D1189406

PLINY'S
NATURAL HISTORY

PHILEMON HOLLAND
in 1632

Part of the title-page from his translation
of Xenophon's *Cyrupaedia*

PLINY'S
NATURAL HISTORY

A SELECTION FROM
PHILEMON HOLLAND'S
TRANSLATION

EDITED BY

J. NEWSOME

OXFORD
AT THE CLARENDON PRESS
1964

Oxford University Press, Amen House, London E.C.4

GLASGOW NEW YORK TORONTO MELBOURNE WELLINGTON
BOMBAY CALCUTTA MADRAS KARACHI LAHORE DACCA
CAPE TOWN SALISBURY NAIROBI IBADAN ACCRA
KUALA LUMPUR HONG KONG

PRINTED IN GREAT BRITAIN

CONTENTS

DR. PHILEMON HOLLAND   *frontispiece*

INTRODUCTION   XV

DEDICATION   3

THE PREFACE TO THE READER   5

THE SUMMARIE OF EVERY BOOKE   13

BOOK I

1. From the Epistle to Vespasian (Titus)   17
2. From the Epistle to Vespasian (Titus)   18

BOOK II

3. Whether the World be finite, and but one   19
4. Of God   20
5. Diverse considerations observed in the nature of winds   24
6. Of the gaping chinks of the earth   25
7. Of the strange wonders of the land   26

BOOK III

8. The Proeme, or Preface   28
9. Of Italy   29

BOOK IV

10. The Corinth Canal   32
11. The paradise of the Hyperboreans   33
12. Britaine and Ireland   34

BOOK V

13. Mount Atlas   36

14. Alexandria   39

15. Jordan, the Dead Sea and the Essenes   40

BOOK VI

16. Of the Black Sea and Bosphorus   42

17. The manifold, strange, and wonderfull formes and shapes of men   43

BOOK VII

18. The Proeme; Nature's mistake   45

19. The strange and wondrous shapes of sundry nations   47

20. The diversitie of nations; India and Ethiopia   48

21. Of Conceptions: and signes distinguishing the sex in great
    bellied women   51

22. Examples of many that have been very like   53

23. The teeth   54

24. Of bodily strength and swiftnesse   55

25. The praise of C. Julius Caesar   56

26. Fortune's lap   58

27. Of Augustus Caesar late Emperor   59

28. Of the longest lives   61

29. Sundry examples of divers diseases   62

30. Of the Ghosts   63

BOOK VIII

31. The praise of Elephants: their wit and understanding 66

32. How the Dragons and Elephants disagree   70

33. Of Lions and Panthers   72

34. Of Wolves   76

35. Of Marmotaines and Urchins or Hedge-hogs   77

36. Of Dogges   79

37. Of Swine, and their natures   81

38. Of Apes and Monkies   82

BOOK IX

39. The Sperm and Killer Whales   84

40. Of Dolphins   86

41. The Barbell and the Belligods   87

42. Of the many-foot fish   88

43. Of the greatest Winkle called Murex, and other kinds of shell-
    fishes   91

44. Of Pearles   92

45. The purple fishes   98

46. Of the Nacre   102

47. Of sea-nettle fishes, and other nastie and filthie creatures   104

48. Of the fish Anthias, and how he is taken   105

BOOK X

49. Of the Cuckow   107

50. Of Peacocks and of Cocks   108

51. Of Cranes and Quailes   109

52. The nightingale   112

53. Of House Doves   114

54. Of the Parrat and other birds that can speake   115

55. Who first devised to cram Hens   118

56. The Auguries and presages of Egges   120

57. The sleepe of living creatures   121

BOOK XI

58. Of the industrie and subtilitie of Nature in framing Insects   123

59. The order that Bees keepe in their worke   125

60. What things be contrarie and hurtfull unto Bees   128

61. Of Indian Pismires   129

62. Of Mans eares and eies   130

63. The resemblance that Apes have to men   132

64. Of Voices   132

BOOK XII

65. Of the Woods and Trees   134

66. Of great Plane trees   135

67. The harvesting of Frankincense   136

BOOK XIII

68. Of Ointments and Perfumes   139

69. Of the nature of Dates   141

BOOK XIV

70. The Decay of ancient knowledge   143

71. Of Vines   146

72. Of avoiding Drunkenesse   147

BOOK XV

73. Cato's Fig   150

BOOK XVI

74. Of Zeland and wonderfull trees in the Northerly regions   152

75. The juice in trees and the nature of their timber   154

76. What wood doth endure and continue always good   156

77. Of Misselto and the priests called Druidae   157

BOOK XVII

78. Of the wonderfull prices of Some Trees 160

79. Of Trees in the winter 162

80. Of the Smell of good ground 164

81. Sundry sorts of Earth and Marle 165

82. Of the nource-garden 168

83. Curious devises to plant vines 169

84. Of the play dayes of vines 170

BOOK XVIII

85. Of the venomes of man 172

86. What famous persons addicted themselves wholly to Husbandrie 174

87. Of good Husbandrie 176

88. Of faults incident to corne, and their remedies 179

89. Of Prevarication and Delirium in husbandrie 180

90. Of the Astronomers 182

91. The Seednes of Corne 184

92. Of the glo-worms 185

93. Democritus and the dearth of olives 186

94. The udder of the Milkeway 187

95. Of Corneharvest 188

BOOK XIX

96. Linnen that will not burne in the fire 190

97. Of the Radish 191

98. Of Colewort and Colliflories 192

99. The Thistle or Artichoke 194

100. Of the simples which are set and sowed in gardens 195

BOOK XX

101. Of garden Cucumbers or Melons   196

102. Of Onions   197

103. Of the garden Cumin   198

BOOK XXI

104. The first invention of the Coronet or Guirland   200

105. A notable act of Queene Cleopatra   201

106. Of Thyme   202

107. Of venomous and poisonfull honey   203

108. Of Nettles   205

109. The medicinable vertues of Cypirus   206

BOOK XXII

110. Of Clothes died with certaine Herbs   208

111. Of the maner of the world in these our daies   210

112. Mushromes or Tad-stoles called Fungi   211

BOOK XXIII

113. Of the sophistication of wines   213

114. Of drinking wine   214

BOOK XXV

115. The cabinet of Mithridates   216

116. Of the sweet Brier or Eglantine and Hydrophobie   217

117. What diseases put men to the greatest paine   219

118. Of Vervaine   221

119. Proper receits for Alopecia and Dandruffe   222

BOOK XXVI

120. Asclepiades and the new practise in Physicke 224

121. Of the infirmities of the Belly 226

BOOK XXVIII

122. Of Spels and Charmes 228

123. Of the properties of a mans spittle 229

BOOK XXIX

124. How many times the order of Physick hath bin changed 232

125. Imperfections and defaults in this art of Physicke 237

BOOK XXX

126. The originall and beginning of Art Magicke 240

BOOK XXXI

127. The fountaines of Cicero 244

128. Of the fishes of Limyra 245

129. Of fresh water from the Sea 246

130. Of the nature of Spunges 246

BOOK XXXII

131. The stay-ship fish 248

BOOK XXXIII

132. Of Mettals and Minerals 250

133. Of Rings 253

134. Other uses besides of gold 255

135. Of Silver and Gold, in money 256

136. The manner of finding gold 259

137. Of Electrum 263

138. Of Silver Mines 264

139. Of Quicksilver 265

140. Of Vermilion 267

141. Of superfluitie and frugalitie touching plate and silver vessels 269

BOOK XXXIV

142. The most renowned Colosses 272

143. Of Praxiteles 273

BOOK XXXV

144. With what colours they painted in old time 276

145. Of Zeuxis 277

146. The great Apelles 279

147. The pictures of Protogenes 286

148. Of other painters 288

149. The wall paintings of Ludius 289

150. Of the last peeces of Painters 291

151. Of drugs that drinke and take colour 291

BOOK XXXVI

152. The excessive expense in columnes and buildings of Marble 293

153. The Venus of Praxiteles 296

154. Of the images of Scopas 298

155. Of the Egyptian Pyramides, and of Sphinx 299

156. Of the Labyrinths 302

157. The temple of Diana in Ephesus 304

158. The sumptuous and admirable aedifices in Rome 306

159. The Load-stone 317

BOOK XXXVII

160. Of Amber   318

161. The Once stone   319

162. Of the Emeraud   320

163. Epilogue   321

GLOSSARY   323

INDEX OF NAMES   329

NOTE

MR. P. TURNER's volume of selections (*Selections from the History of the World . . . introduced by Paul Turner*, Centaur Press, London, 1962) appeared as this was going to press. Material from 96 of his 538 extracts appears in part or whole in this volume also, but he has chosen many passages not included here. The reader who would like to see more of Holland's Pliny, and especially of some parts of it less suitable for general reading, without having to examine the original folios in a library, can consult Mr. Turner. He will find a straight transcript of Holland's text in modern spelling, mistakes included, and, if he does not mind frequent reference to a good glossary and the lack of explanatory notes, he should obtain pleasure and refreshment from a further 'good draught of hens milke'.

Acknowledgement is made to the Trustees of the British Museum for the photograph of the portrait which forms the frontispiece and for permission to reproduce it.

INTRODUCTION

Two years before Queen Elizabeth died, the *Natural History* of Gaius Plinius Secundus, 'the most popular natural history ever published', first appeared in English translation on the book-sellers' counters in Paul's Churchyard. It was in two large folio volumes which, to save money, were often bound in one; it then measured 13 by 9 inches and 4 inches thick. It weighed just over 10 pounds and contained 1,438 printed pages. Even so it was popular, the most popular work which the translator, Dr. Philemon Holland of Coventry, produced for the delight of his contemporaries.

There was a second edition in 1634, three years before his death at the age of 85, in which some of the many errors were corrected, but it has never been reprinted, although it formed the basis of an edition begun by the Wernerian Club in 1847 of which only the first seven books appeared; Holland was bowdlerized, emasculated, modernized, and generally given the mid-Victorian treatment, and it was as well the project lapsed. No other English translation appeared for over 200 years until Bostock and Riley, feeling that Holland was out of date and inaccurate, published their version in 1855–7. White, without acknowledgement, used it for his *Boys' and Girls' Pliny* in 1885. Then, in this century, Rackham began his translation which was continued after his death by Jones; nine of the ten volumes have appeared since 1938. The declared aims of the work were an acceptable Latin text and a literal translation to aid Latin students, who may here study difficult passages in the more specialized chapters, and hope for, but not invariably find, a clear statement of Pliny's account of their subject. It has been used as a check on Holland's translation and on the spellings, sometimes wildly improbable but usually surprisingly correct, of the many proper names and unusual words which the compositors of Adam Islip, the printer, set up in type in 1601 and 1634.

I have no doubt which of these translations to praise most; 'thine be the Bayes, grave learned Holland'. Many are the tributes that great men have paid to his accuracy, knack of translating, and rare, consummate knowledge of English. A complete reprint of his Pliny, corrected and annotated, might well delight our contemporaries, but there is one thing, apart from expense, which is likely to defer its publication for the moment. Pliny interlards what Cuvier calls 'the dryness of his enumerations' with amusing anecdotes, fables, curiosities, and diatribes against contemporary luxury and indolence; but these are so buried beneath interminable ancient geography, pharmacy, and botany that they cannot be exhumed without much spade work. The enumerations, unfortunately, take up at least a quarter of the work, and the capacity of the modern reader would surely be strained by these barren tracts, these endless lists of place names, national boundaries, and pharmacological properties of unidentifiable herbs. Just about half the text is of general interest today, and perhaps, lit by Dr. Holland's 'full smooth *Language*, (yielding unto none;)', it might now or soon be worth reprinting, in an edition of two or three volumes.

Meanwhile, this collection of representative passages is a mere introduction to the first, and greatest, English translation of Pliny, now very difficult to obtain and even more difficult, remembering its weight, to read comfortably when found. Short extracts, however carefully selected, have a bitter-sweet flavour; much of the best is there but divorced from the whole. They may, perhaps, act as an aperitif and whet the appetite for more.

THE *HISTORIA NATURALIS*

Pliny wrote seven books, and all but the last have been lost. His *Natural History* appeared in A.D. 77, and from the number of early manuscripts (one of which, the Nonantulanus palimpsest, is dated to the fifth or sixth century), it seems to have been the most popular of his works. Only a few fragments of his other books are extant.

Hundreds of editions have been published in Latin and in modern languages since the first printing in Venice in 1469. The historical sections of textbooks on many subjects, from astronomy and beekeeping to taxidermy and vermilion pigment, draw on Pliny's material. He did not write a natural history in our sense but included everything pertaining to the world and man; it was a work of reference, an Encyclopedia Romana. The collection of

all this information was indeed 'a brave and magnificent enterprise' and he expected little recognition for it. 'Full well I know,
that I for my part also, shall have but small thanks of many a one
for all my paines taken in writing this history of the world and
Natures works: nay, I am assured that I make my selfe a laughing
stocke, and am condemned of them for spending and losing my
time in such a frivolous piece of worke as this is.' We may hope
that he was pleasantly surprised by the popularity of his book.
His methods of work are mentioned in Holland's preface and
described in more detail by his nephew, Pliny the Younger, in
a letter to Baebius Macer.[1] He must have put his encyclopedia
together from the 160 volumes of annotated selections, written
very small, which he bequeathed to his nephew. Largius Licinus
offered him about ten thousand of our present-day pounds for
them, and it is tempting to imagine what they might be worth
were a copy of them to be discovered now.

For Pliny was the first person to quote his authorities, and many
of the writers whose works he used are unknown except for this
one mention of their names. He makes a great point of this in his
dedicatory letter to the Emperor Titus:

. . . in the front of these books now in hand, I have set down the very
names of those writers, whose help I have used in the compiling of them:
for I have ever bin of this opinion, That it is the part of an honest minded
man, and one that is ful of grace and modesty, to confesse frankly by
whom he hath profited and gotten any good. . . . I have met with some of
our moderne writers, who word for word have exemplified and copied out
whole books of old authors, and never vouchsafed so much as the naming
of them, but have taken their labours and travels to themselves.

But he did not only abstract the things which interested and
amused him from old authors and parcel them up in a rough-and-
ready order. He put himself into the book, recording his views
boldly on all sorts of subjects and reminiscing about many things
he had himself seen. In Holland's translation we get to know
Pliny personally, for Holland, like many of his time, could think
and feel in Latin.

Writers of biographical notes on Pliny are all agreed that the
Historia Naturalis is a great and valuable work; Cuvier calls it

---

[1] Epp. III. 5.

'one of the most precious monuments that have come down to us from ancient times'. Praise for its contents, however, is sometimes tempered by a smug and patronizing attitude to Pliny's Latin style and to his credulity. He was, it seems, too prone to choose from his authors mere stories and marvellous fables; his style at times was affected and slovenly. That he did not accept many of the superstitions current 1,900 years ago is clear enough to anyone who reads him, and it has been suggested that his Latin style is not well represented by the texts which have reached us. Of course some of the sentences are slovenly or obscure after so much manuscript copying. Certainly there are many old wives' tales and marvels, some of which Pliny has not bothered to refute and may perhaps have believed; there were nearly as many sixteen centuries later and Sir Thomas Browne filled much time and paper discussing them in his *Enquiries into Vulgar and Common Errors* (*Pseudodoxia Epidemica*). In our own time Bergen Evans has had to do it all over again. Why should we have to show how superior we are to a cultured Roman gentleman who worked harder than most of us will ever work to produce this delightful personal encyclopedia? He could not, in A.D. 77, have the outlook of 1960 any more than we can use now the knowledge and insight which we hope our 58th descendant will have in the year 3860. We can surely take him as he was, accept the differences between the first century and now, and enjoy this 'immense treasury', this 'storehouse of scattered facts'.

The varied contents of the storehouse, as set out in the Summarie of every Booke will be found on page 13. Twenty thousand subjects are mentioned, two thousand volumes were perused, and the works of a hundred, or as others think five hundred, authors consulted. These nice round numbers may or may not be correct but they give the scale of the undertaking, 'which', as his translator insists, 'for mine owne part I wish to bee immortall'.

GAIUS PLINIUS SECUNDUS

From his nephew's letters we know more of Pliny's character than of the events in his life, and one of the biographical dictionaries speaks of the 'assez légères conjectures' of would-be biographers who claim that he served at sea and also visited Egypt and Judea.

His birthplace seems to have been Como where the Pliny family had estates, but many have tried to give the honour to Verona. He trained as a lawyer and orator in Rome and must have visited North Africa when he was about twenty-two. He served in the army in Germany for some years and then returned to Rome. Vespasian sent him to Spain in charge of the revenue and Titus later made him prefect of the fleet at Misenum. He went to investigate the eruption of Vesuvius in A.D. 79 and was asphyxiated by clouds of gas from the volcano.

He was a cultured and honest man, full of scientific curiosity and interest in all he saw and heard, and unbelievably hard-working. In about thirty years of responsible public and private employment he found time, in ways described by his nephew and summarized in Holland's preface, to compose seven books. These were: a treatise on throwing the javelin from horse-back, a life of General Pomponius Secundus under whom he served in Germany, a history of the German wars, a short course of instruction for orators, a book on problems in grammar written towards the end of Nero's reign, a continuation of Bassus' history which had ended with Claudius, and the *Natural History*.

While he was in Spain his brother-in-law, Lucius Caecilius Cilo, died. Pliny adopted his son, then ten years old, who became known as Gaius Plinius Caecilius Secundus or Pliny the Younger. His letters to Baebius Macer and to Tacitus[1] give a delightful picture of the elder Pliny and a fine account of the eruption of Vesuvius during which he died. Anyone interested in Pliny as a human being will enjoy reading them in full and may come to agree with Holland that here was a man 'worthie to have lived for ever'.

PHILEMON HOLLAND

The biographies of Holland find little to fill his 85 years. Charles Whibley, in his introduction to the Tudor Translations reprint of Holland's Suetonius (1899), has done his best with the materials available and gives us the clearest picture of this quiet, scholarly, kindly man.

Holland was born in Chelmsford in 1552, the son of a clergyman who went into exile because of Queen Mary's persecution.

----

[1] Epp. VI. 16.

He went to the local grammar school, to Trinity College, Cambridge, and later to Oxford where he read medicine. Nothing more is known of him until 1595, when, with a M.D. degree thought to be from a Scottish or continental university, he settled in Coventry and practised as a doctor. By 1608 he was teaching in the Coventry free grammar school and in 1628 he became head-master, but resigned because of his age in less than a year. His medical practice did not make him rich; as Whibley says, 'he tended the sick in charity and grew poor'. His translations did not bring him much money either. Coventry City Council bought his Ammianus for £4 and the English translation of Camden's *Britannia* for £5; it made him grants and in 1632 gave him a pension of £3. 6s. 8d. yearly. Magdalene College, Cambridge, also gave him financial help. He enjoyed good health and all his faculties, notably his sight, until a year before he died in 1637. His wife had died in 1627 and of their seven sons only one, Henry, survived him and edited some of his writings after his death.

He was 48 when he published his first translation, Livy's *History*, in 1600. Within three years two more appeared, Pliny's *Natural History* and Plutarch's *Moralia*. His teaching and medical work must have left him much leisure during his first eight years in Coventry. Yet, a little later, in 1606, he could say that he wrote the translation of Suetonius' *Twelve Caesars* in 'what howres . . . either the doubtful or diseased state of my neighbours, together with meditations of my own mortalitie would afford'; there was a pestilence in Coventry at the time. His output was amazing: 1600, Livy; 1601, Pliny; 1603, Plutarch; 1606, Suetonius; and he continued in 1609 with Ammianus Marcellinus' *Roman History*, and in 1610 with Camden's *Britannia*. None of these are short books; some are very long. Six such translations in ten years is a great feat. Other books followed, notably Xenophon's *Cyrupaedia*, finished in 1620 but not published until 1632. It was 'enterprised by special order and direction' from James I, 'for the contemplation and use of . . . Prince Henry, now in Heaven', and when that paragon of princes died at the age of 18, the publication was 'demurred'.

In the *Cyrupaedia*, and in the *Britannia* which came out in a revised second edition in the year of Holland's death, there are some fulsome poems praising his abilities. By the time he was 80 there was something of a Holland cult; he had become the grand old man of the translators in an age of great translators. No one has troubled to reprint extracts from these commendatory poems, but they bring the man and his times alive; it is impossible to pass them by. There was a good deal of feeling against the translators. The learned were firmly entrenched and attacked translation from the ancient languages as likely to diminish their status. Besides, such knowledge would be bad for the common people. The authors of the poems are at pains to justify making 'common to meere Englishmen' the great works of Rome and Greece, and Fuller finds it necessary to deal with the matter in his life of Holland.

Indeed some decry all translators as interlopers, spoiling the trade of learning, which should be driven amongst scholars alone. Such also allege, that the best translations are rather the work of industry than judgement, and (in easy authors) of faithfulness rather than industry; that many be but bunglers, forcing the meaning of the authors they translate, 'picking the lock when they cannot open it'.

But their opinion presents too much of envy, that such gentlemen who cannot repair to the fountain should be debarred access to the stream. Besides, it is unjust to charge all with the faults of some; and a distinction must be made amongst translators, betwixt cobblers and workmen, and our Holland had the true knack of translating.

Thomas Farnaby, Armig., in the first of the *Cyrupaedia* poems makes the same point.

> Yet can it [thy skill] not escape that blatant Beast
> Which at the heeles dogges vertue; whose chiefe feast
> Is gall of base Detraction; which barkes
> That learning earst engross'd by languag'd Clarks,
> Entail'd on Gownes, by the Translatours pen
> Is now made common to meere Englishmen.

He adds a wish we all can share, especially those of us who are nowadays forced to read the scientific press.

> I wish in Arts as Story we might save
> Labour and time for language; wee should have
> Sooner and sounder Science, fill our mind
> With things, not words, eat fruit, not gnaw the rind.

The malice of the Clarks appears again in the piece by Io. Hall, Hosp: Gray: Gen: who loudly declares:

> How well hast thou laid out thy aged sweat
> To benefit thy Country, to repeat

Those sober Rules, examples, which declare
Thy Authours ripenesse, and thy learned Care!
How sweet a weight dwells in thy cleanly Stile!
Each English tongue must speak't: none can defile
Thy honour, bought with paines, or dare bespaule
Wise Innocence with their ignorant Gall;
Such vertue stands above their Malice blest.
But this Translation shall speake the rest,
  Which shall remaine admir'd till Time betray,
  By breaking of *his Glasse*, the Worlds decay.

W. Lathom, Gen. runs on in an involved panegyric, most remarkable for praising Holland above Xenophon and for the 'dry'd Skelliton'.

To *Hollands* youth *He* [Xenophon] the Greeke Tongue bewray's,
Him teaching t'understand it as his owne;
(In guerdon of whose paines) *Holland* him pays
(Shall I be bold to make the Paragon
The English with the Greeke in equall praise?)
A full smooth *Language*, (yielding unto none;)
That when unequally I come to paize
The *Both* in *Ballance* of Comparison,
My doubtful Mind's devided divers Wayes,
Whom to prayse most with thanks, and thereupon
Determine thus, to say, (as *Paris* say's)
They both deserve the Garland to have won,
Yet (if ought odds there beene) thine be the Bayes
(*Grave learned Holland*) who (so long agon
Dead in his Grave,) thy Master now dost raise
And adde new Life, to his dry'd Skelliton,
Making him proud, translated thus to bee
From *Greece* to *England* and to learne of Thee.

After this exercise in the use of italics and brackets, it is pleasant to turn to more sensible and kindly praise.

Of Doctor *Philemon Holland*

Before thy rare Worke I shall truly prize,
Let mee thy Name first Etymologize,
Learned *Philêmon*; which (unlesse I misse)
Wee call *Deosculor i.* sweetly to kisse.
  When Jupiter with Mankinde much offended,
From high *Olympus* to the Earth descended

With Mercury; the better how to know
How all affaires were manag'd here below,
No Creature save *Philêmon* he could find
To give him Food or welcome to his mind.
For which his Cottage he a Temple made:
And lest his memory by Time should fade,
When he grew old (as Thou *Philêmon* now)
To a *faire Oak* with many a spreading bow
He chang'd the good old man; to yield such Mast,
As should both Memory and Time out-last.
    Wee live not in an age so dull and rude,
But of the Gods wee can learne Gratitude,
Acknowledging by many a sweet Translation,
What profit Thou has brought unto our Nation.

. . . .

Joves Tree, decay Thou canst not: or if dead?
Yet from thy Mast how many shall be fed,
Who Thy Translations read? If King CHARLES give
Grace to Thy Worke? King CHARLES shall ever live.

An observer of all true Worth
and learning,
Thomas Heyvvood, Gen.

There is no doubt that in 1632 everyone loved Philemon Holland; even his pens were worth preserving, as a note in the *Cyrupaedia* describes.

Upon the Translatours Pen, wherewith only hee translated and wrote all Plutarchs Moralls, containing above a Reame of Paper,[1] he wrote this Dystick:

This Booke I wrote with *one* poore Pen, made of a grey Goose quill:
A Pen I found it, us'd before, A Pen I leave it still.

Which Pen afterwards was begged by an auntient Gentlewoman (mother to a noble Countesse yet living:) who garnished it in silver, and kept it as a Monument.

This pen was so famous that there are two other versions, Aubrey maintaining it was used to write the Livy and was preserved mounted in silver by Lady Harington, while Fuller says Holland kept it himself and showed it to Fuller's tutor, Dr. Samuel Ward.

---

[1] 1108 folio pages of print.

In 1637 John Davies of Hereford contributed a long and somewhat tiresome poem to the translation of Camden's *Britannia*. He refers, aptly enough, to Holland's work on the *Historia Naturalis*.

> NATURES great Secretarie thou dost teach
> To speake such English as (though he be high
> In cloudy-matter) English eies may reach,
> His highest Pitch; that tries the Eagles eie.
>
> .   .   .   .
>
> Shall English be so poore, and rudely-base
> As not be able (through meere penury)
> To tell what French hath said with gallant grace,
> And most tongues else of lesse fecunditie?
> God shield it should; . . .

Holland, like Pliny, felt or pretended to feel that he would be thought foolish to work so long and hard at his translations. In the preface to the *Natural History* he complains: 'A painfull and tedious travaile I confesse it is; neither make I doubt but many doe note mee for much follie in spending time herein, and neglecting some compendious course of gathering good, and pursing up pence. But when I looke backe to the example of *Plinie*, I must of necessitie condemne both mine owne sloth, and also reprove the supine negligence of these daies.' He was no good at pursing up pence and treated many of his patients free; probably for this reason people had little faith in him as a doctor. We may think of him, perhaps, as happier at his 'tedious travaile' than trying to make a living from his medical practice or teaching in the grammar school.

And perhaps it was because he was happy in this work that he became a great translator. Whibley believed that he 'still remains the first translator of his age', and for three hundred years everyone has praised him. Yet Holland himself, like Pliny, thought he was writing in a 'mean and popular style', and desired only 'to doe a pleasure unto them that could not read these authors in the original'. The eloquence, richness, and flavour of his style have often been extolled, and his modesty may be thought a little artificial. Yet he could be taken at his word. Apart from its happy phrases, his writing gets much of its richness from the constant repetition of synonyms: a great captain and commander; infested and annoyed with elephants; in the field or champian; want and dearth; checked and snibbed; every page is full of them. And they may well have been needed to make the mean and common people understand him, and through him the cloudy matter of the Latin or Greek author. For his translations are not construes. Compare the Rackham and Holland versions of this sentence about the monopoly in hedgehog skins:

magnum fraus et ibi lucrum monopolio invenit,

Even here fraud has discovered a great source of profit by monopoly,

And in very truth, many have gotten great gain and profit by this commoditie and merchandise, and namely, with their crafty devise of monopolies, that all might pass through their hands only.

Or compare the two versions of Pliny's passage about the reaping machine:

messis ipsius ratio varia. galliarum latifundiis valli praegrandes dentibus in margine insertis duabus rotis per segetem impelluntur jumento in contrarium juncto; ita dereptae in vallum cadunt spicae.

There are various methods of actually getting in the harvest. On the vast estates in the provinces of Gaul very large frames fitted with teeth at the edge and carried on two wheels are driven through the corn by a team of oxen pushing from behind; the ears thus torn off fall into the frame.

As touching the manner of cutting downe or reaping corne, there be divers and sundry devices. In France where the fields be large they use to set a jade or an asse unto the taile of a mighty great wheele barrow or cart made in manner of a Van, and the same set with keen and trenchant teeth sticking out on both sides: now is this carre driven forward before the said beast upon two wheeles into the standing ripe corne (contrary to the manner of other carts that are drawne after) the said teeth or sharp tines fastened to the sides of the wheele barrow or car aforesaid, catch hold of the corn eares, and cut them off: yet so, as they fall presently into the body of the wheele-barrow.

Holland tells his readers (p. 7, below) that he consulted divers Latin versions, with their commentaries, and the Italian and French translations; indeed, the frequent marginal references to alternative readings confirm that he was not content to follow the standard sixteenth-century editions of Barbarus and Gelenius. For his Latin text he seems to have made most use of that of Jacques Dalechamp, a new edition of which appeared in 1587. Many of his renderings and remarks in parenthesis, some of which are mentioned here in footnotes, may be traced to Dalechamp who provided readings and notes from many codices and commentators.

The Italian translations of Landino and of Domenichi may have been consulted, but no word or phrase in Holland could definitely be traced to them. On the other hand, Antoine Dupinet's French translation (probably in its third edition of 1584) contributed greatly to Holland's version. The nettles changing their *colour* (p. 104), the walnut oil (p. 158), the Dove or Pigeon marl (p. 167), and the milkway (or Watling Street) on page 187 are all examples that can only have come from Dupinet. Holland, however, did not blindly follow Dupinet and it is easy to find evidence of this in any chapter; for example Dupinet, like most others, allowed Augustus to fall from a tower (p. 60) but Holland preferred his own version, hinted at in Dalechamp, of making Augustus anxious about 'the fall of a bridge and a towne both'.

The source of some of Holland's renderings could not be found in the Latin, the Italian, or the French. The origin of a surprising passage about the fleet gallantly dight which precedes §144 is as obscure as that of the Polypus lacking any sense but that of food and drink, the texts reading food and danger (p. 89). It is clear that Philemon Holland did not do his work the easy way, and his claim to have collated the available texts and translations can be substantiated.

He was certainly well-read in Latin, Greek, French, and Italian literature. He knew how others had translated the terse original and exactly how he meant to translate it himself. Whibley says that he loved to adorn a simple statement, turn it about and trick it out. But Holland firmly tells the readers of his Suetonius that 'brevitie is many times the mother of Obscuritie', and he turns phrases round and repeats himself to make the meaning and context clear. The more one compares his English with the Latin and with other translations, the easier it is to believe that he was modestly striving to present his author for the first time to mere Englishmen as clearly and correctly as he could with the texts at his disposal.

Whatever his motives, his masterpieces remain and have 'descended to us rich treasuries of sound English and wise interpretation'. A chronological list of these treasuries is given below.

1600 *The Romane Historie, written by T. Livius* (second edition, 1659).
1601 *The Historie of the World: commonly called the Natural History of C. Plinius Secundus* (second edition, 1634–5).

1603 *The Philosophie, commonly called the Morals written by the learned Philo-*
      sopher Plutarch of Chaeronea (second edition, 1657).

1606 *The Historie of Twelve Caesars Emperours of Rome* . . . by Suetonius.

1609 *The Romane History* . . . by Ammianus Marcellinus.

1610 *Britain* . . . by William Camden (second edition, 1637).

1615 *Paralipomena,* a supplement to Thomasius' *Dictionarium.*

1616 *Theatrum Imperii Magnae Britanniae,* by John Speed.

1622 *A learned, elegant and religious Speech delivered unto His* . . . *Majesty,*
      at . . . *Coventry.*

1632 *Cyrupaedia, The Institution and Life of Cyrus* . . . *Written* . . . *by the*
      Sage Xenophon.

1632 *Gutta Podagrica: a treatise of the Gout.*

1639 *Pharmacopeia* (Latin, from the French of Bauderon).

1649 *Regimen Sanitatis Salernae, or the School of Salernes Regiment of Health,* . . .
      by Joannes Mediolano.

THE SELECTIONS

The first edition of 1601 was full of mistakes, and many but
not all of them were corrected in the second edition of 1634. The
text of the selected passages is that of 1634 and it has been
tampered with as little as possible. Holland's paragraphs are too
long for enjoyable reading and they have been subdivided. The
important mistakes, mis-spellings, and printer's errors have been
corrected, but the Elizabethan spelling and punctuation have
been retained. Where the sense is not clear an occasional word
has been inserted between square brackets.

The indiscriminate use of u and v, i and j, vv and w, and the
long s makes up part of the pleasure of reading sixteenth- and
seventeenth-century books. It is, of course, illogical, but Shakespeare seems to come alive as a man when his plays are read in the
Yale photostat edition of the first folio; in a modern edition he is
a Great Poet. The old printing and spelling often point up a
phrase which impresses far less in modern dress. 'The froward
peeuiſhnes of ſome Authors' makes them much more tiresome
people. 'Obſcuritie', too, is more obscure and to 'ſtand ſtiffely' is
stiff indeed. Such small pleasures the reader will, regretfully, have
to forgo here, except in the Dedication to Sir Robert Cecil.

It is a great pity that marginal notes are no longer used; they
are in the right place at the right time. Some of Holland's notes

run to more than fifty words but one never fails to read them; a few have been included as footnotes and marked (P. H.).

Passages have been selected from all parts of the book and each is typical of many pages of similar material. Some were chosen for their interest, some to show how Pliny handled his subjects, and a few, unashamedly, to let Dr. Holland exhibit his virtuosity. Together they are meant to give a bird's-eye view of the whole work and suggest something of its range, flavour, and charm.

THE
HISTORIE
OF THE WORLD:
Commonly called,
THE NATVRALL HISTORIE OF
C. PLINIVS SECVNDVS.

Tranſlated into Engliſh by PHILEMON HOLLAND
Doctor of Phyſicke.

The firſt Tome:

LONDON,
Printed by Adam Iſlip.
1634.

SIR *ROBERT CECIL* KNIGHT, PRINCIPALL SECRETARIE TO THE QVEENS MAIESTIE, MASTER OF COVRT OF THE WARDS AND LIVERIES,

Chancellor of the Vniuerſitie of Cambridge, and
one of her
Maieſties moſt Honourable Priuie Counſell.

The friendly acceptance which T. Livius *of Padua hath found in this Realme, ſince time hee ſhewed himſelfe in Engliſh weed unto her ſacred Majeſtie, hath trained over unto him his neighbour* Plinius Secundus, *from Verona. Whome, being now arraied in the ſame habit, yet fearefull to ſet foot forward in the forreine ground, without the countenance of ſome worthie perſonage, who might both giue him his hand at his firſt entrance, in token of welcome, and alſo grace him afterwards with a fauourable regard to win acquaintance, I humbly preſent unto your Honour. For con-ſidering the qualitie of the man, a Philoſopher diſcourſing ſo deeply in all Learning, where may hee looke for better acceptance than of him, who is most iustly ſtyled, Patron of Learning? Which dignitie conferred of late upon your H. by the generall ſuffrages of a Noble Vniuerſitie (and that for your ſingular inſight in all literature) as a complement to thoſe high places whereunto the favour of a moſt prudent and judicious Princeſſe hath advanced you, and the ſame correſpondent to the ſame wiſedom, justice, and eloquence, which concurre in your perſon, like the ſeuerall beauties of the Rubie, Amethyſt, and Emeraud meeting in one faire Opal, giueth a louely luſtre to your other titles, no leſſe, than if the nine* Muſes *and* Apollo, *repreſented naturally in that rich Agat of K.* Pyrrhus, *were inſerted therein. Now if, as wee read of* [1]Alexander *and* [2]Demetrius, *two mightie monarchs, who amid their deſſeines and making conqueſts and beſieging cities, beheld otherwhiles* Apelles *and* Protogenes *how they handled their pencils; it may pleaſe your Honour betweene the managing of State-affaires under her Majeſtie, to caſt your eie eftſoones upon* Plinie *for your recreation,*

[1] Magnus (P. H.).   [2] Polyorcetes (P. H.).

and fee how liuely hee depeincteth, not Venus Anadyomene,[1] *drawne haply to the patterne of* Campafpe *a courtizan; nor* Ialyfus *with his dog,*[2] *in which picture,* fecit Fortuna naturam; *but euen Nature her felfe, the immediat mother and nource of all things under the Almightie; I fhall not onely thinke him patronized thereby and fufficiently commended to the world, but alfo acknowledge my felfe much deuoted to your H. and bound for euer to pray for the encreafe thereof, with long life and true hapineffe.*

Your Honours moft readie at command,

Philemon Holland.

[1] See § 146.   [2] See § 147.

THE PREFACE TO THE READER

HAPPIE were they in times past reputed (and not unworthily) who had that gratious and heavenly gift, *aut facere scribenda, aut scribere legenda*: that is to say, either to do such things as deserved to bee written, or to write that which was worth the reading. Those that could not attaine to these two branches of felicitie, and yet utterly misliked idlenes, contented themselves in a third degree, namely to take in hand the old workes of their ancients, and by new labours to immortalize their memorie.

Thus *Nicophanes* (a famous painter in his time) gave his mind wholly to antique pictures, partly to exemplifie and take out their patternes after that in long continuance of time they were decaied; and in part to repaire and reforme the same, if haply by some injurious accident they were defaced. The ingenious mind of this artizan thus devoted to antiquitie, as I doe highly commend; so I cannot chuse but embrace his policie, seeking hereby to avoid the envie and reproofe of others. In this number I must range those learned men in severall ages, who to illustrate the monuments left by former writers, have annexed unto them their Commentaries; to save them entire and uncorrupt, have set thereto judiciall observations; and to publish them for a generall benefit of posteritie, have translated the same into their mother language. As for my selfe, since it is neither my hap nor hope to attaine to such perfection, as to bring forth somewhat of mine owne which may quit the paines of a reader; and much lesse to performe any action that might minister matter to a writer; and yet so farre bound unto my native countrey and the blessed state wherein I have lived, as to render an account of my yeeres passed and studies employed during this long time of peace and tranquilitie, wherein (under the most gratious and happy governement of a peerelesse Princesse, assisted with so prudent, politique, and learned Counsell) all good literature hath had free progresse and flourished, in no age so much: mee thought I owed this dutie, to leave for my part also (after many others) some small memoriall, that might give testimonie another day what fruits generally this peaceable age of ours hath produced.

Endeavoured I have therefore to stand in this third ranke, and bestowed those houres which might be spared from the practise of my profession, and the necessarie cares of this life, to satisfie my countrimen now living, and to gratifie the age ensuing, in this kinde. Like as therefore I have travelled alreadie in *Titus Livius* a renowmed Historiographer, so I have proceeded to deale with *Plinius Secundus* the elder, as famous a Philosopher. Now albeit my intention and only scope was, to doe a pleasure unto them that could not read these authours in the original: yet needs I must confesse that even my selfe have not only gained therby encrease of the Latine tongue (wherein these workes were written) but also growne to further knowledge of the matter and argument therein contained. For this benefit wee reape by studying the bookes of such ancient authours, That the oftner we read them over, the more still we find and learne in them: as beeing so judiciously and pithily penned, that, as the Poet said very well, *decies repetita placerent.*[1] Well may the newest songs and last devised plaies delight our ears at the first, and for the present ravish our senses: like as horarie and earely Summer fruits content our tast and please the appetite: but surely it is antiquitie that hath given grace, vigor, and strength to writings; even as age commendeth the most generous and best wines.

In which regard, and upon this experience of mine owne, I nothing doubt but they also whom I might justly feare as hard censours of these my labours, will not onely pitie mee for my paines, but also in some measure yeeld mee thankes in the end, when either by the light of the English (if they be young students) they shall bee able more readily to goe away with the darke phrase and obscure constructions of the Latine; or (being great schollers and taking themselves for deepe Critickes) by conferring the one with the other, haply to espie wherein I have tripped, they shall by that meanes peruse once againe, and consequently gather new profit out of that authour whom peradventure they had laid by for many yeers as sufficiently understood. When some benefit (I say) shall accrew unto them likewise by this occasion, I lesse dread their fearefull doome, to which so wilfully I have exposed my selfe. Well I wist, that among the Athenians, order was taken by law, That an enterlude newly acted should be heard with silence and

[1] Still please at the tenth repetition.

applause: which custome, as it was respective and favourable to the first endeavours of the actours, so it implied an inevitable danger of hissing out an utter disgrace, if afterwards they chanced to misse and faile in their parts. Having shewed my selfe once before upon the stage,[1] presuming upon this priviledge and the curtesie of the theatre, I might have now sitten still and so rested: In mounting up thus soon againe, I may seeme either in the assured confidence of mine owne worthinesse, to proclaime a challenge to all mens censures; or else upon a deepe conceit of some generall connivencie make reckoning of an extraordinarie and wonderfull favor. But as the choise that I have made to publish the monuments of other men, without fathering anything of mine owne, doth excuse and acquit mee for the one; so the froward disposition of carpers in these daies wherein wee live, will checke the other.

Howbeit considering such paines undergone by me one man, for the pleasure of so many; so much time spent of mine, for gaining time to others; and some opportunities of privat lucre overslipt and lost, to win profit unto all; I feare not but these regards may deserve a friendly acceptance and counterweigh all defects and faults escaped, whatsoever. The persuasion hereof, but principally the privitie of my affectionat love unto my countrey (which assured me of a safe-conduct to passe peaceably through their hands who are of the better sort and well affected) induced mee to a resolution not onely to enter upon this new taske, but also to breake through all difficulties, untill I had brought the same, if not to a full and absolute perfection, yet to an end and finall conclusion. Besides this naturall inclination and hope which carried mee this way, other motives there were that made saile and set mee forward. I saw how diverse men before me had dealt with this authour, whiles some laboured to reforme whatsoever by injurie of time was growne out of frame: others did their best to translate him into their own tongue, and namely, the Italian and French: moreover, the Title prefixed therto so universall as it is, to wit, *The Historie of the World*, or *Reports of Nature*, imported (no doubt) that hee first penned it for the generall good of mankind. Over and besides, the Argument ensuing full of varietie, furnished with

---

[1] This refers to his translation of Livy's *Roman History*, published in 1600. See also the Dedication, p. 3.

discourses of all matters, not appropriate to the learned only, but accommodat to the rude peisant of the countrey; fitted for the painefull artizan in towne and citie: pertinent to the bodily health of man, woman, and child; and in one word, suiting with all sorts of people living in a societie and commonweale. To say nothing of the precedent given by the authour himselfe who endited the same, not with any affected phrase, but sorting well with the capacitie even of the meanest and most unlettered: who also translated a good part thereof out of the Greeke.

What should I alledge the example of former times, wherein the like hath evermore been approved and practised? Why should any man therefore take offence hereat, and envie this good to his naturall countrey, which was first meant for the whole world? and yet some there be so grosse as to give out, That these and such like bookes ought not to bee published in the vulgar tongue.[1] It is a shame (quoth one) that *Livie* speaketh English as hee doth: Latinists onely are to bee acquainted with him: as Who would say, the souldiour were to have recourse unto the universitie for militarie skill and knowledge: or the scholler to put on armes and pitch a campe. What should *Plinie* (saith another) bee read in English, and the mysteries couched in his bookes divulged: as if the husbandman, the mason, carpenter, goldsmith, painter, lapidarie, and engraver, with other artificers, were bound to seeke unto great clearkes or linguists for instructions in their severall arts. Certes, such *Momi*[2] as these, besides their blind and erronious opinion, thinke not so honourably of their native countrey and mother tongue as they ought: who if they were so well affected that way as they should be, would wish rather, and endeavour by all meanes to triumph now over the Romans in subduing their literature under the dent of the English pen, in requitall for the conquest sometime over this Island, atchieved by the edge of their sword. As for our speech, was not Latine as common and naturall in Italie, as English here with us. And if *Plinie* faulted not but deserved well of the Romane name, in laying abroad the riches and hidden treasures of Nature, in that Dialect or Idiome which was familiar to the basest clowne: why should any man be blamed for enterprising the semblable, to the commoditie of that countrey

---

[1] See Introduction, p. xxi, for more about these gross views.
[2] Μῶμος; Momus, the critic god.

in which and for which he was borne. Are wee the onely nation under heaven unworthie to tast of such knowledge? or is our language so barbarous, that it will not admit in proper tearmes a forreine phrase?

I honor them in my heart, who having of late daies troden the way before mee in *Plutarch*, *Tacitus*, and others, have made good proofe, that as the tongue in an Englishmans head is framed so flexible and obsequent, that it can pronounce naturally any other language; so a pen in his hand is able sufficiently to expresse Greeke, Latine, and Hebrew. And my hope is, that after mee there will arise some industrious *Flavii*[1] who may at length *cornicum oculos configere*.[2] For if my selfe, a man by profession otherwise carried away, for gifts farre inferiour to many, and wanting such helps as others bee furnished with, have in some sort taught those to speake English who were supposed very untoward to bee brought unto it; what may be expected at their hands, who for leisure may attend better; in wit are more pregnant; and being graced with the opinion of men and favour of the time, may attempt what they will, and effect whatsoever they attempt with greater felicitie? A painfull and tedious travaile I confesse it is; neither make I doubt but many doe note mee for much follie in spending time herein, and neglecting some compendious course of gathering good, and pursing up pence. But when I looke backe to the example of *Plinie*, I must of necessitie condemne both mine owne sloth, and also reprove the supine negligence of these daies.

A courtiour he was, and great favourit of the *Vespasians* both father and sonne:[3] an oratour besides, and pleaded many causes at the barre: a martiall man withall, and served often times a leader and commander in the field: within the citie of Rome hee mannaged civile affaires, and bare honourable offices of State. Who would not thinke but each one of these places would require a whole man? and yet amid these occasions wherewith he was possessed, he penned Chronicles, wrate Commentaries, compiled Grammaticall treatises, and many other volumes which at this day are utterly lost. As for the Historie of Nature now in hand, which

[1] The Emperors Vespasian and Titus were said to be descended from the distinguished Flavian family. Holland hopes for modern Flavii, and describes their attributes in the next sentence.

[2] Transfix the eyes of crows—wary birds; anglice, deceive the most wary.

[3] The emperors Vespasian and Titus.

sheweth him to be an excellent Philosopher and a man accomplished in all kinds of literature (the onely monument of his that
hath escaped all dangers, and as another Palladium[1] beene reserved
entire unto our time) wherein hee hath discoursed of all things
even from the starrie heaven to the centre of the earth; a man
would marveile how hee could possibly either write or doe any
thing else, But considering the agilitie of mans spirit alwaies in
motion: an ardent desire to benefit posteritie, which in these
volumes hee hath so often protested; his indefatigable studie both
day and night, even to the injurie of nature, and the same continued in everie place, as well abroad as within-house; in his
journey upon the high way, where his manner was to read and to
indite; in his ordinarie passage through the streets betweene court
and home, where he gave himselfe no rest, but either read, or else
found his notarie worke to write; and for that purpose rode usually
in an easie litter, with the said Notarie close by his side: lesse
wonder it is, that hee performed his service to Prince and state
according to his calling; and withall delivered unto posteritie so
many fruits of wit and learning. For what is not the head of man
able to compasse? especially making saile with a fervent desire and
resolution to see an end, and besides taking the vantage of all
moments, and losing no time, whereof hee was *unus omnium parcis-
simus.*[2] Touching his affection to search into the secrets of Nature,
it was that and nothing else that shortened his daies, and hastened
his untimely death: for having lived not much above the middle
age of man, desirous he was to know the reason, Why the hill
Vesuvius burned as it did? and approched so neare, that with the
strong vapours and smoake issuing from thence, his breath was
suddenly stopped, and himselfe found dead in the place: a man
worthie to have lived for ever.

What remaineth now, but onely to recommend unto my countrimen this worke of his (which for mine owne part I wish to bee
immortall) were it not for one scruple to bee cleared, which at the

---

[1] A Palladium was a statue of Pallas Athene. The best-known Palladium was
said to have been brought to Rome from Troy by Aeneas. It was kept in the
temple of Vesta, and was saved by the pontifex maximus, L. Caecilius Metellus,
at the cost of his sight, when the temple was burned in 241 B.C. Its subsequent
history is obscure. Presumably Holland is comparing one long-preserved object
with another and is not stating that the Palladium still existed in his time.

[2] One of the most thrifty of men.

first troubled my selfe a little, and might peradventure otherwise offend some readers. In attributing so much unto Nature, *Plinie* seemeth to derogat from the Almightie God, to him ἄγνωτος;[1] and therefore dangerous (saith one) to bee divulged. Farre be it from mee, that I should publish any thing to corrupt mens manners, and much lesse to prejudice Christian religion. After conference therefore with sundrie divines about this point, whom for their authoritie I reverence; whose learning I honor and embrace; and in whom for judgement & synceritie of religion I rest, confirmed I was in my first purpose, and resolved to finish that which I had begun, namely, not to defraud the world of so rich a gem, for one small blemish appearing therein. And that it may appeare how I did not abound in mine owne sence, but had regard as well to satisfie the conscience of others as mine owne, I have thought good to annex immediately hereunto, in manner of a Corollarie,[2] the opinion of one grave and learned preacher concerning this doubt as it was delivered unto mee in writing; which for that it is grounded upon sufficient reasons, and according with the judgement of the rest, the lesse I respect the rash projects of some fantasticall spirits: nothing doubting but the same will settle the minds of the weake, and free my labours from the taint of irreligion.

[1] Unknown.
[2] This has been omitted. The Corollarie is entitled: 'The copie of the said Letter, written as touching the Translation of *Plinie*.' It ends: 'Junii xii, 1601. Your loving friend in the Lord, H. F.'

THE SUMMARIE OF EVERY BOOKE

The first Booke containeth the Dedicatorie Epistle or Preface of the whole worke, addressed to *Titus Vespasian* the Emperour. Also the names of the Authors out of which hee gathered the Historie, which he prosecuteth in 36 Bookes: together with the Summarie of everie Chapter:

The second, treateth of the World, Elements, and Starres:

The third, describeth the first and second gulfe, which the Mediterranean sea maketh in Europe:

The fourth, compriseth the third gulfe of Europe,

The fifth, containeth the description of Affricke,

The sixt, handleth the Cosmographie of Asia,

The seventh treateth of man, and his inventions,

The eighth sheweth unto us, land creatures and their kindes,

The ninth, laieth before us all fishes, and creatures of the water,

The tenth speakes of flying foules and birds,

The eleventh telleth us of Insects,

The twelfth treateth of drugs and odoriferous plants,

The thirteenth describeth strange and forreine trees:

The fourteenth sheweth of vine-plants &c.,

The fifteenth comprehendeth all fruitfull trees,

The sixteenth describeth unto us all wild trees,

The seventeenth containeth tame trees within hortyards,

The eighteenth booke treateth of the nature of corne, and all sorts thereof, together with the profession of husbandmen, and agriculture,

The nineteenth discourseth of Flax, Spart, and Gardenage,

The twentieth sheweth of garden herbs, good to serve both the kitchin for meat, and the Apothecaries shop for medicine,

The one and twentieth treateth of flours and garlands,

The two and twenty containeth the chaplets and medicines made of hearbes,

The three and twentie sheweth the medicinable vertues of wine, and tame trees growing in hortyards,

The foure and twentie declareth the properties of wild trees serving in Physick,

The five and twentie treateth of the herbes in the field comming up of their own accord,

The six and twentie sheweth of many new and strange maladies, the medicinable vertues also of certaine herbes, according to sundry diseases,

The seven and twenty goeth forward to certaine other hearbes and their medicines,

The eight and twentie setteth downe certaine receits of remedies in Physicke, drawne from out of man and other bigger creatures,

The nine and twentie treateth of the first authours and inventors of Physicke, also of medicines taken from other creatures,

The thirtieth booke speaketh of Magicke, and certaine medicines appropriat to the parts and members of mans bodie,

The one and thirtie containeth the medicinable vertues of fishes and water creatures,

The two and thirtie sheweth other properties of fishes, &c.,

The three and thirtie treateth of gold and silver mines,

The foure and thirtie speaketh of copper and brasse mines, also of lead, also of excellent brasse-founders and workemen in copper,

The five and thirtie discourseth of painting, colour, and painters,

The six and thirtie treateth of marble and stone for building,

The seven and thirtie concludeth with pretious stones.

THE
SELECTED
PASSAGES

THE EPISTLE DEDICATORIE TO
PRINCE VESPASIAN
[TITUS]

§ I

MOREOVER, the way that I have entred into, hath not bin troden beforetime by other writers, being indeed so strange and uncouth, as a mans mind would not willingly travell therin. No Latin author among us hath hitherto once ventured upon the same argument, no one Grecian whatsoever hath gone through it and handled all: and no marvell, for many of us love not to take any paines, but study rather to pen matters of delight and pleasure. True it is, I must needs say, that others have made profession hereof, but they have done it with such subtiltie and deepenesse, that all their travels and writings by that means, lie as it were dead and buried in darkenesse. Now come I, and take upon me to speak of every thing, and to gather as it were a compleat body of arts and sciences (which the Greeks call ἐγκυκλοπαιδεία[1]) that are either altogether unknowne, or become doubtfull, through the overmuch curiositie of fine wits: again, other matters are deciphered in such long discourses, that they are tedious to the readers, insomuch as they loath and abhor them.

A difficult enterprise it is therfore to make old stuffe new, to give authoritie and credit to novelties, to polish and smooth that which is worne and out of use, to set a glosse and lustre upon that which is dim and darke, to grace and countenance things disdained, to procure beleefe to matters doubtful; and in one word, to reduce nature to all, and al to their own nature. And verily to give the attempt only and shew a desire to effect such a desseigne as this, although the same be not brought about and compassed, were a brave and magnificent enterprise. Certes of this [same] spirit am I, that [of] those learned men and great students, who making no stay, but breaking through al difficulties, have preferred the profit

---

[1] ἐγκύκλιος παιδεία, the circle of the sciences, the round of learning.

C

of posteritie before the tickling and pleasure of itching eares in
these daies; which I may protest that I have aimed at, not in this
worke only, but also in other of my bookes alreadie.[1]

§ 2

N o w as touching the titles and inscriptions of Bookes, the Greekes
therein have a wonderfull grace and great felicitie: some have
intituled them *Κηρίον*, whereby they would give us to understand
of A sweet hony-combe: others *Κέρας Ἀμαλθείας*, that is to say,
The horne of plenty and store: in such sort, that whosoever
readeth these goodly titles, must needs hope for some great matters
in such bookes, and as the proverb goeth, looke to drinke there or
else no where,[2] a good draught of hens milke. . . .[3]

For mine owne part, although I nothing repent mee that I have
devised no pretier Title for my Booke than plaine *Naturalis Historia*,
i. The reports of Nature, without more ceremonie; yet because I
would not be thought altogether to course and rate the Greekes,
I can be content, nay I am willing to bee thought in this behalfe
like unto those excellent grand masters in Greece, for Painting and
Imagerie, whom you shall finde in these Reports of mine, to have
entituled those rare and absolute peeces of worke (which the more
wee view and looke upon, the more wee admire and wonder at for
their perfection) with halfe titles and unperfect inscriptions, in this
manner, *Apelles went in hand with this Picture*: or, *Polycletus was a making this Image*: as if they were but begun, never finished and laid
out of their hands: which was done (no doubt) to this end, that for
all the varietie and diversitie of mens judgements scanning of their
workemanship, yet the Artificer thereby had recourse to make
excuse; had meanes (I say) to crave and have pardon for any faults
and imperfections that could be found, as if hee meant to have
amended any thing therein amisse or wanting, in case hee had not
beene cut off and prevented by death.

---

[1] A passage which is a good example of the happy marriage of Pliny and
Holland. Pliny's unexceptionable sentiments about his book are hammered home
by the translator; it remains difficult to make old stuff new, and easy to write
only to tickle the itching ears of today.

[2] Alternatively; expect to find there even (*vel*) a draught of hen's milk.

[3] ὀρνίθων γάλα, a proverbial name for rare and dainty things.

In

THE SECOND BOOKE

is contained

the discourse of the World, of coelestiall
impressions and meteors, as also of them
that appeare in the Aire, and upon the Earth

§ 3

Whether the World be finite, and but one

(Chap. 1)

THE World, and this, which by another name men have thought
good to call heaven (under the pourprise and bending cope whereof, all things are emmanteled and covered) beleeve we ought in all
reason to be a God, eternall, unmeasurable, without beginning,
and likewise endlesse. What is without the compasse hereof, neither
is it fit for men to search, nor within mans wit to reach and conceive. Sacred it is, everlasting, infinit, all in all, or rather it selfe all
and absolute: finite and limited, yet seeming infinite: in all motions
orderly and certaine: howbeit in shew and judgement of man,
uncertaine: comprehending and containing all whatsoever, both
without and within: Natures worke, and yet very Nature it selfe,
producing all things.

Great folly it is then, and meere madnesse, that some have
devised and thought in their minde to measure it; yea, and durst
in writing set down the dimensions thereof: that others againe, by
occasion hereupon taken or given, have delivered and taught, That
worlds there were innumerable: as if we were to beleeve so many
natures as there were Heavens: or if all were reduced to one, yet
there should be so many Sunnes and Moones nevertheless, with
the rest also of those unmeasurable and innumerable starres in that
one: as though in this pluralitie of worlds we should not alwaies

meet with the same question still at every turne of our cogitation, for want of the utmost and some end to rest upon: or if this infinite-nesse could possibly be assigned to Nature, the worke-mistresse and mother of all; the same might not be understood more easily in that one Heaven which wee see; so great a worke especially and frame as it is. Now surely a fantasticall folly it is of all other follies, to go forth of it, and so to keepe a seeking without, as if all things within were well and clearely knowne already: as who would say, a man could take the measure just of any third thing, who knoweth not his owne: or the minde of man see those things, which the very World itselfe may not receive.[1]

§ 4

Of God

(Chap. 7)

I SUPPOSE therefore that to seeke after any shape of God, and to assigne a forme and image to him, bewraieth mans weakenesse. For God, whosoever hee be (if haply there be any other, but the very world) and in what part soever resiant,[2] all sense he is, all sight, all hearing: he is all life, all soule, all of himselfe. And verily to beleeve that there be gods innumerable, and those according to mens vertues and vices, to wit, Chastitie, Concord, Understand-ing, Hope, Honour, Clemencie, Faith; or (as *Democritus* was of opinion) that there are two gods onely, and no more; namely, Punishment, and Benefit: These conceits, I say, make mens idle-nesse and negligence the greater. But all commeth of this, That fraile and crasie mortall men, remembring wel their owne infirmitie, have digested these things apart, to the end that each one might from thence chuse to worship and honour that whereof he stood

---

[1] Or, 'which the very world itself may not contain' (*non capiat*). The arguments here are partly redeemed by the idea that much more should be known of this world before speculating on the heavens. Pliny returns often to this theme, the ignorance of his contemporaries, and it is one of the main reasons why he com-piled the *Natural History*.

[2] Resident.

in need most. And hereupon it is, that in sundry nations we finde the same gods named diversly, according to mens devotion: and in one region ye shall have innumerable gods. The infernall powers beneath likewise, yea, and many plagues have been raunged by themselves, and reckoned for gods in their kinde, whilest with trembling feare wee desire that they were pacified. Which superstition hath caused a chappell to be dedicated to the Fever, in the mount Palatium, even by publicke order from the State. Likewise an altar to *Orbona*,[1] neere the temple of *Lares*: because another erected to Bad Fortune in Esquiliae. And thereby we may conceive that there are a greater number of gods in heaven above, than of men upon earth: since that every one of their owne accord make so many gods as they list, fitting themselves with *Junoes* and *Genii* for their patrons. Now certain Nations there be that account beasts, yea, and some filthie things for gods; yea and many other matters more shamefull to be spoken: swearing by stinking meats, by garlicke, and such like. But surely, to beleeve that gods have contracted mariage, and that in so long continuance of time no children should be borne between them: also that some are aged, and ever hoarie and gray: others againe young and alwaies childien: that they be blacke of colour and complexion, winged, lame, hatched of egs, living and dying each other day; are meere fooleries, little better than childish toies. But it passeth and exceedeth all shamelesse impudencie, to imagine adulteries amongst them: eftsoones also chiding, scolding, hatred, and malice: and more than that, how there be gods, patrons of theft and wickednesse. Whereas in very deed, a god unto a man is he, that helpeth a man: and this is the true and direct path-way to everlasting glory. . . .

Now, That the soveraigne power and deity, whatsoever it is, should have regard of mankind[2] is a toy and vanity worthy to be laughed at. For can we chuse but beleeve, can we make any doubt, but needs that Divinity and Godhead must be polluted with so base and manifold a ministery? And hardly in manner may it be judged, whether of the twain be better and more expedient for mankinde to beleeve, that the gods have regard of us; or to be persuaded that they have none at all: considering, That some men

---

[1] Goddess of parents bereft of children.
[2] Here let Christians take heed, and be thankefull to God for the light revealed unto them out of the holy scriptures (P. H.).

have no respect and reverence at all of the gods; others againe so much, as it is a very shame to see their superstition. Addicted these are and devoted to serve them by forrein magicke ceremonies: they weare their gods upon their fingers in rings, yea, they worship and adore monsters: they condemne and forbid some meats; yet they devise others for them. Impose they do upon them hard and vengible charges to execute, not suffering them to rest and sleep in quiet. They chuse neither mariages nor children, ne yet any one thing els, but by the approbation and allowance of sacred rites and mysteries. Contrariwise, others there are so godlesse, that in the very capitoll they use deceit, and forsweare themselves even by *Jupiter*, for all that he is ready to shoot his thunderbolts: and as some speed wel enough with their wicked deeds and irreligion; so others again feele the smart and are punished by the saints whom they adore, and the holy ceremonies which they observe.

Howbeit, betweene both these opinions, men have found out to themselves a middle Godhead and divine power, to the end that we should give stil a more uncertaine conjecture as touching God indeed. For throughout the whole world, in every place, at all times, and in all mens mouths, Fortune alone is sought unto and called upon: she only is named and in request; shee alone is blamed, accused and endited. None but she is thought upon; she only is praised, she only is reproved and rebuked: yea, and worshipped is she with railing and reprochfull tearms: and namely when she is taken to be wavering and mutable: and of the most sort supposed also blind; roving at random, unconstant, uncertaine, variable, and favoring the unworthy: whatsoever is laid forth, spent, and lost, whatsoever is received, woon and gotten: all that comes in, all that goes out is imputed to Fortune: and in all mens reckonings and accounts she makes up the booke and sets all streight. So abject we are, so servile also and enthralled to Lots, that even the very chance of Lots is taken for a god, than which nothing maketh us more doubtfull and ignorant of God.

Now there are another sort, that reject Fortune and Chance both, and wil not abide them, but attribute the events and issues of things, to their owne severall stars, and go by the fatall horoscope or ascendent of their nativitie: affirming that the same shall ever befall, which once hath bin set downe and decreed by God: so as he forever after may sit still and rest himselfe. And this opinion beginneth now to settle and take deep root, insomuch as both the learned, and also the rude and ignorant multitude, run that way on end. From hence (behold) proceed the warnings and admonitions of lightenings, the fore-knowledge by Oracles, the predictions of Soothsayers, yea, and other contemptible things not worthy to be once spoken of; as sneesing, and stumbling with the foot, are counted as matters of presage. *Augustus Caesar* of famous memorie hath made report and left in writing, that his left foot shooe was untowardly put on before[1] the right, on that very day, when he had like to have miscarried in a mutiny among his souldiers.

Thus these things every one doe enwrap and entangle silly mortall men, void of all forecast and true understanding: so as this only point among the rest remaines sure and certain, namely, That nothing is certaine: neither is there ought more wretched and more proud withall; than man. For all lively creatures else take care onely for their food, wherein Natures goodnes and bountie of it selfe is sufficient: which one point verily is to be preferred before all good things whatsoever, for that they never thinke of glory, of riches, of seeking for dignities and promotions, nor over and above, of death. Howbeit, the beleefe that in these matters the gods have care of mens estate, is good, expedient, and profitable in the course of this life: as also that the vengeance and punishment of malefactors may well come late (whiles God is busily occupied otherwise in so huge a frame of the world) but never misseth in the end: and that man was not made next in degree unto God, for this, That he should be wel-neare as vile and base as the bruit beasts. Moreover, the chiefe comfort that man hath, for his imperfections in Nature, is this, That even God himselfe is not omnipotent, and cannot do all things: for neither he is able to worke his owne death, would he never so faine, as man can do when he is wearie of his life; the best gift which he hath bestowed upon him, amid so great miseries of his life: nor indow mortall men with everlasting life: ne yet recall, raise, and revive those that once are departed and dead: nor bring to passe that one who lived, did not live; or he that bare honorable offices, was not in place of rule and dignity. Nay, he hath no power over things done and past, save only oblivion: no more than he is able to effect (to come with pleasant reasons and arguments to

---

[1] ? for. Probably the left shoe was put on instead of the right (*praepostere*).

prove our fellowship therin with God) that twise ten should not make twenty: and many such things of like sort. Whereby (no doubt) is evidently proved, the power of Nature, and how it is she, and nothing els, which we call God. I thought it not impertinent thus to divert and digresse to these points, so commonly divulged, by reason of the usuall and ordinarie questions as touching the Essence of God.

§ 5

Diverse considerations observed in the nature of winds

(Chap. 46)

THE old Greeke writers, not so few as twentie, have set downe and recorded their observations of the Winds. I marvell so much the more, that the World being so at discord, and divided into kingdomes, that is to say, dismembred as it was; so many men have had care to seek after these things, so intricate and hard to be found out, and namely in time of wars, and amid those places where was no safe lodging nor abode, and especially when pyrats and rovers, common enemies to mankinde, held welneere all passages: I marvell, I say, that at this day each man in his owne tract and countrey taketh more light and true knowledge of some things by their commentaries and bookes, who never set foot there, than they doe by the skill and information of home-born inhabitants; whereas now in time of so blessed and joious peace, and under a prince who taketh such delight in the progresse of the State and of all good arts, no new thing is learned by farther inquisition,[1] nay, nor so much as the inventions of old writers are throughly understood. And verily it cannot be said, that greater rewards were in those daies given, considering that the bountie of Fortune was dispersed, and put into many mens hands: and in truth most of these deepe Clerkes and learned men, sought out

---

[1] Research.

these secrets for no other reward or regard, than to doe good unto posteritie. But now mens manners are waxen old and decay; now, all good customes are in the waine: and notwithstanding that the fruit of learning be as great as ever it was, and the recompences as liberall, yet men are become idle in this behalfe. The seas are open to all, an infinite multitude of saylers have discovered all coasts whatsoever, they saile through and arrive familiarly at every shore: all for gaine and lucre, but none for knowledge and cunning. Their mindes altogether blinded, and bent upon nothing but covetousnesse, never consider that the same might with more safetie be performed by skill and learning. And therfore seeing there be so many thousand poore sailers that hazard themselves on the seas, I will treat of the winds more curiously and exquisitly than perhaps beseemes the present worke that is begun.

§ 6

Of the gaping chinks of the earth

(Chap. 80)

AFTER many and sundry sorts the earth therefore is shaken, and thereupon ensue wondrous effects: in one place the walls of cities are laid along: in another they be swallowed up in a deepe and wide chawne:[1] here are cast up mighty heaps of earth; there are let out Rivers of water, yea and somtimes fire doth breathe forth, and hot springs issue abroad: in another place the course and chanell of rivers is turned clean away and forced backward. There goeth before and commeth with it a terrible noise: one while a rumbling more like the loowing and bellowing of beasts: otherwhiles it resembles a mans voice, or else the clattering and rustling of armor and weapons, beating one upon another according to the qualitie of the matter that catcheth and receiveth the noise, or the fashion either of the hollow cranes[2] within, or the cranny by which it passeth, whiles in a narrow way it taketh on with a more slender and whistling noise: and the same keepeth an hoarse din in winding

---

[1] Chasm or cleft.   [2] Tunnels, tubes.

and crooked caves, rebounding againe in hard passages; roaring in moist places, waving and floting in standing waters, boiling and chafing against solid things. And therefore a noise is often heard without any earthquake, and never at any time shaketh it simply after one and the same manner, but trembles and waggeth to and fro.

As for the gaping chink, sometimes it remaineth wide open, and sheweth what it hath swallowed up; otherwhiles it closeth up the mouth, and hideth all, and the earth is knit together so againe, as there remaine no marks and tokens to be seene: notwithstanding many times it hath devoured cities, and drawne into it a whole tract of ground and fields. Sea coasts and maritime regions most of all other feele earthquakes. Neither are the hilly countries without this calamitie: for I my selfe have known for certain, that the Alps and Apenine have often trembled. In the Autumne also and Spring there happen more earthquakes than at other times, like as lightnings. And hereof it is that France and Egypt least of all other are shaken: for that in Egypt the continuall Sommer, and in France the hard Winter, is against it. In like manner, earthquakes are more rife in the night than in the day time: but the greatest use to be in the morning and evening. Toward day light there be many; and if by day, it is usually about noon. They fortune also to be when the Sun and Moone are eclipsed, because then all tempests are asleepe and laid to rest. But especially, when after much raine there followes a great time of heate; or after heate store of raine.

§ 7

Of the strange wonders of the land

(Chap. 93)

FOR let us speake no more of Earthquakes, and whatsoever else of that kind, as of graves and sepulchres of cities buried, and extant to be seen; but discourse we rather of the wonders, than the mischiefes wrought by Nature in the earth. And surely the story of coelestiall things was not more hard to be declared: the wealth is such of mettals and mines, in such varietie, so rich, so fruitfull, rising still one under another for so many ages, notwithstanding daily there is so much wasted and consumed throughout the world, with fires, ruines, shipwrecks, wars, and fraudulent practises: yea and so much spent in ryot and superfluous vanities, that it is infinite: yet see how many sorts of jemmes there be still, so painted and set out with colors? in precious stones what varieties of sundry colours, and how bespotted are they: and amongst them behold the brightnesse and white hue of some, excluding all else but onely light! The vertue and power of medicinable fountaines: the wonderfull burning so many hundred yeres together of fire issuing forth in so many places: the deadly dampes and exhalations in some places, either sent out of pits when they are sunke, or else from the very native seat and position of the ground; present death in one place to the birds and foules of the aire only (as at Soracte, in a quarter neere the city:) in other, to all other living creatures save only man: yea and sometimes to men also, as in the territories of Sinuessa and Puteoli. Which damp holes breathing out a deadly aire some call *Charoneae Scrobes*, i. *Charons* ditches. Likewise in the Hirpines land, that of Ampsanctus, a cave neere unto the temple of Mephitis, wherinto as many as enter dy presently. After the like manner at Hierapolis in Asia there is another such, hurting all that come to it, except the priest of *Cybele*, the great mother of the gods. In other places there be also caves and holes of a propheticall power; by the exhalation of which men are intoxicate and as it were drunken, and so foretell things to come, as at Delphi that most renowned Oracle. In all which things what other reason can any mortall man make, than the divine power of Nature, diffused and spred through all, which breaketh forth at times in sundry sorts.

THE THIRD BOOKE
describeth
the first and second gulfe, which the
Mediterranean sea maketh in Europe

§ 8

The Proeme, or Preface

HITHERTO have we written of the position and wonders of the
Earth, Waters, and Starres: also we have treated in generall termes,
of the proportion and measure of the whole world. Now it followeth, to discourse of the parts thereof: albeit this also be judged an
infinite piece of worke, nor lightly can be handled without some
reprehension: and yet in no kinde of enterprise pardon is more due;
since it is no marvell at all, if he who is borne a mortall man,
knoweth not all things belonging to man. And therefore I will not
follow one Author more than another, but every one as I shall
thinke him most true in the description of each part. Forasmuch
as this hath been a thing common in manner to them all, namely,
to learn or describe the scituations of those places most exactly,
where themselves were either borne, or which they had discovered
and seene: and therefore neither will I blame nor reprove any man.
The bare names of places shall be simply set downe in this my
Geographie, and that with as great brevitie as I can: the excellency,
as also the causes and occasions thereof, shall be deferred to their
severall and particular treatises: for now the question is as touching the whole earth in generalitie, which mine intent is to represent unto your eies: and therefore I would have things thus to be
taken, as if the names of countries were put downe naked, and void
of renowne and fame, and such onely as they were in the beginning,
before any acts there done; and as if they had indeed an indument
of names, but respective onely to the World and universall Nature
of all.

Now the whole globe of the earth is divided into three parts,

Europe, Asia and Africa. The beginning we take from the West and the Firth of Gades, even whereas the Atlanticke Ocean breaking in, is spred into the Inland and Mediterranean seas. Make your entrance there, I meane at the Streights of Gibralter, and then Africa is on the right hand, Europe on the left, and Asia before you just betweene. The bounds confining these, are the rivers Tanais[1] and Nilus. The mouth of the ocean at Gades (whereof I spake before) lyeth out in length 15 miles, and stretcheth forth in breadth but five, from a village in Spaine called Mellaria, to the promontorie of Africke, called the *White*, as *Turranius Gracilis* born thereby, doth write. *T. Livius*, and *Cornelius Nepos* have reported, that the breadth thereof where it is narrowest, is seven miles over, but ten miles where it is broadest. From so small a mouth (a wonder to consider) spreadeth the sea so huge and so vast as we see; and withall, so exceeding deepe, as the marvell is no lesse in that regard. For why? in the verie mouth thereof, are to be seen many barres and shallow shelves of white sands (so ebbe is the water) to the great terrour of shippes and sailers passing that way. And therefore many have called those Streights of Gibralter, The entrie of the Mediterranean Sea. Of both sides of this gullet, neere unto it, are two mountaines set as frontiers and rampiers to keepe all in: namely Abila for Africke, Calpe for Europe, the utmost end of *Hercules* Labours. For which cause, the inhabitants of these parts call them, the two pillars of that God; and doe verily beleeve, that by certaine draines and ditches digged within the Continent, the maine Ocean, before excluded, made way and was let in, to make the Mediteranean seas, where before was firme land: and so by that meanes the very face of the whole earth is cleane altered.

§ 9

Of Italy

(Chap. 5)

NEITHER am I ignorant, that it might be thought and that justly, a point of an unthankefull mind and idle withall, if briefely

[1] Don.

in this sort, and as it were by the way, that land should be spoken of which is the nource of all lands. She also is the mother, chosen by the powerfull grace of the gods, to make even heaven it selfe more glorious; to gather into one the scattered empires, to soften and make civill the rude fashions of other countries; and whereas the languages of so many nations were repugnant, wilde, and savage, to draw them together by commerce of speech, conference, and parley; to indue man with humanitie; and briefly, that of all nations in the world, there should be one onely countrey. But here, what should I do? so noble are all the places that a man shal come unto, so excellent is every thing, and each state so famous and renowned, that I am fully possessed with them all, and to seeke what to say. Rome citie, the only faire face therein, worthy to stand upon so stately a necke and pair of shoulders, what worke would it aske thinke you, to bee set out as it ought?[1] the very tract of Campaine by it selfe, so pleasant and goodly, so rich and happie, in what sort should it be described? So as it is plaine and manifest, that in this one place there is the workmanship of Nature wherein she joieth and taketh delight.

Now besides all this, the whole temperature of the aire is evermore so vitall, healthy, and wholesome, the fields so fertile, the hills so open to the Sun, the forrests so harmlesse, the groves so coole and shadie, the woods of all sorts so bounteous and fruitfull, the mountaines yeelding so many breathing blasts of winde; the corne, the vines, the olives so plentifull; the sheep so inriched with fleeces of the best wooll, the bulls and oxen so fat and well fed in the necke; so many lakes and pooles, such store of rivers and springs watering it throughout; so many seas and havens, that it is the very bosom lying open and ready to receive the commerce of all lands from all parts; and yet it selfe full willingly desireth to lie far into the sea to helpe all mankinde.[2] Neither do I speake now of the natures, wits, and fashions of the men; ne yet of the nations abroad subdued with their eloquent tongue, and strong hand. Even the Greekes (a nation of all other most given to praise themselves beyond measure) have given their judgement of her, in that they called some small part thereof, Great Greece. But in good faith, that which we did in the mention of the heaven, namely, to touch

---

[1] Set out in § 158, q.v.
[2] A similar passage appears in § 163, the Epilogue.

some knowne planets and a few stars, the same must we likewise do in this one part: only I would pray the Readers to remember and carry this away, That I hasten to rehearse every particular thing through the whole round globe of the earth.

THE FOURTH BOOKE
compriseth
the fourth gulfe of Europe

§ 10

The Corinth Canal

(Chap. 4)

PELOPONNESUS, called beforetime Apia and Pelasgia, is a demy Island, worthie to come behinde no other land for excellency and name; lying betweene two seas, Aegeum and Ionium: like unto the leafe of a plane tree, in regard of the indented creekes and cornered nouks thereof: it beareth a circuit of 563 miles, according to *Isodorus*. The same, if you comprise the creekes and gulfes, addeth almost as much more. The streight where it beginneth to passe on and go forward, is called Isthmos. In which place the seas abovenamed gushing and breaking from divers waies, to wit, from the North and the East, do devoure all the breadth of it there: untill by the contrary running in of so great seas, the sides on both hands being eaten away, and leaving a space of land betweene, five miles over, Hellas with a narrow necke doth meet with Peloponnesus. The one side thereof is called the Corinthian gulfe, the other, the Saronian. Lecheae of the one hand, and Cenchreae of the other, do bound out and limit the said streights where the ships are to fetch a great compasse about with some danger, such vessels I meane as for their bignesse cannot be conveighed over upon wains. For which cause, *Demetrius* the king, *Caesar* the Dictator, prince *Caius*,[1] and *Domitius Nero*, assaied to cut through the narrow foreland, and make a channell navigable with ease: but the attempt and enterprise was unhappie,[2] as appeared by the issue and end of them all.

[1] Caligula.
[2] After these four attempts, the canal was completed on, it is said, the original trace of Nero, by a French company in 1893.

§ 11

The paradise of the Hyperboreans

(Chap. 12)

WITHIN a little appeare the Ripaean hils, and a countrey called Pterophoros, for the resemblance of certain wings or feathers, occasioned by the continuall fall of snow. A part of the world thus is condemned by dame Nature, and drowned in deepe and thick darkenes, dwelling within no other houses but the workes of frozen cold, and the ycie harbors of the chilling Northerne wind. Behind those hills and beyond the North pole,[1] there is a blessed and happy people (if we may beleeve it) whom they call Hyperborei, who live exceeding long, and many fabulous and strange wonders are reported of them. In this tract are supposed to be the two points or poles about which the world turns about, and the very ends of the heavens revolution. For 6 moneths together they have one entire day; and night as long, when the Sunne is cleane turned from them: but their day beginneth not at the spring Aequinoctiall (as the leaud and ignorant common people do imagine) and so continueth to the Autumne: for once in the yeere, and namely at our mid-sommer when the Sun entreth into Cancer, the Sun riseth with them: and once likewise it setteth, even in the midwinter with us, when the Sun entreth Capricorne. The countrie is open upon the Sunne, of a blissefull and pleasant temperature, void of all noisome wind and hurtfull aire. Their habitations be in woods and groves, where they worship the gods both by themselves, and in companies and congregations: no discord know they; no sicknes are they acquainted with. They never die, but when they have lived long enough: for when the aged men have made good cheere, and annointed their bodies with sweet ointments, they leape from off a certain rocke into the sea. This kind of sepulture, of all others is most happy.

Some Writers have seated them in the first part of the sea coasts in Asia, and not in Europe, for that indeed some be there resembling the like manners and customes, and even so scituate, named Attaci.

---

[1] *ultra Aquilonem,* beyond the N. wind; but the sense of the rest of the passage is that the Pole was there.

Some have set them just in the mids between both Sunnes to wit, the setting of it with the Antipodes, and the rising of it with us: which cannot possibly be, considering so vast and huge a sea comming betweene. As for those that have placed them no where but in the six moneths day-light, [they] have written thus much of them, That they sow in the morning, reape at noone, at sunsetting gather the fruits from the trees, and in the nights lie close shut up within caves. Neither may we make doubt of that nation, since that so many Authors doe testifie, That they were wont to send the first fruits of their corne, as far as Delos to *Apollo*, whom above all others they honour. And virgins they were that had the carriage of this present; who for certaine yeeres were venerable, and courteously entertained of all nations, untill such time as upon breach of faithfull hospitalitie, they took up an order to bestow those sacred oblations in the next marches of their neighbour borderers: and they againe to conveigh the same to their neighbours that confined upon them, and so forward as far as to Delos. But soone after, this custome was for-let and cleane given over.

§ 12

Britaine and Ireland[1]

(Chap. 16)

OVER against this tract lieth Britannia, betweene the North and West, being an Island renowned both in Greeke and Roman records: opposite it is unto Germanie, Gaule, and Spaine, the greatest parts by far of all Europe, and no small sea betweene. It was some time named Albion, when all the Isles were called Britanniae, of which anon we wil speak. This Island is from Gesoriacum, a coast towne of Morini, fifty miles, taking the next and shortest cut. In circuit, as M. *Pitheas* and *Isidor* report, it containeth 3825 miles. And now for these thirtie yeeres well-neere, the Romane Captaines grow into farther knowledge thereof, and

[1] This chapter, and those following up to § 16, are examples from the geographical books in which the 'names of countries were put down naked'. The distances vary with the texts and many are inaccurate; e.g., Gesoriacum

yet not beyond the forrest of Caledonia, as neere as it is. *Agrippa* supposeth that it is in length 800 miles, and in bredth 300. Also that Ireland is as broad, but not so long by 200 miles. This Isle is seated above it, and but a very short cut or passage distant from it, to wit, 30 miles from the people Silures. Of other Islands in this Ocean there is none by report in circuit more than 125 miles. Now there be Orcades 40, divided asunder by small spaces betweene: Acmodae 7, and 30 Haebudes. Also betweene Britaine and Hibernia, Mona, Monapia, Ricnea, Vectis, Silimnus, and Andros: but beneath them, Siambis and Axantos: and on the contrary side towards the Germane Sea there lie scattering the Glessariae, which the later Greeke Writers have named Electrides, for that Amber was there ingendred or bred. The farthest of all knowne or spoken of, is Thule, in which there be no nights at all, as we have declared, about Midsummer, namely when the Sun passeth through Cancer: and contrariwise no daies in mid-winter: and each of these times they suppose do last six moneths, all day or all night. *Timaeus* the Historiographer saith, that farther within-forth, and six daies sailing from Britain, there lieth the Island Mictis, in which white lead grows; and that the Britans do saile thither in winter vessels, covered with leather round about, and wel sowed. There be that make mention of others beside, to wit, Scandia, Dumna, Bergos, and Nerigos the biggest of all the rest, from the which men saile to Thule. Within one daies sailing from Thule is the frozen sea, named of some Cronium.

(Boulogne) is not 50 miles from Britain. The place-names will be found in the index, but to save page-turning a list of them is repeated here:

Silures,	people of S. Wales.	Silimnus,	(Silumnus) Dalkey.
Orcades,	Orkneys.	Andros,	Bardsey I.
Acmodae,	Shetlands.	Siambis,	Sian.
Haebudes,	Hebrides.	Axantos,	Ushant.
Hibernia,	Ireland.	Glessariae,	Is. near Jutland (see § 160).
Mona,	Anglesey.	Thule,	Iceland (or Shetland or N.
Monapia,	I. of Man.		Norway).
Ricnea,	Rathlin (or Islay).	Mictis,	St. Michael's Mount sug-
Vectis,	I. of Wight (or		gested in spite of the six
	White-horn).		days' sail.

Scandia, Dumna, Bergos, and Nerigos are unidentified but possibly Hebrides. It has been suggested that Scandia was Sweden and Nerigos (Norge) was Norway, both at that time being thought to be islands.

THE FIFTH BOOKE
containeth the description of Africke

§ 13

Mount Atlas

(Chap. 1)

As many miles from it[1] is the towne Sala, standing upon a river of
the same name, neere now unto the wildernesse, much infested and
annoied with whole heards of Elephants, but much more with the
nation of the Autololes, through which lies the way to Atlas the
most fabulous mountaine of all Africk. For writers have given
out, that this hill arising out of the very midst of the sea sands,
mounteth up to the skie, all rough, ill favored, and overgrowne on
that side that lieth to the shore of the Ocean, unto which it gave
the name; and yet the same is shadowie, full of woods, and watered
with veines of spouting Springs that way which looketh to Africke,
with fruitfull trees of all sorts, springing of their own accord, and
bearing one under another, in such sort, that at no time a man can
want his pleasure and delight to his full contentment. Moreover,
that none of the inhabitants there are seene all day long: all is still
and silent, like the fearfull horror in desert wildernesse: and as men
come neerer and neerer unto it, a secret devotion ariseth in their
hearts, and besides this feare and horrour, they are lifted up above
the clouds,[2] and even close to the circle of the Moone. Over and
besides, that the same hill shineth oftentimes with many flashes of
fires, and is haunted with the wanton lascivious Aegipanes and
Satyres, whereof it is full, that it resoundeth with noise of Haut-
boies, pipes, and fifes, and ringeth againe with the sound of tabers,
timbrels, and cymbals. These be the reports of great and famous
writers, to say nothing of the labors and works both of *Hercules* and
Perseus there; and to conclude, that the way unto it is exceeding
great, and not certainely knowne.

[1] The river Subur, now Sebou.
[2] This could be fear and horror of the peak rising above the clouds, but
Holland had *elati super nubila* (following Dalechamp) and preferred the idea of
the approaching travellers being lifted above the clouds as they climbed higher.

Bookes there were besides of *Hanno*, a great captain and commander among the Carthaginians, who in the time of the most flourishing state of Carthage, had a charge and commission to discover and survey the whole compasse of Africk. Him, most of the Greeks as well as our countreymen following, among some other fabulous stories, have written that hee also built many cities there; but neither memoriall upon record, nor any token of them at all is left extant. . . . The first time that the Romans warred in Mauritania, was in the time of prince *Claudius* Emperor: at what time as *Aedemon* the freed servant of king *Ptolomaeus*, by *C. Caesar*[1] slaine, went about to revenge his death; for as the barbarous people retired and fled back, certaine it is that the Romans came as far as to the hill Atlas. And not only such Generals as had bin Consuls, and were of the Senatours degree and calling, who at that time managed and conducted the wars, but knights also and gentlemen of Rome, who from that time had government and command there, tooke it for an honor and glory, that they had pierced and entred into Atlas . . . and by that common fame and report, there may seeme to lie a thorow faire thither. But that is found for the most part by daily experience, most decciveable of all things else; because persons of high place and great worth, when they are loath to search out narrowly into the truth of matters, sticke not for shame of ignorance, to give out untruths: and never are men more credulous and apt to beleeve and be deceived, than when some grave personage fathereth a lie.

And verily I lesse marvell, that they of gentlemens degree, yea, and those now of Senators calling, have not come to the certaine knowledge of some things there: seeing they set their whole affection and mind upon nothing but excesse and riot; which how powerfull it is and forcible, is seen by this most of all, when forests are sought out far and neere for Ivory and Citron trees; when all the rocks in Getulia are searched for Murices and Purpurae (shell fishes that yeeld the purple crimson colour.)

Howbeit, the natural inhabitants of that country do write, That in the sea coast 150 miles from Sala, there is the river Asana, that receiveth salt water into it, but hath in it a goodly faire haven; and not far from it another fresh river, which they call Fut: from which to Dyris (for that is the name in their language of Atlas, by a

[1] Caligula.

generall consent) are 200 miles, with a river comming betweene, named Ivor. And there, the speech so goeth, are to be seene the certain tokens of a ground somtimes inhabited; to wit the reliques of vine-yards and date tree groves. *Suetonius Paulinus* (a Consull in our time) who was the first Roman leader, that for certaine miles space went over Atlas, also hath reported verily as touching the height thereof. . . .: and moreover, that the foot thereof, toward the bottom, stand thick and ful of tall woods, with trees therein of an unknown kinde, but the heigth of them is delectable to see to, smooth and even without knots, the leaves and branches like Cypresse, and besides the strong smell they yeeld, are covered all over with a thinne downe, of which (with some help of Art) fine cloath may be made, such as the silk-worm doth yeeld. That the top and crest thereof is covered over with deepe snow even in Sommer time. Moreover, that he reached up to the pitch of it at the tenth daies end, and went beyond it, as far as a river called Niger,[1] through wildernesses ful of blacke dust; where otherwhiles there stood out certaine cliffes, and craggie rocks, as they were scortched and burnt; and that those places by reason of partching heat were not habitable, albeit a man made triall thereof in the winter season: furthermore, that the pesants who dwelt in the next forests, were pestred with Elephants, wilde beasts, and serpents of all sorts; and those people were called Canarii; for that they and dogs feed together one with another, and part among them the bowels of wild beasts. For certaine it is knowne, that a nation of the Aethyopians whom they cal Perorsi, joineth upon them.

Juba the father of *Ptolomaeus*, who before time ruled over both Mauritanes, a man more memorable and renowned for his study and love of good letters, than for his kingdome and royall port, hath written the like concerning Atlas: and he saith moreover, that there is an herb growing there called Euphorbia, of his Physitions name that first found it: the milkie juice whereof he praiseth wondrous much, for to cleare the eies,[2] and to be a preservative against all serpents and poisons whatsoever; and thereof hath he written a treatise, and made a book by it selfe: thus much may suffice, if it be not too much, as touching Atlas.

§ 14

Alexandria

(Chap. 10)

BUT right worthy of praise is Alexandria, standing upon the coast of the Egyptian sea, built by *Alexander* the Great on Africke side, 12 miles from the mouth of Canopus, neere to the lake Mareotis, which was before-time called Arapotes.[1] *Dinochares* the Architect (a man renowned for his singular wit many waies) laid the modell and platforme therof by a subtil and witty devise; for having taken up a circuit of 15 miles for the city, he made it round like to a Macedonian cloke, ful in the skirts, bearing out into angles and corners, as wel on the right hand as the left, so as it seemed to lie in folds and plaits, and yet even then he set out one fifth part of all this plot for the kings palace. The lake Mareotis from the South side, meeteth with an arme of the river Nilus, brought from out of the mouth of the said river called Canopicus: for the more commodious trafficke and commerce out of the firme ground and inland Continent. This lake containeth within it sundry Islands, and (according to *Claudius Caesar*) it is thirty miles over. Others say, that it lieth in length 40 Schoeni, and so, whereas every Schoene is 30 stadia, it commeth by that account to be 150 miles long, and as many broad.[2] Over and besides, there be many goodly faire townes of great importance, standing upon the river Nilus where he runneth, and those especially which have given name to the mouthes of the river, and yet not to all those neither (for there be 11 of them in all, over and besides foure more, which they themselves call bastard mouthes) but to 7 of the principall.

[1] Rachotes (P. H.). Rachotes or Rachotis is correct. It was a small Greek village with a good port, where Alexander decided to build the capital of his western conquests.

[2] Another example of the geographical descriptions. Lake Mareotis or Mariut used to be 42 miles long and 22 wide before its connexion with the sea was closed. It is now a shallow lake behind the Alexandria coastline with an approximate maximum length of 25 miles and width of 10 miles.

§ 15

Jordan, the Dead Sea and the Essenes

(Chaps. 15–17)

T HE river Jordan springeth from the fountaine Panias, which gave the Syrname to the citie Caesarea, whereof we will speake more. A pleasant river it is, and as the site of the countrey will permit and give leave, winding and turning in and out, seeking as it were for love and favour, and applying it selfe to please the neighbor inhabitants. Full against his will, as it were, he passeth to the lake of Sodom, Asphaltites,[1] that ill-favored and cursed lake: and in the end falleth into it, and is swallowed up of it, where amongst those pestilent and deadly waters, he loseth his owne that are so good and wholesome. And therefore to keep himselfe out of it as long as he possibly could, upon the first opportunity of any vallies, hee maketh a lake, which many call Genesara, which is 16 miles long, and 6 broad. The same lake is environed with divers faire and beautifull townes; to wit, on the East side, with Julias and Hippo; on the South, with Tarichea, of which name, the lake by some is called Tarichion; and on the West, with Tiberias, an healthfull place for the baines there of hot waters.

Asphaltites, or the lake of Sodom, breedeth and bringeth forth nothing but Bitumen; and thereupon it tooke the name. No living body of any creature doth it receive into it: buls and camels swim and flote aloft upon it. And hereupon ariseth that opinion which goeth of it, That nothing there wil go downe and sink to the bottome. This lake in length exceedeth 100 miles, 25 miles over it is at the broadest place, and six at the narrowest.[2] On the East, the Arabian Nomades confront it; and on the South side, Machaerus regardeth it: in time past, the second fortresse of Judaea, and principall next to Jerusalem. On the same coast, there is a fountain of hot waters, wholesome and medicinable, named Callirhoe, and good against many diseases. The very name that it carrieth, importeth no lesse praise and commendation.

[1] Dead Sea.
[2] The Dead Sea is now about 40 miles long by 8 wide.

Along the West coast inhabit the Esseni.[1] A nation this is, living alone and solitarie, and of all others throughout the world most admirable and wonderfull. Women they see none: carnal lust they know not; they handle no mony; they lead their life by themselves, and keepe company onely with Date trees. Yet neverthelesse, the countrey is evermore well peopled, for that daily numbers of strangers resort thither in great frequencie from other parts: and namely, such as be weary of this miserable life, are by the surging waves of frowning fortune driven hither, to sort with them in their manner of living. Thus for many thousand yeares (a thing incredible, and yet most true) a people hath continued without any supply of new breed and generation. So mightily increase they evermore, by the wearisome estate and repentance of other men. Beneath them stood sometime Engedi, for fertilitie of soile and plenty of Date-tree groves, accounted the next city in all Judaea, to Jerusalem. Now, they say, it serveth for a place only to inter their dead: beyond it, there is a castle or fortresse scituat on a rock, and the same not far from the lake of Sodom Asphaltites.[2] And thus much as touching Judaea.

[1] Holland follows Dalechamp, *ab occidente litora Esseni habitant usquequaque*, instead of the usual *fugiunt (fugitant) usque qua nocent*, which suggests that the Essenes kept away from the noxious exhalations of the coast.

[2] This castle is named Masada in some texts. It was identified from Josephus' description of the fortress and was explored in 1842. The site is the cliff and hill-top of Sebbeh, visible from Engedi.

THE SIXTH BOOKE
Handleth the Cosmographie of Asia

§ 16

Of the Black Sea and Bosphorus

(Chap. 1)

THE sea called Pontus Euxinus, and named by the Greeks in old time, Axenos, for the hard usage that passengers found at the hands of those savage Nations upon the coasts thereof, is spred also betwixt Europ and Asia, upon a very spite and speciall envy of Nature, as it seems, to the earth, and a wilfull desire to maintaine the sea still in his greatnesse, and to fulfill his greedy and endlesse appetite. For shee was not contented to have invironed the whole earth, with the main Ocean, yea and taken from it a great part thereof, with exceeding rage overflowing the same, and laying all empty and naked: it sufficed not, I say, to have broken through the mountaines, and so to rush in, and after the sea had dismembred Calpe[1] from Affricke, to have swallowed up much more by far than is left behind to be seen: no nor to have let Propontis[2] gush through Hellespont, and so to encroach again upon the earth and gaine more ground: unlesse from the streights of Bosphorus also he enlarge himselfe into another huge and vast sea, and yet is never content, untill the lake Mœotis[3] also with his streight, meet with him as he thus spreadeth abroad and floweth at liberty, and so joine together and part as it were, their stolen good betweene them. And verily that all this is happened maugre the earth, and that it made all resistance that it could, appeareth evidently by so many streights and narrow passages lying between these two elements of so contrary nature (considering that in Hellespont, the space is not above 875 [double] paces from land to land; and at the two Bosphori the sea is so passeable, that oxen or kine may swim at ease from the one side to the other: and hereupon they both tooke their name:) the which vicinitie serveth very wel to

---

[1] Gibraltar.   [2] Sea of Marmora.   [3] Sea of Azov.

entertaine and nourish amity among nations, separated by nature one from another; and in this disunion as it were, appeareth yet a brotherly fellowship and unitie. For the cocks may be heard to crow, and the dogs to bark, from the one side to the other; yea and men out of these two worlds may parly one to another with audible voice, and have commerce of speech together, if the weather be calme, and that the windes doe not carry away the sound thereof.

§ 17

The manifold, strange, and wonderfull formes and shapes of men

(Chap. 30)

ALL Ethyopia in generall was in old time called Aetheria: afterwards Atlantia: and finally of *Vulcans* son *Aethiops*, it took the name Ethyopia. No wonder it is, that about the coasts thereof there be found both men and beasts of strange and monstrous shapes, considering the agilitie of the suns fierie heat, so strong and powerfull in those countries, which is able to frame bodies artificially of sundry proportions, and to imprint and grave in them divers forms. Certes, reported it is, that far within the country Eastward there are a kinde of people without any nose at all on their face, having their visage all plain and flat. Others again without any upper lip, and some tonguelesse. Moreover, there is a kind of them that want a mouth, framed apart from their nose-thrils: and at one and the same hole, and no more, taketh in breath, receiveth drinke by drawing it in with an oaten straw; yea, and after the same maner feed themselves with the grains of oats, growing of their own accord without mans labour and tillage, for their only food. And others there be, who in stead of speech and words, make signes, as well with nodding their heads, as moving their other members. There are also among them, that before the time of *Ptolomaeus Lathyrus* king of Egypt, knew no use at all of fire.

Furthermore, writers there be, who have reported, that in the countrey neere unto the meeres and marishes from whence Nilus issueth, there inhabit those little dwarfes called Pygmei. . . . But then he [Dalion, the historian] telleth fabulous and incredible tales of those countries. Namely, that Westward there are people called Nigroi, whose king hath but one eie, and that in the mids of his forehead. Also he talketh of the Agriophagi, who live most of panthers and lions flesh. Likewise of the Pomphagi, who eat all things whatsoever. Moreover, of the Anthropophagi, that feed on mans flesh. Furthermore, of the Cynamolgi,[1] who have heads like dogs. Over and besides, the Artabatites who wander and go up and downe in the forests like fourefooted savage beasts. Beyond whom, as he saith, be the Hesperioi, and Perorsi, who, as we said before, were planted in the confines of Mauritania. In certain parts also of Ethyopia the people live of Locusts only, which they pouder with salt, and hang up in smoke to harden, for their yerely provision, and these live not above 40 yeares at the most.

[1] Dog-milkers.

THE SEVENTH BOOKE
treateth of man, and his inventions

§ 18

The Proeme; Nature's mistake

THUS, as you see, we have in the former books sufficiently treated of the universall world; of the Lands, Regions, Nations, Seas, Islands, and renowned Cities therein contained. It remaines now to discourse of the living creatures comprised within the same, and their natures: a point doubtlesse that would require as deepe a speculation as any part else thereof whatsoever, if so be the spirit and minde of man were able to comprehend and compasse all things in the world. And to make a good entrance into this treatise and history, me thinkes of right we ought to begin at Man, for whose sake it should seeme that Nature made and produced all other creatures besides: though this great favour of hers, so bountifull and beneficiall in that respect, hath cost them full deare. Insomuch as it is hard to judge, whether in so doing she hath done the part of a kinde mother, or a hard and cruell step-Dame.

For first and formost, of all other living creatures, man she hath brought forth all naked, and cloathed him with the good and riches of others. To all the rest she hath given sufficient to clad them every one according to their kinde; as namely, shells, cods, hard hides, prickes, shag, bristles, haire, downe feathers, quills, skales, and fleeces of wooll. The very trunkes and stems of trees and plants she hath defended with barke and rinde, yea and the same sometimes double, against the injuries of heat and cold: Man alone, poore wretch, she hath layed all naked upon the bare earth, even on his birth day, to cry and wraule presently from the very first houre that hee is borne, in such sort as among so many living creatures there is none subject to shed teares and weepe like him. And verily to no babe or infant is it given once to laugh before he be forty daies old, and that is counted very early, and with the soonest. Moreover, so soone as he is entred in this manner to enjoy the light of the Sunne, see how he is immediately tyed and bound fast, and hath no member at libertie:[1] a thing that is not practised upon the yong whelpes of any beast among us, be he never so wilde. The childe of man thus untowardly borne, and who another day is to rule and command all other, loe how he lieth bound hand and foot, weeping and crying, and beginning his life in miserie, as if he were to make amends and satisfaction by his punishment unto Nature, for this onely fault and trespasse, that he is borne alive.

O folly of all follies, ever to thinke (considering this simple beginning of ours) that we were sent into this world to live in pride, and cary our heads aloft! The first hope that we conceive of our strength, the first gift that Time affourdeth us, maketh us no better yet than foure footed beasts. How long is it ere we can go alone? how long before we can prattle and speake, feed our selves, and chew our meat strongly? what a while continueth the mould and crowne of our heads to beate and pant, before our braine is well settled;[2] the undoubted marke and token that bewraieth our exceeding great weakenesse above all other creatures? What should I say of the infirmities and sicknesses that do soone seise upon our feeble bodies? what need I speake of so many medicines and remedies devised against these maladies: besides the new diseases that come every day, able to checke and frustrate all our provision of physicke whatsoever? As for all other living creatures, there is not one, but by a secret instinct of nature knoweth his own good, and wherto he is made able; some make use of their swift feet, others of their flight wings; some are strong of limne; others are apt to swim, and practise the same: man only knoweth nothing unlesse he be taught; hee can neither speake, nor goe, nor eate, otherwise than he is trained to it: and to be short, apt and good at nothing he is naturally, but to pule and cry. And hereupon it is, that some have beene of this opinion, That better it had been, and simply best for a man, never to have been borne, or else speedily to die.

None but we doe sorrow and waile, none but we are given to excesse and superfluitie infinitely in every thing, and shew the same in every member that we have. Who but we againe are ambitious and vain-glorious? who but we are covetous and greedie

---

[1] It is still common, in parts of the Mediterranean area and the Middle and Far East, to bind infants so firmly that they cannot move.
[2] The fontanelle closes at about 18 months.

of gathering good? we and none but we desire to live long and
never to die, are superstitious, carefull of our sepulture and buriall,
yea and what shall betide us when we are gone. Mans life is most
fraile of all others; and in least securitie he liveth: no creature
lusteth more after every thing than he: none feareth like unto him,
and is more troubled and amazed in his fright: and if he be set once
upon anger, none more raging and wood than he. To conclud, all
other living creatures live orderly and well, after their owne kinde:
we see them flocke and gather together, and ready to make head
and stand against all others of a contrary kinde: the lyons as fell
and savage as they be, fight not one with another: serpents sting
not serpents, nor bite one another with their venomous teeth: nay
the very monsters and huge fishes of the sea, war not among themselves in their owne kinde: but beleeve me, Man at mans hand
receiveth most harme and mischiefe.

§ 19

The strange and wondrous shapes of sundry nations

(Chap. 1)

IN our Cosmographie and reports of nations and countries, wee
have spoken in generall of all mankinde, spred over the face of the
whole earth: neither is it our purpose at this present to decipher
particularly all their customes and manners of life, which were
a difficult enterprise, considering how infinit they be, and as many
in manner as there be societies and assemblies of men. Howbeit,
I thinke it good, not to over-passe all, but to make relation of some
things concerning those people especially, who live farthest remote
from our seas: among whom I doubt not but I shall find such
matter, as to most men will seeme both prodigious and incredible.
And verily who ever beleeved that the Aethiopians had bin so
blacke, before he saw them with his eies: nay what is it, I pray
you, that seemeth not a wonder at the first sight? How many
things are judged impossible before they are seene done and
effected? And certes, to speake a truth, The power and majestie of
Nature, in every particular action of hers and small things, seemeth
incredible, if a man consider the same severally, and enter not
into a generall conceit of her wholly as she is.

For to say nothing of the painted peacocks feathers, of the sundry spots of tygres, luzernes, and panthers, of the variable colours and markes of so many creatures besides: let us come to one only point, which to speake of seemes but small, but being deepely weighed and considered, is a matter of exceeding great regard, and that is, The varietie of mens speech; so many tongues and divers languages are amongst them in the world, that one stranger to another seemeth well-neere to be no man at all. But come to view and marke the variety that appeares in our face and visage, albeit there be not past ten parts or little more therein, see how among so many thousands as we are, you shall not find any two persons, who are not distinct in countenance and different one from another: a thing that no artificer nor painter (be he never so cunning and his craftmaster every way) can performe, but in a few pictures, and take what heed he can with all his curious affectation.

And yet thus much must I advertise the readers of this mine history by the way, that I will not pawne my credit for many things that herein I shall deliver, nor bind them to beleeve all I write as touching strange and forrein nations: refer them rather I will to mine authors, whom in all points (more doubtful than the rest) I will cite and alledge, whom they may beleeve if they list: onely let them not thinke much to follow the Greeke writers, who from time to time in this behalfe have been more diligent in penning, and more curious in searching after antiquities.[1]

§ 20

The diversitie of nations; India and Ethiopia

(Chap. 2)

BUT principally above all other countries, India and the whole tract of Aethiopia is full of these strange and miraculous things.

---

[1] This sentence defines very clearly Pliny's attitude to reported marvels. The nineteenth-century critics, conscious of scientific discoveries being made all around them, blamed Pliny for setting down, and even believing, too many fables; it is possible they had not noticed this passage and others like it (see Introduction, p. xviii). While Pliny is less than fair in condemning the Greeks *en masse*, he does soften the blow by suggesting that they are not always so 'curious'. He never loses an opportunity to have at them; see, for example, § 160 where he rates Sophocles for his views on amber.

And first and formost the beasts bred in India be very big, as it may appeare by their dogs, which for proportion are much greater than those in other parts. And trees grow there to that tallnesse, that a man cannot shoot a shaft over them. The reason hereof is the goodnesse and fatnesse of the ground, the temperat constitution of the aire, and the abundance of water: which is the cause also that under one fig tree (beleeve it that list) there may certaine troupes and squadrons of horsmen stand in covert, shaded with the boughes. And as for reeds, they be of such a length, that between every joint they will yeeld sufficient to make boats able to receive three men apeece, for to row therein at ease. There are to be seene many men there above five cubits tall:[1] never are they known once to spit, troubled they are not with pain in the head, tooth-ach, or griefe of the eies; and seldome or never complaine they of any sorance in other parts of the body, so hardy are they, and of so strong a constitution thorough the moderat heat of the Sun. Over and besides, among the Indians be certain Philosophers, whom they call Gymnosophists, who from the Sun rising to the setting thereof are able to endure all the day long, looking full against the Sunne, without winking or once moving their eies: and from morning to night can abide to stand somtimes upon one leg, and sometimes on the other in the sand, as scalding hot as it is. Upon a certaine mountaine named Nulus, there be men whose feet grow the tother way backward, and of either foot they have eight toes, as *Megasthenes* doth report. And in many other hils of that countrey, there is a kind of men with heads like dogs, clad all over with skins of wild beasts, who in lieu of speech use to bark: armed they are and well appointed with sharp and trenchant nailes: they live upon the prey which they get by chasing wild beasts, and fowling. *Ctesias* writes that there were discovered and knowne of them above 120000 in number.

By whose report also, in a certaine country of India the women beare but once in their life, and their infants presently waxe grey so soone as they are borne into the world.[2] Also, that there is a kind of people named Monocoli, that have but one leg apeece, but they are most nimble, and hop wondrous swiftly. The same men are

---

[1] 7 feet 6 inches.
[2] This may be because dark skin pigmentation does not appear until shortly after birth.

also called Sciopodes, for that in hotest season of the Summer, they ly along on their back, and defend themselves with their feet against the Suns heate: and these people as he saith are not farre from the Troglodites. Againe, beyond these Westward, some there be without heads standing upon their necks, who cary eies in their shoulders. Among the Westerne mountains of India the Satyres haunt, (the country wherein they be, is called the region of the Catarcludi) creatures of all other most swift in footmanship: which one whiles run with all foure; otherwhiles upon two feet only like men: but so light footed they are, that unlesse they be very old and sick, they can never be taken. *Tauron* writeth, That the Choromandae are a savage and wild people: distinct voice and speech they have none, but in stead thereof, they keep an horrible gnashing and hideous noise: rough they are and hairy all over their bodies, eies they have red like the houlets, and toothed they be like dogs. *Eudoxus* saith, That in the Southern parts of India, the men kind have feet a cubit long, but the women so short and smal, that thereupon they be called Struthopodes, *i.* sparrow footed.

Megasthenes is my Author, that among the Indian Nomades there is a kind of people, that in stead of noses have only two smal holes, and after the manner of snakes they have their legs and feet limmer,[1] wherwith they crawle and creep, and named they are Sciritae. In the utmost marches of India, Eastward, about the source and head of the river Ganges, there is a nation called the Astomes, for that they have no mouths: all hairy over the whole body, yet clothed with soft cotton and down that come from the leaves of trees: they live only by the aire, and smelling to sweet odors, which they draw in at their nosthrils: No meat nor drinke they take, only pleasant savours from divers and sundry roots, floures, and wild fruits growing in the woods they entertaine: and those they use to carry about with them when they take any farre journey, because they would not misse their smelling. And yet if the sent be any thing strong and stinking, they are soone therwith overcome, and dy withal. Higher in the country, and above these, even in the edge and skirts of the mountains, the Pygmaei Spythamaei[2] are reported to be: called they are so, for that they

---

[1] Bandy, or supple.
[2] *Trispithami*, the three-span men.

are but a cubit or three shaftments (or spannes) high, that is to say, three times nine inches. The clime wherein they dwel is very wholsome, the aire healthy, and ever like to the temperature of the Spring: by reason that the mountains are on the North side of them, and beare off all cold blasts. And these prety people *Homer* also hath reported to be much troubled and anoied by cranes. The speech goeth, that in the Spring time they set out all of them in battell aray, mounted upon the backe of rammes and goats, armed with bowes and arrowes, and so downe to the sea side they march, where they make foule worke among the egges and yong crane-lings newly hatched, which they destroy without all pitty. Thus for three months this their journy and expedition continueth, and then they make an end of their valiant service: for otherwise if they should continue any longer, they were never able to with-stand the new flights of this foule, grown to some strength and bignesse. As for their houses and cottages, made they are of clay or mud, fouls feathers, and birds egge shels. . . .

See how nature is disposed for the nones to devise full wittily in this and such like pastimes to play with mankinde, thereby not only to make her self merry, but to set us a wondring at such strange miracles. And I assure you, thus dayly and hourely in a manner playeth she her part, that to recount every one of her sports by themselves, no man is able with all his wit and memory. Let it suffice therfore to testifie and declare her power, that we have set downe those prodigious and strange workes of hers shewed in whole nations: and then go forward to discourse of some particulars approved and knowne in man.

§ 21

*Of Conceptions: and signes distinguishing
the sex in great bellied women*

(Chaps. 6, 7)

IF ten dayes after a woman hath had the company of a man shee feele an extraordinary ache in the head, and perceive giddinesse in the brain as if all things went round; finde a dazling and mistinesse in the eies, abhorring and loathing meat, and withall a turning and wambling[1] in the stomacke; it is a signe that she is conceived, and beginneth to breed: if she goe with a boy better coloured will she be all the time, and delivered with more ease, and by the 40 day she shall feele a kinde of motion and stirring in her wombe. But contrarie it falleth out in the breeding of a girle, she goeth more heavily with it, and findeth the burthen heavier, her legs and thighes about the share will swell a little. And ninetie dayes it will be before she absolutely perceiveth any moving of the infant. But be it male or female shee breeds, they put her to much paine and grievance when their haire beginneth to bud forth, and ever at the full of the Moone: and even the very infants after they are borne are most amisse and farthest out of frame about that time. And verily great care must be had of a woman with child all the time she goeth therewith, both in her gate, and in every thing else that can be named: for if women feed upon over-salt and poudered[2] meat they wil bring forth a child without nailes: and if they hold not their wind[3] in their labor, longer it will be ere they be delivered, and with more difficultie. Much yawning in the time of travell is a deadly signe: like as to sneese presently upon conception threatneth abortion or a slip.

I am abashed much, and very sory to thinke and consider what a poore and ticklish beginning man hath, the proudest creature of all others, when the smel only of the snuffe of a candle put out is the cause oft times that a woman fals into untimely travel. And yet see, these great tyrans, and such as delight only in carnage and bloudshed have no better original. Thou then that presumest upon thy bodily strength, thou that standeth so much upon Fortunes favors, and hast thy hands full of her bountifull gifts, taking thy self not to be a foster-child and nurceling of hers, but a naturall son borne of her owne body: thou I say that busiest thy head evermore, and setteth thy minde upon conquests and victories: thou that art upon everie good successe and pleasant gale of prosperity puffed up with pride, and takest thy selfe for a god, never thinkest that

---

[1] *redundatio stomachi*; a modern translation has 'vomiting', but Lewis and Short, quoting this reference, give 'a rising', a description which any pregnant woman will confirm.
[2] Spiced, salted.
[3] Hold not their breath.

thy life when it was hung upon so single a thred, with so small a matter might have miscarried.

Nay more than that, even at this day art thou in more danger than so, if thou chance to be but stung or bitten with the little tooth of a Serpent; or if but the verie kernell of a raisin go downe thy throat wrong, as it did with the poet *Anacreon*, which cost him his life. Or, as *Fabius* a senator of Rome, and Lord chiefe Justice besides, who in a draught of milk fortuned to swallow a small haire, which strangled him. Well then, thinke better of this point, for he verily that will evermore set before his eies and remember the frailty of mans estate, shall live in this world uprightly and in even ballance, without inclining more to one side than unto another.

§ 22

Examples of many that have been very like

(Chap. 12)

TORANIUS a merchant slave-seller, sold unto *M. Antonius* (now one of the two great Triumvirs)[1] two most beautiful and sweet faced boyes, for twins, so like were they one to the other, albeit the one was borne in Asia, and the other beyond the Alps. But when *Antony* afterwards came to know the same, and that this fraud and cousenage was bewraied and detected by the language and speech of the boyes, he fell into a furious fit of choler, and all to berated the foresaid *Toranius*. And when among other challenges he charged him with the high price he made him pay (for they cost him two hundred[2] Sesterces, as for twins, when they were none such) the wily merchant being his craftmaster answered, That it was the cause why he held them so deare, and sold them at so deare a rate: for (quoth he) it is no marvell at all that two

---

[1] *jam triumviro*, when he was one of the triumvirate (Antony, Octavian, and Lepidus). Either Holland felt that Lepidus was insignificant or 'two' is a printer's error'.

[2] Or 200,000.

brethren twins that lay both together in one belly do resemble one the other; but that there should be any found borne as these were in divers countries, so like in all respects as they, he held it for a most rare and wonderfull thing. This answer of his was delivered in so good time, and so fitly to the purpose, that *Antonie* the great man, who never was well but when he outlawed citisens of Rome, and did confiscat their goods, he I say that erewhile was all enraged and set upon reviling and reprochfull termes, was not only appeased, but also contented so with his bargaine, that he prised those two boies as much as any thing else in all his wealth.

§ 23

The teeth

(Chap. 16)

SOME children are borne with an entire whole bone that taketh up all the gum, instead of a row of distinct teeth; as a son of *Prusias* king of the Bythinians, who had such a bone in his upper chaw. This is to be observed about teeth, that they onely check the fire and burn not to ashes with other parts of the body: and yet as invincible as they are and able to resist the violence of the flame, they rot and become hollow with a little catarrhe or waterish rheume that droppeth and distilleth upon them:[1] white they may be made, with certaine mixtures and medicines called *Dentifrices*. Some weare their teeth to the very stumps onely with use of chawing; others againe loose them first[2] out of their head; they serve not onely to grind our meat for our daily food and nourishment, but necessary also they be for the framing of our speech. The fore-teeth stand in good stead to rule and moderate the voice by a certaine consent and tuneable accord, answering as it were to the stroke of the tongue: and according to that row and ranke of theirs wherein they are set, as they are broader or narrower,

---

[1] An alternative translation, 'teeth are hollowed out by the poisons in corrupt phlegm', makes this clearer.
[2] *Primum*, first, may be read *prius*; the sense then is that some lose their teeth (presumably from decay) earlier than those who wear them down by chewing.

greater or smaller, they yeeld a distinction and varietie in our words, cutting and hewing them thicke and short, framing them pleasant, plaine, and ready, drawing them out at length, or smuddering and drowning them in the end: but when they bee once falne out of the head, man is bereaved of all means of good utterance and explanation of his words.

§ 24

Of bodily strength and swiftnesse

(Chap. 20)

V A R R O in his treatise of prodigious and extraordinary strength, maketh report of one *Tritanus*, a man that of body was but little and lean withall, howbeit of incomparable strength, much re-nowned in the fence schoole, and namely, in handling the Samnites weapons, wearing their manner of armor, and performing their feats and masteries of great name. He maketh mention also of a sonne of his, a souldier, that served under *Pompeius* the Great, who had all over his body, yea and throughout his armes and hands, some sinewes running streight out in length, others cross-ing overthwart lattise-wise; and he saith moreover of him, that when an enemie out of the camp gave him defiance and challenged him to a combat, he would neither put on defensive harnesse, ne yet arme his right hand with offensive weapon; but with naked hand made meanes to foile and overcome him, and in the end when hee had caught hold of him, brought him away perforce into his own camp with one finger. *Vinnius Valens* a captaine, pensioner or centurion of the gard-souldiers about *Augustus Caesar*, was woont alone to beare up a charriot laden with certain hogsheads or a butt of wine, untill it was discharged thereof, and the wine drawne out: also his manner was with one hand to stay a coach against all the force of the horses striving and straining to the contrary; and to perform other wonderfull masteries, which are to be seen engraven upon his tombe; and therefore (quoth *Varro*) being called *Hercules*[1]

[1] Rusticellus was nicknamed Hercules for his feats of strength; hence 'there-fore'.

Rusticellus, he tooke up his mule upon his back and carried him away. *Fufius Salvius* having two hundred pound weights at his feet, and as many in his hands, and twise as much upon his shoulders, went withall up a paire of staires or a ladder. My selfe have seene one named *Athanatus,* do wonderfull strange matters in the open shew and face of the world, namely, to walke his stations upon the stage with a cuirace of lead weighing 500 pound, booted besides with a pair of buskins or greives about his legges that came to as much in weight. As for *Milo* the great wrestler of Crotona, when he stood firm upon his feet, there was not a man could make him stir one foot; if he held a pomegranat fast within his hand, no man was able to stretch a finger of his and force it out at length.

It was counted a great matter, that *Phidippides* ran 1140 stadia,[1] to wit, from Athens to Lacedaemon in two daies, untill *Anystis* a courier of Lacedaemon, and *Philonides* footman to *Alexander* the great, ran between Sicyon and Elis in one day, 1200 stadia. But now verily at this day we see some in the grand cirque, able to indure in one day the running of 160 miles. And but a while agoe we are not ignorant, that when Fonteius and Vipstanus were Consuls, a yong boy but 9 yeres old, between noon and evening ran 75 miles. And verily a man may wonder the more at this matter, and come to the full conceit thereof, if he do but consider, that it was counted an exceeding great journy that *Tiberius Nero* made with three chariots (shifting from one to the other fresh) in a day and a night, riding post haste unto his brother Drusus then lying sicke in Germany, and all that was but 200 miles.[2]

§ 25

The praise of C. Julius Caesar

(Chap. 25)

F O R vigor and quicknesse of spirit, I take it, that *C. Caesar* Dictatour, went beyond all men besides. I speake not now of his vertue

[1] 130 miles.
[2] These distances are given in thousands of paces and the texts vary. Holland's mileages have been reduced by 5 to 10 per cent. by Rackham.

and constancie, neither of his high reach and deep wit, whereby he apprehended the knowledge of all things under the cope of heaven; but of that agilitie of minde, that prompt and ready conceit of his, as nimble and active as the verie fire. I have heard it reported of him, that he was wont to write, to reade, to indite letters, and withall to give audience to suiters and heare their causes all at one instant. And being emploied, as you know he was, in so great and important affaires, he ordinarily indited letters to foure secretaries or clerkes at once: and when he was free from other greater businesse, he would otherwise finde seven of them work at one time. The same man in his daies fought 50 set battels with banners displaied against his enemies: in which point, he alone out-went *M. Marcellus*, who was seene 40 times save one in the field. Besides the carnage of citizens that hee made in the civill wars when he obtained victory, he put to the sword 1,192,000 of his enemies, in one battell or other. And certes for mine owne part, I hold this for no speciall glory and commendation of his, considering so great injurie done to mankind by this effusion of bloud; which in some part he hath confessed himselfe, in that he hath forborne to set downe the overthrowes and bloudshed[1] of his adversaries (fellow citizens) during the civill wars. Yet *Pompey* the great deserves honour more justly for scouring the seas, and taking from the rovers 846 saile of ships.

But to return again to Caesar, over and above the qualities of worth before rehearsed, an especiall property of his owne he had, for clemency and mercy, wherein he so far forth surmounted all other men, that hee repented therof in the end. As for his magnanimity, it was incomparable, and he left such a president behind him, as I forbid all men to match or second it. For to speake of his sumptuosities, of his largesses, of the magnificent shewes exhibited to the people, the exceeding cost and charges therein bestowed, with all the stately furniture thereto belonging, were a point of him that favored such lavish expence and superfluities. But herein appeared his true hautinesse of mind indeed, and that unmatchable spirit of his, that when upon the battel at Pharsalia, as wel the cofers and caskets with letters and other writings of *Pompey*, as also those of *Scipio's* before Thapsus, came into his hands, he was most true to them, and burnt all without reading one scrip or scrol.

[1] The casualty list.

§ 26

Fortunes lap

(Chap. 40)

DOUBTLESSE it is, and past all question, that of all Nations under the Sun, the Romans excell and are the only men for all kinde of vertues. But to determine who is the happiest man in all the world is above the reach of humane wit; considering that some take contentment and repose felicitie in this thing, others in that, and every one measureth it according to his severall fancy and affection: but to say a truth, and judge aright indeed, laying aside all the glosing flatteries of fortune, and without courting her to determin this point, There is no man to be counted happy in this world. Right well it is on our side, and Fortune dealeth in exceeding favor with us, if we may not justly be called unhappy: for put case there be no other miserie and calamitie besides, yet surely a man is ever in feare lest Fortune will frowne upon him, and do him a shrewd turne one time or other: and admit this feare once, there can be no sound happinesse and contentment in the minde. What shall I say moreover than this, that no man is at all times wise and in his perfect wits? Would God that this were taken of most men for a Poets word only, and not a true saying indeed.

But such is the vanity and folly of poore mortall men, that they flatter themselves, and are very witty to deceive themselves, making their accounts and reckonings of good and evill fortune like to the Thracians, who by certain white and blacke stones which they cast into a certain vessell, and there laid up for the better proofe and triall of every dayes fortune; and at the last day and time of their death they fall to parting these stones one from another, and telling them apart, and according to the number of the white and blacke, give judgement and pronounce of each ones fortune. But what say they to this, that many times it falleth out, that the day marked with a white stone, for a good day, had in it the beginning and overture of some great misfortune and calamitie? How many men have seemed to fall into Fortunes lap, and entred upon great empires and dominions, which in the end turned to their afflictions and miseries? How many have we seen overthrowne, punished extremely, and brought to utter ruine, even by means of their owne good parts and commendable gifts? Certes these be good things and great favors, if a man could make ful account to enjoy them but one houre with contentment.

But thus verily stands the case, and this is the ordinary course of this world: one day is the judge of another, and the day of death judgeth and determineth all: and therefore there is no trust in them, neither may wee assure our selves of any. To say nothing of this, that our good fortunes are not in number equall to our bad: and say there were as many of the one as of the other, Is there any one joy to be weighed in true ballance against the least grief and sorrow that commeth? Foolish and sottish men that we are for all our curiositie! for we reckon our daies by tale and number, whereas we should ponder and peise them by weight.

§ 27

Of Augustus Caesar late Emperor

(Chap. 45)

As touching the late Emperor *Augustus*, whom all the world rangeth in this ranke of men fortunat: if we consider the whole course of his life we shal find the wheele to have turned often, and perceive many changes of variable fortune. First, his owne uncle[1] by the mothers side put him by the Generalship of the horse; and notwithstanding all his earnest suit preferred *Lepidus* to that place before him: secondly, he was noted and thought hardly of for those outlawries of Roman citisens, and thereby purchased himselfe much hatred and displeasure: tainted also he was for being one of those three in the Triumvirate, yoked and matched with wicked companions and most dangerous members to the weal publique: and this galled him the more, that in this fellowship, the Roman empire was not equally and indifferently parted among them three, but *Antonie* went away with the greatest share by odds. Also his ill fortune was in the battell before Philippi to fall sicke, to take his flight, and for three daies, diseased as he was, to lurke

---

[1] Julius Caesar (actually great-uncle).

and lie hidden within a marish: whereupon (as *Agrippa* and *Maecenas* confesse) he grew into a kinde of dropsie, so as his belly and sides were puffed up and swelled with a waterish humor, gotten and spred betwixt the flesh and the skin. Furthermore, he suffered shipwrecke in Sicily, and there likewise he was glad to skulk within a cave in the ground. What should I say, how when he was put to flight at sea, and the whole power of his enemies at his heeles, he besought *Proculeius* in that great danger to rid him out of his life: how he was perplexed for the quarrels and contentions at Perusia: in what feare and agonie hee was in the battell of Actium (a towne of Albanie) as also for the issue of the Pannonian warre, for the fall of a bridge and a towne both.[1] So many mutinies among his soldiers; so many dangerous diseases: the jealousie and suspition that he had evermore of *Marcellus*: the reproch and shame he sustained for confining and banishing *Agrippa*: his life so many times laid for by poison and other secret traines: the death of his children,[2] suspected to have bin by indirect meanes: the double sorrow and grief of heart thereby, and not altogether for his childelesse estate. The adulterie of his owne daughter, and her purpose of taking his life away, detected and published to the World: the reprochfull departure and slipping aside of *Nero*[3] the sonne of his Wife: another adulterie commited by one of his owne Neeces.[4]

Over and above all this, thus many more crosses and troubles comming one in the necke of another: namely, want of pay for his souldiers, the rebellion of Sclavonia, the mustering of slaves and bond-servants to make up his army, for want of other able youths to levy unto the warres: Pestilence in Rome Citie: famin and

---

[1] Most commentators have *ruina e turri*, for his fall from a tower. Dalechamp gives other readings, *ruine in curru*, and *ruinae pontis* which Holland uses; the fall of the town is not in the text. In an annotation to his translation of Suetonius' *Twelve Caesars*, Holland returns to this accident. Suetonius mentions that Augustus hurt both arms with a fall from a bridge and Holland's note reads: 'A turret of wood. Some take this bridge to be a kind of fabric or scaffold reared for the assault of the town Metulum and not an ordinary bridge built over some river.' The town which fell may have been Metulum, the chief town of the Iapodes on the river Kulpa. It is believed to have been on the site of Metlika, a small town on the Kupa river not far from Zagreb.

[2] Lucius and Gaius, sons of Julia and Agrippa, were adopted.

[3] The future Emperor Tiberius.

[4] Holland uses niece for granddaughter. In this case, it is Augustus' granddaughter, Julia.

drought universally throughout Italy: and that which more is, a deliberat purpose and resolution of his to famish and pine himselfe to death, having to that end fasted 4 dayes and 4 nights; and in that time received into his body the greater part of his owne death. Besides, the overthrow and rout of *Varus* his forces, the foule staine and blemish to the touch of his honor and majestie very neere: the putting away of *Postumus Agrippa* after his adoption, and the misse that he had of him after his banishment: then, the suspition that hee conceived of *Fabius* for disclosing his secrets: adde hereto the opinion and conceit he tooke of his owne wife and *Tiberius*, which surpassed all his other cares. To conclude, that god, and he who I wot not whether obtained heaven, or deserved it more, departed this life, and left behinde him as heire to the crowne his enemies sonne.

§ 28

Of the longest lives

(Chap. 48)

EPHORUS testifieth, that ordinarily the kings of Arcadia were 300 yeares old ere they died. *Alexander Cornelius* writeth of one *Dando* a Sclavonian, who lived 500 yeres. *Xenophon* in his treatise of old age,[1] makes mention of a King of the Latmii, or as some say, over a people upon the sea coasts, who lived 600 yeares; and because he had not lied loud enough already, he goes on still and saith, that his son came to 800. All these strange reports proceed from the ignorance of the times past, and for want of knowledge how they made their account; for some reckoned the Summer for one yeare, and the Winter for another. There were againe that reckoned every quarter for a yeare, as the Arcadians, whose yeare was but three moneths. Ye shall have some, and namely the

---

[1] There are many readings here. Most give Xenophon's treatise as a narrative of a coasting voyage; *in periplo Lutmiorum* (*Latinorum*, *Lutimorum*, *Lamiorum*), and this may have described the area of Mount Latmus in Caria near the mouth of the Maeander river. Holland follows Pinet in making the treatise of old age and this reading is mentioned by Dalechamp from the Chiffletianus codex.

Egyptians, that count every change or new Moon for a yeare: and therefore no marvell if some of them are said to live 1000 yeares.

§ 29

Sundry examples of divers diseases

(Chap. 50)

CERTES this gift of life that we have from nature, be it more or lesse, is fraile and uncertain; and say that it be given to any in largest measure, it is but scant yet, and very short, yea and of but small use, if wee consider the whole course thereof from the beginning to the end. For first, if we count our repose and sleep in the night season, a man can be truly said to live but halfe his life; for surely a good moity and halfe deale thereof which is spent in sleeping, may be likened well to death: and if he cannot sleep, it is a pain of all pains, and a very punishment. I reckon not in this place the yeares of our infancie, which age is void of reason and sense; ne yet of old age, which the longer it continueth, the more are they plagued that be in it. What should I speake of so many kindes of dangers, so many diseases, so many feares, so many pensive cares, so many prayers for death, as that in maner we pray for nothing oftner? In which regards how can a man be said to live the while? and therefore Nature knoweth not what better thing to give a man than short life.

First and formost, the senses wax dull, the members and limmes grow benummed, the eye sight decaieth betimes, the hearing followeth soone after, then faile the supporters, the teeth also and the very instruments that serve for our food and nourishment: and yet forsooth all this time so full of griefe and infirmities is counted a part of our life. Hereupon it is taken for a miraculous example, and that to which again we canot find a fellow, that *Xenophilus* the musitian lived 105 yeares, without any sicknesse or defect in all his body. For all other men, beleeve me, are vexed at certain houres (like as no other creatures besides) with the pestiferous heats and shaking colds of the fever in every joynt, sinew, and muscle of the bodie, which go and come, keeping their times in their severall fits, not for certain houres in the day only, but from one day to another, and from night to night; one while every third day or night, otherwhiles every fourth, yea and somtime a whole yeare together.[1] Moreover, what is it but a very disease, to know the time and houre of a mans death, and so to die forsooth in wisedome?

For maladies there be in which Nature hath set down certain rules and lawes: namely a quartaine fever never lightly[2] begins in the shortest daies of the yeare, neither in the 3 moneths of winter (to wit, December, Januarie, Februarie.) Some diseases are not incident to those that are above 60 yeares of age: others againe do end and passe away when youths begin to be undergrowne,[3] and especially this is observed in yong maidens. Moreover, old folke of all other are least subject to take the plague. Furthermore, sicknesses there be that follow this region or that, assailing and infecting the inhabitants generally therein. There be some againe that surprise and take hold of servants only, both all and some: others touch the best persons alone of the highest calling, and so from degree to degree. But in this place observed usually it is by experience, That a pestilence beginning in the South parts, goeth alwaies towards the West, and never lightly but in winter, neither continueth it above three moneths.

§ 30

Of the Ghosts

(Chap. 55)

AFTER men are buried, great diversitie there is in opinion, what is become of their souls and ghosts, wandering some this way, and others that. But this is generally held, that in what estate they were before men were born, in the same they remain when they

---

[1] It is interesting that malaria was so common that 'all other men' except Xenophilus suffered from it.
[2] Commonly.
[3] At puberty.

are dead. For neither body nor soule hath any more sence after our dying day, than they had before the day of our nativitie. But such is the folly and vanitie of men, that it extendeth stil even to the future time; yea, and in the very time of death flattereth it selfe with fond imaginations, and dreaming of I know not what life after this: for some attribute immortality to the soule: others devise a certain transfiguration therof: and there be again who suppose, that the ghosts sequestred from the body, have sense: whereupon they do them honour and worship, making a god of him that is not so much as a man. As if the maner of mens breathing differed from that in other living creatures; or as if there were not to be found many other things in the World, that live much longer than men, and yet no man judgeth in them the like immortality. But shew me what is the substance and body as it were of the soule by it selfe? what kind of matter is it apart from the body? where lieth her cogitation that she hath? how is her seeing, how is her hearing performed? what toucheth she? nay, what doth she at al? How is she emploied? or if there be in her none of all this, what goodnesse can there be without the same? But I would know where shee setleth and hath her abiding place after her departure from the body? and what an infinit multitude of souls like shadows would there be, in so many ages, as well past as to come? now surely these be but fantastical, foolish, and childish toies; devised by men that would faine live alwaies, and never make an end.

The like foolery there is in preserving the bodies of dead men: and the vanity of *Democritus* is no lesse, who promised a resurrection thereof, and yet himself could never rise again. And what a folly is this of all follies to think (in a mischief) that death should be the way to a second life? what repose and rest should ever men have that are borne of a woman, if their soules should remain in heaven above with sence, whiles their shadows tarried beneath among the infernall wights? Certes, these sweet inducements and pleasing persuasions, this foolish credulitie and light beliefe, marreth the benefit of the best gift of Nature, to wit, Death; it doubleth besides the paine of a man that is to die, if he happen to thinke and consider what shall betide him the time to come. For if it be sweet and pleasant to live, what pleasure and contentment can one have, that hath once lived, and now doth not. But how much more ease and greater securitie were it for each man to beleeve himselfe in this point, to gather reasons, and to ground his resolution and assurance upon the experience that he had before hee was borne.[1]

[1] This may refer to the belief, developed in Plato's *Meno*, that all knowledge was but memory of the soul's existence before birth. It is more likely that Pliny meant to deny the existence of the soul before birth and after death.

In
THE EIGHTH BOOKE
are contained the natures of land beasts
that go on foot

§ 31

The praise of Elephants: their wit and understanding

(Chaps. 1, 3, 5)

PASSE we now to treat of other living creatures, and first of land-beasts: among which, the Elephant is the greatest, and commeth neerest in wit and capacitie to men; for they understand the language of that country wherin they are bred, they do whatsoever they are commanded, they remember what duties they be taught, and withall take a pleasure and delight both in love and also in glory, nay more than all this, they embrace goodnesse, honestie, prudence, and equitie (rare qualities I may tel you to be found in men) and withal have in religious reverence (with a kinde of devotion) not only the stars and planets, but the sun and moon they also worship. And in very truth, writers there be who report thus much of them, That when the new moon beginneth to appeare fresh and bright, they come downe by whole heards to a certaine river named Amilo, in the desarts and forests of Mauritania, where after that they are washed and solemnly purified by sprinckling and dashing themselves all over with the water, and have saluted and adored after their manner that planet, they returne again into the woods and chases, carrying before them their yong calves that be wearied and tired. Moreover, they are thought to have a sense and understanding of religion and conscience in others; for when they are to passe the seas into another country, they wil not embarke before they be induced thereto by an oath of their governors and rulers, That they shall returne again: and seene there have bin divers of them, being enfeebled by sicknesse (for as big and huge as they be, subject they are to grievous maladies) to lie upon their backs, casting and flinging herbes up toward heaven, as if they had procured and set the earth to pray for them. . . .

This is knowne for certaine, that upon a time there was an Elephant among the rest, not so good of capacity, to take out his lessons, and learn that which was taught him: and being beaten and beaten again for that blockish and dull head of his, was found studying and conning those feats in the night, which he had bin learning in the day time. But one of the greatest wonders of them was this, that they could mount up and clime against a rope; but more wonderfull, that they should slide downe again with their heads downward. *Mucianus*, a man who had in his time bin thrice Consull, reporteth thus much of one of them, that he had learned to make the Greeke characters, and was wont to write in that language thus much, *Thus have I written, and made an offering of the Celticke spoiles.* Likewise hee saith, that himselfe saw at Puteoli, a certain ship discharged of Elephants embarked therein; and when they should be set ashore, and forced to go forth of the vessel, to which purpose there was a bridge made for them to passe over, they were affrighted at the length thereof, bearing out so far from the land into the water: and therefore to deceive themselves, that the way might not seeme so long, went backward with their tails to the banke, and their heads toward the sea.

They are ware, and know full well that their only riches (for love of which, men lay wait for them) lieth in their armes and weapons that Nature hath given them: king *Juba* calleth them their hornes: but *Herodotus*, who wrote long before him, and the custome of speech, hath tearmed them much better, teeth. And therefore when they are shed and fallen off, either for age, or by some casualtie, the Elephants themselves hide them within the ground. And this in truth is the only yvory: for all the rest, yea, and these teeth also so far as lay covered within the flesh, is of no price, and taken for no better than bone. And yet of late daies, for great scarcitie and want of the right teeth, men have bin glad to cut and saw their bones into plates, and make yvorie therof. For hardly can we now come by teeth of any bignes, unlesse we have them out of India. For all the rest that might be gotten in this part of the world between us and them, hath bin imploied in superfluities only, and served for wanton toies. You may know yong Elephants by the whitenes of these teeth: and a speciall care and regard have these beasts of them above all. They looke to one of them alwaies, that the point be sharp; and therefore they forbeare to occupie it, least it should bee blunt against they come to fight: the other they use ordinarily, either to get up roots out of the earth, or to cast down any banks or mures that stand in their way. When they chance to be environed and compassed round about with hunters, they set formost in the rank to be seen, those of the heard that have the least teeth: to the end, that their price might not be thought worth the hazard and venture in chase for them. But afterwards, when they see the hunters eager, and themselves overmatched and weary, they breake them with running against the hard trees, and leaving them behind, escape by this ransome as it were, out of their hands. . . .

The Elephants march alwaies in troups. The eldest of them leadeth the vaward, like a captaine: and the next to him in age, commeth behind with the conduct of the arrereguard. When they are to passe over any river, they put formost the least of al their company, for feare, that if the bigger should enter first, they would, as they trod in the channell, make the water to swell and rise, and so cause the fourd to be more deepe. *Antipater* writeth, that K. *Antiochus* had two Elephants, which he used in his wars above all the rest; and famous they were for their surnames, which they knew well enough, and wist when any man called them thereby: and verily, *Cato* reciting in his Annals the names of the principall captaine Elephants,[1] hath left in writing, That the Elephant which fought most lustily in the point of the Punick war, had to name Surus, by the same token, that the one of his teeth was gone.[2] When *Antiochus* on a time would have sounded the fourd of a certaine river, by putting the Elephants before, Ajax refused to take the water, who otherwise at all times was wont to lead the way. Whereupon the king pronounced with a loud voice, That look which Elephant passed to the other side, he should be the captain and chiefe. Then Patroclus gave the venture: and for his labor had

[1] This can read, 'although Cato removed the names of military captains from his annals, he left in writing that . . .'.
[2] The meaning is that the elephant was named 'Syrian' and had broken one tusk.

a rich harnish and caparison given him, and was all trapped in silver (a thing wherin they take most delight) and made besides the soveraigne of all the rest. But the other that was disgraced thus, and had lost his place, would never eat any meat after, but died for very shame of such a reprochfull ignominy. For among other qualities, marvellous bashfull they are: for if one of them be overmatched and vanquished in fight, he wil never after abide the voice and braying of the conqueror, but in token of submission, giveth him a turfe of earth, with vervaine or grasse upon it.

Upon a kind of shamefaced modesty, they never are seen to ingender together, but perform that act in some covert and secret corner. They go to rut, the male at 5 yeres of age, the femal not before she is 10 yeres old. And this they do every third yere: and they continue therein five daies in the yeare (as they say) and not above:[1] for upon the sixt day they all to wash themselves over in the running river: and before they be thus purified, return not to the heard. After they have taken one to another once, they never change: neither fall they out and fight about their femalls, as other creatures do most deadly and mortally. And this is not for want of love and hot affection that way: for reported it is of one Elephant, that he cast a fancy and was enamoured upon a wench in Aegypt that sold nosegaies and garlands of floures. And lest any man should thinke that hee had no reason thereto, it was no ordinary maiden, but so amiable, as that *Aristophanes* the excellent Grammarian, was wonderfully in love with her. Another there was, so kind and full of love, that he fansied a youth[2] in the army of *Ptolomaeus*, that scarce had never an haire upon his face, and so entirely he loved him, that what day soever he saw him not, he would forbeare his meat, and eat nothing. K. *Juba* likewise reporteth also of an Elephant that made court to another woman, who made and sold sweet ointments and perfumes. All these testified their love and kindnes, by these tokens: joy they would at the sight of them, and looke pleasantly upon them: make toward them they would (after their rude and homely manner) by all means of flatterie: and especially in this, that they would save whatsoever people cast to them for to eat, and lay the same ful kindly in their

---

[1] This can read, 'they go to rut only for two years and then only for five days in each year'; much of this about elephants is inaccurate.

[2] 'a Syracusan named Menander' appears in most texts.

laps and bosomes. But no marvel it is that they should love who are so good of memorie. For the same *Juba* saith, That an Elephant tooke knowledge and acquaintance of one man in his old age, and after many a yere, who in his youth had bin his ruler and governor. He affirmeth also, that they have by a secret divine instinct, a certain sence of justice and righteous dealing. For when K. *Bocchus* meant to be revenged of 30 Elephants, that he had caused to be bound unto stakes, and set other 30 to run upon them, appointing also certain men among to pricke and provoke them thereto; yet for all that, could not one of them be brought for to execute this butcherie, nor be ministers of anothers crueltie.

§ 32

How the Dragons and Elephants disagree

(Chaps. 11, 12)

ELEPHANTS breed in that part of Africke which lieth beyond the desarts and wildernesse of the Syrtes: also in Mauritania: they are found also amongst the Aethyopians and Troglodites, as hath beene said: but India bringeth forth the biggest: as also the dragons[1] that are continually at variance with them, and evermore fighting, and those of such greatnesse, that they can easily clasp and wind round about the Elephants, and withall tye them fast with a knot. In this conflict they die, both the one and the other: the Elephant he fals downe dead as conquered, and with his heavy weight crusheth and squeaseth the dragon that is wound and wreathed about him.

Wonderfull is the wit and subtilty that dumbe creatures have, and how they shift for themselves and annoy their enemies; which is the only difficulty that they[2] have to arise and grow to so great an heigth and excessive bignes. The dragon therfore espying the Elephant when he goeth to reliefe,[3] assaileth him from an high tree

---

[1] The dragons may well be pythons.
[2] The dragons.
[3] To pasture, *ad pabula.*

and launceth himselfe upon him; but the Elephant knowing well enough he is not able to withstand his windings and knittings about him, seeketh to come close to some trees or hard rocks, and so for to crush and squise the dragon between him and them: the dragons ware hereof, entangle and snarle his feet and legs first with their taile: the Elephants on the other side, undo those knots with their trunk as with a hand: but to prevent that againe, the Dragons put in their heads into their snout, and so stop their wind, and withall fret and gnaw the tenderest parts they find there. Now in case these two mortall enemies chance to re-incounter on the way, they bristle and bridle one against another, and addresse themselves to fight; but the chiefe thing the dragons make at is the eie, whereby it comes to passe, that many times the Elephants are found blinde, pined for hunger, and worne away, and after much languishing, for very anguish and sorrow die of their venome.

What reason should a man alledge of this so mortall warre betweene them, if it be not a very sport of Nature, and pleasure that she takes, in matching these two so great enemies together, and so even and equall in each respect? But some report this mutuall war betwecn them after another sort, and that the occasion thereof ariseth from a naturall cause: for (say they) the Elephants bloud is exceeding cold, and therefore the dragons be wonderful desirous thereof to refresh and coole themselves there-with during the parching hot season of the yeare. And to this purpose they ly under the water, waiting their time to take the Elephants at a vantage when they arc drinking: where they catch fast hold first of their trunke, and they have not so soone clasped and intangled it with their taile, but they set their venomous teeth in the Elephants eare (the onely part of all their body which they cannot reach unto with their trunke) and so bite it hard: now these dragons are so big withal, that they are able to receive all the elephants bloud: thus are they sucked dry untill they fall down dead: and the dragons also, drunke with their bloud, are squeesed under them, and so dy together.[1]

[1] See also § 140.

§ 33

Of Lions and Panthers

(Chaps. 16, 17)

LIONS there be also in Europe (only between the rivers Achelous
and Nestus)[1] and these verily be far stronger than those of Africke
or Syria. Moreover, there are two kinds of Lions: the one short, wel
trussed, and compact, with more crisp and curled mains, but these
are timerous and cowards to them that have long and plain haire;
for those passe not for any wounds whatsoever. The Lions lift up
a leg when they pisse, as dogs do: and moreover, they have
a strong and stinking breath, their very body also smelleth rank.
Seldom they drink, and eate but each other day; and if at any time
they feed til they be full, they wil abstain from meat three daies
after. In their feeding, whatsoever they can swallow without chewing, downe it goes whole: and if they finde their gorge and
stomacke too full, and not able indeed to receive according to their
greedy appetite, they thrust their pawes down their throats, and
with their crooked clees fetch out some of it again, to the end they
should not be heavy and slow upon their fulnesse, if haply they be
put to find their feet and fly. Mine Author *Aristotle* saith moreover,
That they live very long: and hee proveth it by this argument,
That many of them are found toothlesse for very age. *Polybius*, who
accompanied (*Scipio*) *Aemylianus* in his voiage of Africke, reporteth
of them, That when they be growne aged they will prey upon
a man: the reason is, because their strength will not hold out to
pursue in chase any other wild beasts: then they come about the
cities and good towns of Africke, lying in wait for their prey, if any
folk come abroad: and for that cause, he saith, that while hee was
with *Scipio*, hee saw some of them crucified and hanged up, to the
end that upon the sight of them other Lions should take example,
and be skarred from doing the like mischiefe.

The Lion alone of all wilde beasts, is gentle to those that humble
themselves unto him, and will not touch any such upon their submission, but spareth what creature soever lieth prostrate before
him. As fell and furious as he is otherwiles, yet he dischargeth

[1] In Thrace.

his rage upon men, before he sets upon women, and never preyeth on babes unlesse it be for extreme hunger. They are verily persuaded in Lybia,[1] that they have a certain understanding when any man doth pray or intreat them for anything. I have heard it reported for a truth, by a captive woman of Gaetulia (which being fled was brought home again to her master) that she had pacified the violent fury of many Lions within the woods and forests, by faire language and gentle speech; and namely, that for to escape their rage, shee hath been so hardy as to say, she was a silly woman, a banished fugitive, a sickly, feeble, and weak creature, an humble suiter and lowly suppliant to him the noblest of all other living creatures, the Soveraigne and commander of all the rest, and that she was too base and unworthy for his glorious Majestie to prey upon her. Many and divers opinions are currant, according to the sundry occurrences that have hapned, or the inventions that mens wits have devised as touching this matter; namely, that savage beasts are dulced and appeased by good words and faire speech: as also that fell serpents may be trained and fetched out of their holes by charmes; yea and by certaine conjurations and menaces restrained and kept under for a punishment: but whether it be true or no, I see it is not yet by any man set downe or determined.

To come againe to our Lions, the signe of their intent and disposition is their taile; like as in horses, their eares: for these two marks and tokens certainly hath Nature given to the most couragious beasts of all others, to know their affections by: for when the Lion stirs not his taile, he is in a good mood, gentle, mild, pleasantly disposed, and as if he were willing to be plaied withall: but in that fit he is seldome seen, for lightly he is alwaies angry. At the first when he entreth into his choler; he beateth the ground with his taile: when he groweth into greater heats, he flappeth and jerketh his flanks and sides withall, as it were to quicken himselfe, and stir up his angry humour. . . .

Lions are nothing at all crafty and fraudulent, neither be they suspitious: they never look askew, but alwaies cast their eye directly forward, and they love not that any man should in that sort looke side-long upon them. It is constantly beleeved, that

[1] An alternative reading is, 'Juba [the king of Numidia who wrote histories at Rome] was persuaded that . . .'.

when they ly a dying they bite the earth, and in their very death shed teares. This creature, so noble as hee is, and withall so cruell and fell, trembleth and quaketh to heare the noise of cart-wheeles, or to see them turne about; nay hee cannot abide of all things Chariots when they be void and empty: frighted hee is with the cockes combe, and his crowing much more, but most of all with the sight of fire. The Lion is never sicke but of the peevishnesse of his stomacke, loathing all meat: and then the way to cure him is to ty unto him certaine shee Apes, which with their wanton mocking and making mowes at him, may move his patience, and drive him for the very indignitie of their malapert saucinesse, into a fit of madnesse; and then so soone as he hath tasted their bloud he is perfectly wel again: and this is the only help. . . .

. . . we find in histories many examples also of their clemencie and gentlenesse, seen upon divers casuall occasions. *Mentor* the Syracusan fortuned in Syria to meet with a Lion, who after an humble maner in token of obedience and submission, seemed to tumble and wallow before him: he, astonied for feare, started backe and began to fly, but the wild beast followed him still, and was ready at every turne to present himselfe before him, licking the very tracks of his foot-steps as he went, in flattering manner, as if he would make love unto him. *Mentor* at length was ware that the Lion had a wound in his foot, and that it swelled therwith: whereupon he gently plucked out the spill of wood that had gotten into it, and so eased the beast of his paine. This accident is for a memoriall represented in a picture at Syracusa.

Semblably, *Elpis*, a Samian being arrived and landed in Africk, chanced to espy neer the shore a Lion gaping wide, and seeming afar off to whet his teeth at him in menacing wise: he fled apace to take a tree, calling upon god *Bacchus* to help him (for then commonly wee fall to our praiers when we see little or no hope of other helpe:) but the Lion stopt him not in his flight, albeit he could have crossed the way well enough, but laying himselfe downe at the tree root, with that open mouth of his wherewith he had skared the man, made signes to move pitty and compassion. Now so it was, that the beast having lately fed greedily, had gotten a sharp bone within his teeth, that put him to exceeding paine: besides that, hee was almost famished: and he looking pittifully up to the man, shewed how he was punished himselfe among those verie weapons wherewith he was wont to anoy others, and after a sort with dumb and mute prayers besought his help. *Elpis* avised him well a pretty while; and besides that hee was not very forward to venture upon the wilde beast, he staied the longer and made the lesse hast, while he considered rather this strange and miraculous accident, than otherwise greatly feared. At last he comes downe from the tree and plucks out the bone, whiles the Lion held his mouth handsomly to him, and exposed himselfe to his helpfull hand as fitly as he possibly could. In requitall of which good turne, it is said, that so long as this ship of his lay there at anchor, the Lion furnished him and his company with good store of venison ready killed to his hand. . . .

Demetrius the philosopher, so wel seen into the speculation of natures works, and the causes thereof, makes mention of as memorable a case as the former, touching a Panther:[1] for as he saith there was a Panther desirous to meet with a man, and therefore lay in the mids of an high-way untill some passenger should come by, and suddenly was espied by the father of *Philinus* the Philosopher, who travailed that way. The man (for feare) began to retire and go backe againe, but the wild beast kept a tumbling and vanting all about him; doubtlesse and by all apparance after a flattering sort, as if it would have had somwhat; and such a tossing and tormenting of it selfe she made, so piteously, that it might soone be seene in what griefe and pain the Panther was. The poore beast had but lately kindled, and her young whelps were falne into a ditch, afarre off: well, the first point that the man shewed of pitty and commiseration was, not to be affraid, and the next was, to have regard and care of her: follow he did the Panther, as she seemed to train and draw him by his garment (which with her clawes shee tooke hold of daintily) untill they were come to the pit or ditch above-said. So soon then as he knew the cause of her griefe and sorrow, and withall what might be the reward of his courtesie, even as much as his life came to, he drew forth her little ones that were fallen into the said pit: which don, she and her whelps together leaping and shewing gambols for joy, accompanied him, and through the wildernesse directed him untill he was gotten forth. So as it appeared in her, that shee was thankfull unto him,

---

[1] A leopard: its skin is described as 'white, beset all over with little black spots like eies'.

and requited his kindnesse, albeit there passed no covenant nor promise between them of any such recompence: a rare example to be found even among men.

§ 34

Of Wolves

(Chap. 22)

IT is commonly thought likewise in Italy, that the eye sight of wolves is hurtful; in so much as if they see a man before hee espy him, they cause him to lose his voice for the time. They that be bred in Affrick and Aegypt, are but little, and withal nothing lively, but without spirit. In the colder clime, they be more cruell and eger. That men may be transformed into wolves, and restored againe to their former shape, we must confidently beleeve to be a lowd lie, or else give credit to all those tales which we have for so many ages found to be meere fables. But how this opinion grew first, and is come to be so firmly setled, that when we would give men the most opprobrious words of defiance[1] that we can, we terme them *Versipelles*,[2] I thinke it not much amisse in a word to shew.

Euanthes (a writer among the Greekes, of good account and authority) reporteth, that he found among the records of the Arcadians, That in Arcadia there was a certaine house and race of the *Antaei*, out of which one evermore must needs be transformed into a wolfe: and when they of that family have cast lots who it shall be, they use to accompany the party upon whom the lot is falne, to a certaine meere or poole in that country: when he is thither come, they turne him naked out of all his clothes, which they hang upon an oke thereby: then he swimmeth over the said lake to the other side, and being entered into the wildernesse, is presently transfigured and turned into a wolfe, and so keepeth

---

[1] *ut in maledictis versipelles habeat*; Rackham translates that public opinion 'classes werewolves among persons under a curse'. *Versipelles* meant also cunning, sly, and crafty—opprobrious words, and Holland's sense seems preferable.
[2] i. Turn coats (P. H.).

company with his like of that kind for nine yeeres space: during[1] which time, (if he forbeare all the while to eat mans flesh) he returneth againe to the same poole or pond, and being swomme over it, receiveth his former shape againe of a man, save only that he shall look nine yeeres elder than before. *Fabius*[2] addeth one thing more and saith, That he findeth againe the same apparell that was hung up in the oake aforesaid. A wonder it is to see, to what passe these Greekes are come in their credulity: there is not so shamelesse a lye, but it findeth one or other of them to uphold and maintaine it.

§ 35

Of Marmotaines and Urchins or Hedge-hogs

(Chap. 37)

THE Rats of Pontus, which be onely white,[3] come not abroad all winter: they have a most fine and exquisit taste in their feeding; but I wonder how the authours that have written this, should come to the knowledge of so much. Those of the Alps likewise, *i.* Marmotanes, which are as bigge as Brocks or Badgers, keepe in, during winter: but they are provided of victuals before hand which they gather together and carry into their holes. And some say, when the male or female is loden with grasse and herbs, as much as it can comprehend within all the foure legges, it lieth upon the backe with the said provision upon their bellies, and then commeth the other, and taketh hold by the taile with the mouth, and draweth the fellow into the earth: thus doe they one by the other in turnes: and hereupon it is, that all that time their backes are bare and the haire worne off. Such like Marmotaines there be in Aegypt; and in the same manner they sit ordinarily upon their buttocks, and upon their two hinder feet they goe, using their fore-feet in stead of hands.

Hedgehogs also make their provision before-hand of meat for

---

[1] After.

[2] *addit quoque fabulosius* or *Fabius*; it may well be Euanthes who added something even more fabulous.

[3] White all over.

winter, in this wise. They wallow and roll themselves upon apples and such fruit lying under foot, and so catch them up with their prickles, and one more besides they take in their mouth, and so carry them into hollow trees. . . . When they perceive one hunting of them, they draw their mouth and feet close together with all their belly part, where the skin hath a thin downe and no pricks at all to do harme, and so roll themselves as round as a foot-ball, that neither dog nor man can come by any thing but their sharpe-pointed prickles. So soon as they see themselves past all hope to escape, they let their water go and pisse upon themselves. Now this urine of theirs hath a poisonous qualitie to rot their skin and prickles, for which they know well enough that they be chased and taken. And therefore it is a secret and speciall policie, not to hunt them before they have let their urine go; and then their skin is very good, for which chiefly they are hunted: otherwise it is nought ever after, and so rotten, that it will not hang together, but fall in pieces: al the pricks shed off, as being putrified, yea although they should escape away from the dogs and live still: and this is the cause that they never bepisse and drench themselves with this pestilent excrement, but in extremitie and utter despaire: for they cannot abide themselves their owne urine, of so venomous a qualitie it is, and so hurtfull to their own body; and do what they can to spare themselves, attending the utmost time of extremitie, insomuch as they are ready to be taken before they do it.

When the Urchen is caught alive, the devise to make him open again in length, is to besprinkle him with hot water; and then by hanging at one of their hin[d]feet without meat they die with famine: otherwise it is not possible to kill them and save their case or skin. There be writers who bash not to say, That this kinde of beast (were not those pricks) is good for nothing, and may well be missed of men: and that the soft fleece of wooll that sheepe bear, but for these prickes were superfluous and to no purpose bestowed upon mankind: for which [of] the rough skin of these Urchins, are brushes and rubbers made to brush and make cleane our garments.[1] And in very truth, many have gotten great gain and profit by this commoditie and merchandise, and namely, with their crafty devise of monopolies, that all might passe through their hands only, notwithstanding there hath not bin any one disorder more repressed

[1] Or rather instead of tazels that sharemen use (P. H.).

and reformation sought by sundry edicts and acts of the Senate in that behalfe: every prince hath been continually troubled hereabout with grievous complaints out of all provinces.

§ 36

Of Dogges

(Chap. 40)

A MONG those domesticall creatures that converse with us, there be many things worth the knowledge: and namely, as touching dogges (the most faithfull and trustie companions of all others to a man) and also horses. And in very truth, I have heard it credibly reported, of a dogge, that in defence of his master, fought hard against theeves robbing by the high way side: and albeit he were sore wounded even to death, yet would he not abandon the dead body of his master, but drave away both wild foule and savage beast, from seizing of his carkasse. Also of another in Epirus, who in a great assembly of people knowing the man that had murdered his Mr. flew upon him with open mouth, barking and snapping at him so furiously, that he was ready to take him by the throat, untill he at length confessed the fact that should cause the dog thus to rage and fome against him. There was a king of the Garamants exiled, and recovered his royall state againe by the meanes of 200 dogs that fought for him against al those that made resistance, and brought him home maugre his enemies. The Colophonians and Castabulians, maintained certain squadrons of mastive dogs, for their war service: and those were put in the vaward to make the head and front of the battell, and were never knowne to draw back and refuse fight. These were their trustiest auxiliaries and aid-soldiers, and never so needy as to call for pay.... The Chronicles report of a dog that *Nicomedes* king of Bithynia kept, which flew upon the queene *Consingis* his wife, and al to mangled and worried her, for toying and dallying overwantonly with the king her husband. . . .[1]

---

[1] *propter lasciviorem cum marito jocum*. This sounds better in Holland's rendering than the more recent 'for playing a rather loose joke with her husband'.

But this passeth al, which happened in our time, and standeth upon record in the publicke registers, namely, in the yeere that *Appius Julius* and *P. Silius* were Consuls, at what time as *T. Sabinus* and his servants were executed for an outrage committed upon the person of *Nero*, sonne of *Germanicus*: one of them that died had a dog which could not be kept from the prison dore, and when his master was throwne down the staires (called Scalae Gemoniae[1]) would not depart from his dead corps, but kept a most pitteous howling and lamentation about it, in the sight of a great multitude of Romanes that stood round about to see the execution and the manner of it: and when one of the companie threw the dogge a piece of meat, he straightwaies carried [it] to the mouth of his master lying dead. Moreover, when the carkasse was thrown into the river Tiberis, the same dog swam after, and made all the means he could to beare it up aflote that it should not sink: and to the sight of this spectacle and fidelitie of the poore dogge to his master, a number of people ran forth by heapes out of the citie to the water side.

They be the onely beasts of all others that know their masters; and let a stranger unknown be come never so suddenly, they are ware of his comming, and will give warning. They alone know their owne names, and all those of the house by their speech. Be the way never so long, and the place from whence they came never so farre, they remember it, and can go thither againe. And surely, setting man aside, I know not what creature hath a better memorie. As furious and raging as they be otherwhiles, yet appeased they will be and quieted, by a man sitting down upon the ground. Certes, the longer we live, the more things we observe and marke still in these dogges. As for hunting there is not a beast so subtle, so quick, and so fine of sent, as is the hound: he hunteth and followeth the beast by the foot, training the hunter that leads him by the coller and leash, to the very place where the beast lieth. Having once gotten an eie of his game, how silent and secret are they notwithstanding? and yet how significant is their discoverie of the beast unto the hunter? first with wagging their taile, and afterwards with their nose and snout, snuffing as they doe. And therefore it is no marvell, if when hounds or beagles be over old,

---

[1] Steps of lamentation, leading to the Tiber, down which criminals' bodies were dragged with hooks.

wearie, and blind, men carry them in their armes to hunt, for to wind the beast, and by the verie sent of the nose to shew and declare where the beast is at harbour.

§ 37

Of Swine, and their natures

(Chap. 51)

SWINE having lost one eie, are not thought to live long after; otherwise they may continue untill they be fifteen yeares old, yea and some to twenty. But they grow to be wood and raging other-whiles: and besides are subject to many maladies more, and most of all to the squinancie,[1] and wen or swelling of the kernels in the neck. Will ye know when a swine is sick or unsound, pluck a bristle from the back and it will be bloudie at the root: also he will cary his neck at one side as he goeth. A sow, if she be over-fat, soone wanteth milke; and at her first farrow bringeth fewest pigs. All the kind of them love to wallow in dirt and mire. They wrinkle their taile; wherin this also is observed, that they be more likely to appease the gods in sacrifice, that rather writh & turn their tailes to the right hand, than the left. Swine wil be fat and wel larded in sixtie daies; and the rather, if before you begin to frank them up, they be kept altogether from meat three daies. . . .

This is known for a truth, that when certaine theeves had stolne and driven away a companie of them, the swinheard having fol-lowed them to the water side (for by that time were the theeves imbarged with them) cried aloud unto the swine, as his manner was: whereupon they knowing his voice, leaned all to one side of the vessel, turned it over and sunke it, tooke the water, and so swam againe to land unto their keeper. Moreover, the hogs that use to lead and goe before the heard, are so well trained, that they wil of themselves goe to the swine-market place within the citie, & from thence home againe to their maisters, without any guid to direct them. The wild bores in this kind, have the wit to cover their tracks with mire, and for the nones to run over marish

[1] Quinsy.

G

ground where the prints of their footing will not be sene; yea and to be more light in running to void their urine first. Sowes also are splaied as well as camels, but two daies before, they be kept from meat: then hang they by the fore-legs, for to make incision into their matrice, and to take forth their stones: and by this means they will sooner grow to be fat.

There is an Art also in cookerie, to make the liver of a sow, as also of a goose, more daintie (and it was the devise of *M. Apicius*) namely, to feed them with drie figges, and when they have eaten till they bee full, presently to give them mead or honied wine to drink, untill they die with being overcharged. There is not the flesh of any other living creature, that yeeldeth more store of dishes to the maintenance of gluttonie, than this; for fiftie sundrie sorts of tastes it affordeth, whereas other have but one a peece. From hence come so many edicts and proclamations, published by the Censors, forbidding and prohibiting to serve up at any feast or supper, the belly and paps of a sow, the kernels about the neck, the brizen, the stones, the womb, and the fore-part of the bores head: and yet for all that, *Publius* the Poet and maker of wanton songs, after that he was come to his freedom, never (by report) had supper without an hogs belly with the paps.

§ 38
Of Apes and Monkies
(Chap. 54)

ALL the kinde of these Apes approch neerest of all beasts to the resemblance of a mans shape: but they differ one from another in the taile. Marvellous crafty and subtill they be to beguile themselves: for by report, as they see hunters doe before them, they will imitate them in every point, even to besmeare themselves with glew & birdlime, & shoo their feet within gins and snares, and by that means are caught. *Mucianus* saith, that he hath seene Apes play at chesse and table:[1] and that at first sight they could know nuts made of waxe from others. He affirmes also, that when

---

[1] *latrunculis lusisse*; play with draughtsmen or pawns.

the moon is in the wain, the monkies & Marmosets (which in this kinde have tailes) are sad and heavy, but the new moone they adore and joy at, which they testifie by hopping and dancing. As for the eclipse of Sun or Moone, all other foure footed beasts also do greatly dread and feare. The she Apes of all sorts are wondrous fond of their little ones: and such as are made tame within house will carry them in their armes all about so soone as they have brought them into the world, keepe a shewing of them to every bodie, and they take pleasure to have them dandled by others, as if thereby they tooke knowledge that folke joyed for their safe deliverance: but such a culling and hugging of them they keep, that in the end with very clasping and clipping they kill them many times.[1] Apes that be headed and long snouted like dogs, and thereof called Cynocephali,[2] are of all others most curst, shrewd and unhappy: like as the Marmozets and Monkies called Sphinges & Satyri,[3] are gentlest and most familiar.

[1] Monkeys and baboons in captivity often kill their young in this way.
[2] Baboons.
[3] Perhaps chimpanzees and orang-outangs.

THE NINTH BOOKE
laieth before us all fishes, and creatures
of the water

§ 39
Of the Sperm and Killer Whales

(Chap. 6)

THESE monstrous Whales named Balaenae,[1] otherwhiles come
into our seas also. They say that in the coast of the Spanish Ocean
by Gades, they are not seen before midwinter when the daies be
shortest: for at their set times they lie close in a certain calme deep
and large creeke, which they chuse to cast their spawn in, and
there delight above all places to breed. The Orcae, other monstrous
fishes, know this full well, and deadly enemies they be unto the
foresaid whales. And verily, if I should pourtrait them, I can
resemble them to nothing else but a mightie masse and lumpe of
flesh without all fashion, armed with most terrible, sharpe, and
cutting teeth. Well, these being ware that the Whales are there,
breake into this secret by-creek out of the way, seeke them out,
and if they meet either with the young ones, or the dammes that
have newly spawn'd,[2] or yet great with spawn, they all to cut and
hack them with their trenchant teeth: yea, they run against them
as it were a foist or ship of warre armed with sharp brazen pikes in
the beake-head. But contrariwise, the Balaenes or Whales aforesaid,
that cannot wind and turne aside for defence, and much lesse make
head and resist, so unweldie as they bee by reason of their owne
weightie and heavie bodie, (and as then either big bellied, or else
weakened lately with the paines of travell and calving their young
ones) have no other meanes of helpe and succor but to shoot into
the deepe, and gaine sea-roome to defend themselves from the
enemie. On the other side, the Orcae labour (to cut them short of
their purpose) to lie betweene them and home in their very way,

[1] Sperm whales.   [2] Calved.

and otherwhiles kill them unawares in the streights, or drive them upon the shelves and shallows, or else force them against the very rocks, & so bruise them. When these combats and fights are seen, the sea seemes as if it were angry with it selfe: for albeit no winds are up, but all calme in that creek and gulfe, yet ye shall have waves in that place where they encounter (with the blasts of their breath, and the blowes given by the assailant) so great, as no tempestuous whirle windes whatsoever are able to raise.

In the haven of Ostia likewise there was discovered one of these Orcaes, and the same assailed by *Claudius* the Emperour.[1] It chanced to come as he was making the said harbour or pere, drawne and trained thither with the sweetnes of certaine beasts hides that were brought out of Gaule, and were cast away and perished by the way. Of them for certaine daies she had fed, and still following them, with the weight of her heavie bodie had made a furrow and channel (as it were) with her bellie in the bottome among the shelves: and by reason of the flowing of the sea she was so invested and compassed in with the sands, that by no means possible she could turn about: but stil while she goes after these hides whereof she fed, she was by the billows of the sea cast aflote on the shore, so as her back was to be seene a great deale above the water, much like to the bottome or keele of a ship turned upside downe. Then the Emperour commanded to draw great nets and cords with many folds along the mouth of the haven on every side behind the fish, himselfe accompanied with certaine Pretorian cohorts, for to shew a pleasant sight unto the people of Rome, came against this monstrous fish, and out of many hoies and barks the souldiers launced darts and javelines thicke. And one of them I saw my selfe sunke downe right with the abundance of water that this monstrous fish spouted and filled it withall. The Whales called Balenae have a certaine mouth or great hole in their forehead, and therefore as they swim aflote aloft on the water, they send up on high (as it were) with a mighty strong breath a great quantity of water when they list, like stormes of rain.

---

[1] Claudius' whale is thought to have been a Cachalot. Pliny saw this stranded whale himself and calls it an Orca, which may mean a Killer-whale; other suggested identifications for the Orca are the Grampus and the Narwhal.

§ 40

Of Dolphins

(Chap. 8)

THE Dolphin is a creature that carries a loving affection not only
unto man, but also to musicke: delighted he is with harmony in
song, but especially with the sound of the water instrument, or
such kind of pipes. Of a man he is nothing affraid, neither avoides
from him as a stranger: but of himselfe meeteth their ships, plaieth
and disportes himselfe, and fetcheth a thousand friskes and
gamboles before them. He will swim along by the mariners, as it
were for a wager, who should make way most speedily, and
alwaies outgoeth them, saile they with never so good a fore-wind.

In the daies of *Augustus Caesar* the Emperour, there was a Dolphin
entred the gulfe or poole Lucrinus, which loved wondrous well
a certain boy a poore mans son: who using to go every day to
schoole from Baianum to Puteoli, was woont also about noone-tide
to stay at the water side, and to call unto the Dolphin, *Simo, Simo,*[1]
and many times would give him fragments of bread, which of
purpose he ever brought with him, and by this meanes allured the
Dolphin to come ordinarily unto him at his call. (I would make
scruple and bash to insert this tale in my storie and to tell it out,
but that *Maecenas, Fabianus, Flavius Alfius,* and many others have
set it downe for a truth in their chronicles.) Well in processe of
time, at what houre soever of the day, this boy lured for him and
called *Simo,* were the Dolphin never so close hidden in any secret
and blind corner, out he would and come abroad, yea and skud
amaine to this lad: and taking bread and other victuals at his hand,
would gently offer him his back to mount upon, and then downe
went the sharpe pointed prickles of his fins, which he would put
up as it were within a sheath for fear of hurting the boy. Thus
when he had him once on his back, he would carry him over the
broad arme of the sea as farre as Puteoli to schoole; and in like
manner convey him backe again home: and thus he continued for
many yeeres together, so long as the child lived. But when the boy
was fallen sicke & dead, yet the Dolphin gave not over his haunt,

[1] Snubnose.

but usually came to the wonted place, & missing the lad, seemed to be heavie and mourne againe, untill for very griefe & sorrow (as it is doubtles to be presumed) he also was found dead upon the shore.

Another Dolphin there was not many yeeres since upon the coast of Affricke, neere to the citie Hippo, called also Diarrhytus, which in like manner would take meat at a mans hand, suffer himselfe gently to be handled, play with them that swom and bathed in the sea, and carrie on his backe whosoever would get upon it. Now it fell out so, that *Flavianus* the Proconsull or lieutenant Generall in Affrick under the Romans, perfumed and besmeered this Dolphin upon a time with a sweet ointment: but the fish (as it should seem) smelling this new & strange smel fell to be drowsie and sleepie, and hulled to and fro with the waves, as if it had bin halfe dead: and as though some injurie had bin offered unto him, went his way and kept aloufe, and would not converse any more for certaine moneths with men, as before-time. Howbeit in the end he came again to Hippo, to the great wonder & astonishment of all that saw him. But the wrongs that some great persons and lords did unto the citizens of Hippo, such I mean as used to come for to see this sight: and namely, the hard measure offered to those townesmen, who to their great cost gave them entertainement, caused the men of Hippo to kill the poore Dolphin.

§ 41

The Barbell and the Belligods

(Chap. 17)

OUR great belligods say, that a Barbell[1] when he is dying, changeth his hue, and turneth into an hundred colours: the proofe and experience whereof may be seen if he be put into a glasse: for through it, it is a pretty sport to see how he altereth and changeth his skales beeing ready to die, one way into a pale and wan colour, otherwhiles into a reddish hue, one after another for many times together. *M. Apicius* (who was a man of all others most inventive

[1] Red mullet.

and wonderful for his witty devises to maintain riot and excesse) thought it was a singular way to stifle and kill these Barbels in a certain pickle, called the Roman Allies sauce (see how even such a thing as that, hath found a syrname forsooth & a proper addition.) And he also went about to provoke men to devise a certain manger or broth made of their livers, like to that dripping or gravie called Allec[1] that commeth of Fishes when they pine and corrupt. For surely it is more easie for me to say who set men a work that way first, than set down who woon the best game in the end, and was the greatest glutton. *Asinius Celer*, a man of great calling and high place, who sometime had bin Consull, shewed his prodigalitie in this Fish, & it was when *C. Caligula* was Emperor: for he gave for one Barbell eight thousand Sesterces. Certes, the consideration hereof ravisheth my mind, and carrieth it away to behold & wonder at those, who in their reproofs of gluttonie and gourmandise, complained that a cooke carried a greater price in the market than a good horse of service. For now adaies a cooke will cost as much as the charge of a triumph:[2] and one Fish as deare as a cook. And to conclude, no man is better esteemed and regarded more, than he that hath the most cunning cast to wast the goods, & consume the substance of his lord and master.

§ 42

Of the many-foot fish

(Chap. 30)

I CANNOT overpasse but record the reports of *Trebius Niger*, one of the traine and retinue of *L. Lucullus* Proconsull in Baetica which he upon his knowledge delivered as touching these Many-feet fishes called Polypi, namely, That they are most desirous and

---

[1] Allec or Alex was a costly fish paste, the sediment from the fish sauce, called Roman Allies sauce, which was made from mackerel. The method was probably the same as that still used in lower Egypt; fresh fish are slightly salted and allowed to 'pine and corrupt'.

[2] Or, as three horses: *triumphorum* or *trium equorum*, probably the latter. If people once complained that a cook cost more than a horse, nowadays a cook was worth three horses.

greedie of cockles, muscles, and such like shell-fishes: and they againe on the contrarie side, so soone as they feele themselves touched of the Polypes, shut their shels hard, and therwith cut asunder their clawes or armes, that were gotten within: and thus fall they to feed upon those, who sought to make a prey of them. (Now in very truth these shel-fishes, all of them see not at all, neither have they any other sense, but tasting of their meat, & feeling of their drinke.)[1] These Polypi foreseeing all this, lie in wait to spie when the said cockles, etc. gape wide open, and put in a little stone between the shels, but yet beside the flesh and bodie of the fish, for feare lest if it touched and felt it, she would cast it forth again: thus they theeve, and without all daunger and in securitie get out the fleshie substance of the meat to devoure it: the poore cockles draw their shels together for to clasp them between (as is above-said) but all in vaine, for by reason of a wedg between, they will not meet close nor come neere together. See how subtle and craftie in this point these creatures be, which otherwise are most sottish and senselesse.

Moreover, the said *Trebius Niger* affirmeth, that there is not any other beast nor fish in the sea more daungerous to doe a man a mischiefe within the water, than is this Pourcuttle or Many-feet Polypus: for if he chance to light on any of these divers under the water, or any that have suffered shipwracke and are cast away, he assailes them in this manner: He catcheth fast hold of them with his clawes or armes, as if he would wrestle with them, and with the hollow concavities and noukes between, keepeth a sucking of them; and so long he suckes and sokes their bloud (as it were cupping-glasses set to their bodies in divers places) that in the end he draweth them drie. But the only remedie is this, to turne them upon their backe, and then they are soone done and their strength gone: for let them lie so, they stretch out themselves abroad, and have not the power to clasp or comprehend any thing. And verily all living creatures in the sea love the smell of them exceeding well, which is the cause that fishers besmare and anoint their nets with them, to draw and allure fishes thither.[2]

---

[1] Or danger: *periculi*. This seems to be a mistake; the 1601 edition has '[danger]'.

[2] This sentence may have been displaced; Rackham takes it after 'would rob them of their salt-fish', in the next sentence.

The rest which mine author hath related as touching this fish, may seem rather monstrous lies and incredible, than otherwise:[1] for he affirmed, that at Carteia there was one of these Polypi, which used commonly to go forth of the sea, and enter into some of their open cesterns and vauts among their ponds and stewes, wherein they keep great sea fishes, and otherwhiles would rob them of their salt-fish, and so go his waies againe: which he practised so long, that in the end he gat himselfe the anger and displeasure of the maisters and keepers of the said ponds and cesterns, with his continuall & immeasurable filching: whereupon they staked up the place and empalled it round about, to stop all passage thither. But this thief gave not over his acustomed haunt for all that, but made meanes by a certaine tree to clamber over and get to the fore-said salt fish; and never could he be taken in the manner, nor discovered, but that the dogges by their quick sent found him out and baied at him: for as he returned one night toward the sea, they assailed and set upon him on all sides, and therwith raised the foresaid keepers, who were afrighted at this so sudden an alarm, but more at the strange sight which they saw.

For first and foremost this Polype fish was of an unmeasurable and incredible bignesse: and besides, he was besmeared and beraied all over with the brine and pickle of the foresaid salt-fish, which made him both hideous to see to, and to stinke withall most strongly. Who would ever have looked for a Polipe there, or taken knowledge of him by such marks as these? Surely they thought no other, but that they had to deale and encounter with some monster: for with his terrible blowing and breathing that he kept, he drave away the dogs, and otherwhiles with the end of his long stringed winding feet, he would lash and whip them; somtimes with his stronger clawes like arms he rapped and knoked them well and surely, as it were with clubs. In summe, he made such good shift for himselfe, that hardly and with much adoe they could kill him, albeit he received many a wound by trout-spears which they launced at him. Wel, in the end his head was brought and shewed to *Lucullus* for a wonder, & as big it was as a good round hogshead or barrel that would take and containe 15 Amphores:[2]

---

[1] Incredible it is; the octopus does not leave the water, nor does it breathe.
[2] 90 gallons.

and his beards (for so *Trebius* tearmed his clawes and long-stringed feet) carried such a thicknesse and bulke with them, that hardly a man could fathome one of them about with both his armes, [with] such knockers they were knobbed and knotted like clubs, and withall 30 foot long. The concavities within them, and hollow vessels like great basons, would hold 4 or 5 gallons apeece: and his teeth were answerable in proportion to the bignes of his bodie. The rest was saved for a wonder to be seene, and weighed 700 pound weight. This author of mine *Trebius* affirmeth, that Cuttels also and Calamaries[1] have been cast upon that shore, ful as big. Indeed in our sea there be Calamaries taken of 5 cubits long, and Cuttels of twaine, in length: and these live not above two yeares.

§ 43

Of the greatest Winkle called Murex, and other kinds of shell-fishes

(Chap. 33)

As for the Pourcelanes or Murices, they have a stronger skaled shell; as also all the kind of Winkles great and small. Wherin a man may see the wonderfull varietie of Nature in this play and pastime of hers, giving them so many and sundry colours, with such diversitie of formes and figures; for of them yee shall have flat and plain, hollow, long, horned like the moon croissant, full round, halfe round, & cut as it were just through the mids, bow-backt, and rising up, smooth, rough toothed and indented like a saw, ridged and chamfered between, wrinkling and winding upward to the top like Caltropes, bearing out sharpe points in the edges, withoutforth broad and spread at large, within rolled in pleits.

Moreover, there be other distinct shapes besides all these, some be striped and raied with long streaks, others crested and blasing with a bush of long haire: some againe crisped and curled, others

---

[1] *saepia*; types of cuttlefish, but Pliny, more cautiously, gives their length in Italian waters as 7½ feet.

made like an hollow gutter or pipe: some fashioned as it were a comb, others waving with plaits one above another tile-wise, others framed in the manner of a net or lattise: some are wrought crooked and byas, others spred out directly in length. A man shall see of them those that are made thick and mossie thrust together and compact, others stretcht forth at large: ye shall have of them wrapt and lapt one within another: and to conclude, yee shall find them run round into a short fast knot, and all their sides united together in one: some flat and plain good to give a clap, others turning inward crooked like a cornet, made as it were to sound and wind withall. Of all these sorts, the Pourcelanes or Venus-Winkles swim above the water, and with their concavitie or hollow part which they set into the weather, help themselves in stead of sailes, and so gathering wind, saile as it were aloft upon the sea. The manner of the Scalops is to skip, and otherwhiles they will leap forth of the water. They also can find the means to make a boat of themselves, and so flote above and saile handsomly.

§ 44

Of Pearles

(Chaps. 34, 35)

BUT what meane I all this while to stand upon these small trifling matters, when as in very truth the overthrow of all honestie, the ruin of good maners, and in lieu thereof all riot and superfluity proceeds from these shel-fishes, and from nothing so much? for now the world is grown to this passe that there is nothing in it whatsoever so chargeable to mankind, nothing so hurtfull and dangerous as is the very sea, and that so many waies; namely in furnishing the table with such varietie of dishes, in pleasing and contenting the taste with so many dainty and delicate fishes; and those carry the highest price that be gotten with greatest hazard and danger of those that take them, otherwise they be of no regard and value to speake of. Howbeit al that before named is nothing in comparison of the Purples, pretious Coquils and Pearls

that come from thence.[1] It was not sufficient belike to bring the
seas into the kitchen, to let them down the throat into the belly,
unlesse men and women both caried them about in their hands and
eares, upon their head, and all over their body. And yet what
societie and affinitie is there betwixt the sea and apparell? what
proportion betwixt the waves and surging billowes thereof, and
wooll? for surely this element naturally receives us not into her
bosom unlesse we be stark naked: and set the case there were so
great good fellowship with it and our bellies; how comes our
backe and sides to be acquainted with it? But wee were not contented to feed with the peril of so many men, unlesse we be clad
and araied also therewith. O, the folly of us men! see how there is
nothing that goeth to the pampering and trimming of this our
carcasse, of so great price and account, that is not bought with the
utmost hasard, and costeth not the venture of a mans life!

But now to the purpose. The richest merchandise of all and the
most soveraigne commoditie throughout the whole world are
these Pearles. The Indian ocean is chief for sending them: and yet
to come by them, we must go and search among those huge &
terrible monsters of the sea, which we have spoken of before: we
must passe over so many seas, and saile into far countries so remote, and come into those parts where the heate of the sun is so
excessive and extreme; and when all is done we may perhaps misse
of them: for even the Indians themselves are glad to seeke among
the Islands for them, & when they have done all they can, meet
with very few. The greatest plenty of them is to be found in the
coast of Taprobane,[2] and Stoidis, as hath bin said before in our
Cosmographie and description of the world: and likewise about
Perimula a promontorie and city of India.[3] But the most perfect
and exquisite of all others be they that are gotten about Arabia,
within the Persian gulfe.

This shell-fish which is the mother of Pearle, differs not much

---

[1] Pearls do not come from the purple-bearing winkles. *Conchylia* (the 'coquils')
is also used for shell-fish, and the meaning may be either that all the expensive
fishes are surpassed by the mere shell-fish that carry pearls, or that they are surpassed by the precious purple-fish and the oyster with its pearl.

[2] Ceylon.

[3] Pliny describes Stoidis elsewhere as an island lying next to the desert island
of Cascandrus off the coast of Baluchistan. It has not been identified but Perimula,
on the Aurea Chersonese, was probably Malacca in Malaya.

in the maner of breeding and generation from the Oysters: for when the season of the yeare requireth that they should engender, they seeme to yawne and gape, and so do open wide; and then (by report) they conceive a certaine moist dew as seed, wherewith they swell and grow big, and when time commeth labor to be delivered hereof: and the fruit of these shell fishes are the Pearles, better or worse, great or small, according to the qualitie and quantitie of the dew which they received. For if the dew were pure and cleare which went into them, then are the Pearles white, faire, and Orient: but if grosse and troubled, the Pearles likewise are dimme, foule, and duskish; pale (I say) they are, if the weather were close, darke, and threatning raine in the time of their conception. Whereby (no doubt) it is apparant and plaine, that they participate more of the aire and sky, than of the water and the sea; for according as the morning is faire, so are they cleere: but otherwise, if it were misty and cloudy, they also will be thicke and muddy in colour. If they may have their full time and season to feed, the Pearles likewise will thrive and grow bigge; but if in the time it doth chance to lighten, then they close their shells together, and for want of nourishment are kept hungrie and fasting, and so the pearles keepe at a stay and prosper not accordingly. But if it thunder withall, then suddenly they shut hard at once, and breed only those excrescences which be called Physemata, like unto bladders puft up and hooved with wind, & no corporal substance at all: and these are the abortive & untimely fruits of these shel fishes.

Now those that have their ful perfection, and be sound and good indeed, have many folds and skins wherein they be lapt, not unproperly as it may be thought, a thicke, hard, and callous rind of the body, which they that be skilfull do pill and clense from them. Certes, I cannot chuse but wonder how they should so greatly be affected with the aire, and joy so much therein: for with the same they wax red, and lose their native whitenesse and beautie, even as the bodie of a man or woman that is caught and burnt with the sun. And therefore those shels that keep in the maine sea, and lie deeper than that the sun-beames can pierce unto them, keep the finest and most delicate pearles. And yet they, as orient as they be, waxe yellow with age, become riveled, and looke dead without any lively vigor: so as that commendable orient lustre (so much sought for of our great lords and costly dames) continueth but in their youth, and decaieth with yeares. When they be old, they will prove thicke and grosse in the very shels, and sticke fast unto their sides, so as they cannot be parted from them, unlesse they be filed asunder. These have no more but one faire face, and on that side are round, for the backe part is flat and plaine; and hereupon such are called Tympania, as one would say, Bell pearles. We see daily of these shells which serve as boxes to carrie sweet perfumes and precious ointments, and most commendable they are for this gift, that in them there be pearls of this sort naturally growing together like twins. The pearle is soft and tender so long as it is in the water, take it forth once and presently it hardeneth.

As touching the shell that is the mother of Pearle, as soon as it perceiveth and feeleth a mans hand within it, by and by she shutteth, and by that means hideth and covereth her riches within: for well woteth she that therefore she is sought for. But let the fisher looke well to his fingers, for if she catch his hand between, off it goeth: so trenchant and sharp an edge she carrieth, that is able to cut it quite a two. And verily this is a just punishment for the theefe, and none more: albeit she be furnished and armed with other means of revenge. For they keep for the most part about craggie rocks, and are there found: and if they be in the deepe, accompanied lightly they are with curst Sea-dogs. And yet all this will not serve to skar men away from fishing after them: for why? our dames and gentlewomen must have their eares behanged with them, there is no remedie. Some say, that these mother-pearles have their kings and captaines, as Bees have: that as they have their swarmes led by a master Bee, so every troup and companie of these, have one speciall great and old one to conduct it; and such commonly have a singular dexteritie and wonderfull gift to prevent and avoid all daungers. These they be that the dyvers after pearles are most carefull to come by: for if they be once caught, the rest scatter asunder and be soone taken up within the nets. . . .

As for those [pearls] that are long and pointed upward, growing downeward broader and broader like a peare, or after the manner of Alabaster boxes, full and round in the bottome, they be called Elenchi.[1] Our dames take a great pride in a braverie, to have these

[1] It is not clear why pear-shaped pearls received this name. Rackham has

not only hang dangling at their fingers, but also two or three of them together pendant at their eares. And names they have forsooth newly devised for them, when they serve their turne in this their wanton excesse and superfluitie of roiot: for when they knocke one against another as they hang at their eares or fingers, they call them Crotalia, *i.* Cymbals:[1] as if they tooke delight to heare the sound of their pearles ratling together. Now adayes also it is growne to this passe, that meane women and poore mens wives affect to weare them, because they would be thought rich: and a by-word it is amongst them, That a faire pearle at a womans eare is as good in the street where she goeth as an huisher to make way, for that every one will give such the place. Nay, our gentle-women are come now to weare them upon their feet, and not at their shoo latchets only, but also upon their startops and fine buskins,[2] which they garnish all over with pearle. For it wil not suffice nor serve their turne to carie pearles about them, but they must tread upon pearles, goe among pearles, and walke as it were on a pavement of pearles. . . .

I my selfe have seen *Lollia Paulina* (late wife, and after widdow, to *Caius Caligula* the emperor) when she was dressed and set out, not in stately wise, nor of purpose for some great solemnity, but only when she was to go to a wedding supper, or rather unto a feast when the assurance was made, & great persons they were not that made the said feast: I have seen her, I say, so beset and be-deckt all over with hemeraulds and pearles, disposed in rewes, ranks, and courses one by another: round about the attire of her head, her cawle, her borders, her peruk of hair, her bondgrace and chaplet;[3] at her ears pendant, about her neck in a carcanet, upon

---

'probes' from ἔλεγχος a proof. Ἔλεγχος can also mean a disgrace or a reproach, and the ladies, in their wanton excess, may have called these dangles 'my little disgraces'. The allusion can now only be guessed.

[1] Or castanets used to accompany wanton dancers.

[2] Types of boot.

[3] The Latin has *capite, crinibus, spira, auribus, collo, monilibus, digitis*, or head, hair, plait, ears, neck, bracelets, and fingers. The items of Lollia's dress are:

cawle	netted cap:
borders	plaits of hair used as switches;
bondgrace	veil or scarf attached to the front of a bonnet to keep off the sun;
chaplet	head wreath;
carcanet	necklace.

her wrest in bracelets, & on her fingers in rings; that she glittered & shon again like the sun as she went. The value of these ornaments, she esteemed and rated at 400 hundred thousand[1] Sestertii: and offered openly to prove it out of hand by her bookes of accounts & reckonings. Yet were not these jewels the gifts and presents of the prodigall prince her husband, but the goods and ornaments from her owne house, fallen to her by way of inheritance from her grandfather, which he had gotten together even by the robbing and spoiling of whole provinces. See what the issue and end was of those extortions and outrageous exactions of his: this was it, That *M. Lollius*, slandered and defamed for receiving bribes & presents of the kings in the East; and being out of favor with *C. Caesar*, sonne of *Augustus*, and having lost his amitie, dranke a cup of poison, and prevented his judiciall triall: that forsooth his neece *Lollia*, all to be hanged with jewels of 400 hundred thousand Sestertii, should be seene glittering, and looked at of every man by candle-light all a supper time. . . .

And yet this is not the greatest example that can be produced of an excessive riot and prodigalitie. Two only pearles there were together, the fairest and richest that ever have beene knowne in the world: and those possessed at one time by *Cleopatra* the last queen of *Aegypt*, which came into her hands by means of the great kings of the East, and were left unto her by descent. This princesse, when *M. Antonius* had strained himselfe to doe her all the pleasure he possibly could, & had feasted her day by day most sumptuously, & spared for no cost: in the hight of her pride and wanton braverie (as being a noble curtezan, and a queene withall) began to debase the expence and provision of *Antonie*, and made no reckoning of all his costly fare. When he thereat demanded againe how it was possible to goe beyond this magnificence of his, she answered againe, that she would spend upon him at one supper 100 hundred thousand[2] Sestertii. *Antonie*, who would needs know how that might bee (for he thought it was impossible) laid a great wager with her about it, and shee bound it againe, and made it good. The morrow after, when this was to be tried, and the wager either to be won or lost, *Cleopatra* made *Antonie* a supper (because she would not make default, and let the day appointed to passe) which was sumptuous and roial ynough: howbeit, there was no

[1] 40 millions (P. H.). [2] 10 millions (P. H.).

extraordinarie service seene upon the board: whereat *Antonius* laughed her to scorne, and by way of mockerie required to see a bill with the account of the particulars. She again said, that whatsoever had been served up alreadie, was but the overplus above the rate & proportion in question, affirming still that she would yet in that supper make up the full summe that she was seazed at: yea, her selfe alone would eat above that reckoning, and her owne supper should cost 600 hundred thousand[1] Sestertii, and with that commanded the second service to be brought in. The servitors that waited at her trencher (as they had in charge[2] before) set before her one only crewet of sharpe vineger, the strength whereof is able to resolve pearles.[3] Now she had at her eares hanging these two most precious pearles, the singular and only jewels of the world, and even Natures wonder. As *Antonie* looked wistly upon her, and expected what shee would doe, shee tooke one of them from her eare, steeped it in the vineger, and so soon as it was liquified, dranke it off. And as shee was about to doe the like to the other, L. *Plancus* the judge of that wager, laid fast hold upon it with his hand, and pronounced withall, That *Antonie* had lost the wager. Whereat the man fell into a passion of anger.

There was an end of one pearle: but the fame of the fellow thereof may goe with it: for after that this brave queen the winner of so great a wager, was taken prisoner and deprived of her roiall estate, that other pearle was cut in twaine, that in memoriall of that one halfe supper of theirs, it should remaine unto posteritie, hanging at both the eares of *Venus* at Rome, in the temple of Pantheon.

§ 45

The purple fishes

(Chaps. 36, 38, 39, 40, 41)

PURPLES live ordinarily seven yeers. They lie hidden for 30 daies space about the dogdaies, like as the Murices or Burrets do. They

---

[1] 60 millions (P. H.). [2] Had been told to do.

[3] There seems no doubt that vinegar (*acetum*) is meant, although it has often been pointed out that pearls do not dissolve in vinegar. Rackham suggests that Cleopatra swallowed the pearl whole and recovered it later. Even so it would be unpleasant to take it in vinegar, and little better in soured wine, the original meaning of *acetum*.

meet together by troupes in the spring, and with rubbing one against another, they gather and yeeld a certaine clammie substance and moisture in manner of waxe. The Murices doe the like. But that beautifull colour, so much in request for dying of fine cloth, the Purples have in the midst of the neck and jawes. And nothing else it is, but a little thin liquor within a white veine: & that is it which maketh that rich, fresh, and bright colour of deepe red purple roses. As for all the rest of this fish, it yeeldeth nothing. . . .

The best time to take Purples, is after the dog star is risen, & before the Spring: for, when they have made that viscous muscilage in manner of wax, their juice and humour for colour is over liquid, thin, & waterish. And yet the purple diers know not so much, nor take heed thereof, whereas indeed the skill thereof is a speciall point of their art, and wherein lieth all in all. Well, when they are caught, as is abovesaid, they take forth that vein before mentioned; and they lay it in salt, or else they do not well: with this proportion ordinarily, namely, to every hundredweight of the Purple liquor, a Sestier or pint and halfe of salt.[1] Full three dayes and no more it must thus lie soking in powder. For the fresher that the colour is, so much is it counted richer and better. This don, they seeth it in leads, & to every Amphore, (*i.* which containeth about eight wine gallons) they put one hundred pound and a halfe just, of the colour so prepared. Boile it ought with a soft and gentle fire, and therfore the tunnel or mouth of the furnace must be a good way off from the lead and chawdron. During which time, the workemen that tend the lead, must eftsoones skim off and clense away the fleshie substance, which cannot chuse but stick to the veines which containeth the juice or

---

[1] The amounts of ingredients in this passage are not reliable. The secrets of the Tyrian purple dying methods are said to have been lost in the twelfth century. It is true that anyone can use the shellfish material in small amounts as a fast marking ink, but even Barcroft in his 'Philosophy of permanent colours' contents himself with testing small quantities and does not attempt the method of boiling for ten days. The subject is much complicated by Pliny's nomenclature. Fabius Columna (*De purpura*, Rome, 1616) identified only two types of shell-fish, the purpura or pelagium and the buccinum. He believed murex and conchylium were only generic names for shell-fish and where murex appeared to mean a distinct species it had been mistakenly substituted for buccinum. With such difficulties it is not surprising that the dying secrets remain lost, but the real reason for their disappearance is doubtless their successful replacement.

liquour of purple beforesaid. And thus they continue 10 daies, by which time ordinarily the lead or vessell wil shew the liquour cleere, as if it were sufficiently boiled. And to make a triall thereof, they dip into it a fleece of wool wel rensed & washt out of one water into another: & till such time, that they see it give a perfect die, they stil ply the fire, & give it a higher seething. That which staineth red, is nothing so rich as that which giveth the deep & sad blackish color. When it is come to the perfection, they let the wooll lie to take the liquor 5 houres: then they have it forth, touse and card it, and put it in againe, until it hath drunke up all the colour, as much as it will.

Now this is to be observed, that the sea cornet Buccinum makes no good colour of it selfe: for their dye wil shed & lose the lustre. And therfore usually they joine to it the sea Purple Pelagium, which maketh too deep and brown a colour: unto which it giveth a fresh & lively teinture, as it were in grain,[1] and so maketh that sad purple which they desire. Thus by mixing & medling the force of both together, they mend one another, while the lightnesse or sadnesse of the one doth quicken and raise, or els dorr and take downe the colour of the other. To the dying of a pound of wooll, they use this proportion of two hundred Buccina or sea Cornets, joined with a hundred and eleven Pelagian Purples: & so commeth that rich Amethyst or purple violet colour, so highly commended above all other. But the Tyrians make their deep red purple, by dipping their wool first in the liquor of the Pelagian purples only, whiles it is not throughly boiled to the heigth, but as it were green yet and unripe; and therof they let it take what it can drinke. Soone after they change it into another caudron or lead, where the colour of the sea Cornets alone is boiled. And then it is thought to have a most commendable and excellent dye, when it is as deep a red as bloud that is cold and setled, blackish at the first sight, but looke between you and the light, it carieth a bright and shining lustre. And hereupon it is, that *Homer* calleth bloud, Purple. . . . As for the cloth died with the purple of the shel-fish Conchylia, the maner of making the colour, and dying in all respects is the same, save that there be no sea Cornets used thereto. Moreover, the juice or liquor for that colour, is tempered with water in stead of the filthy pisse and urine of a man, altogether

---

[1] The scarlet dye from the kermes insect.

used in the other:[1] and therein is sodden but the halfe proportion of colours to the foresaid tinctures. And thus is made that light pale stammel[2] so highly commended, for being short of the deep rich colour: and the lesse while that the wooll is suffered to drinke the fill, the more bright and fresh it seemeth.

As for these colours, they are valued dearer or cheaper, according to the coasts where these fishes are gotten more or lesse. Howbeit, it was never known that in any place, a pound of the right purple wooll, died with the Pelagian colour, or of the colour it selfe, was more worth than 500 Sesterces: nor a pound of the Cornets purple cost above one hundred. I would they knew so much that pay so deare for these wares by retaile here at home, and cannot have them, but at an excessive rate. But here is not all, neither is this an end of expence that way, for one still draweth on another: and men have a delight to spend and lay on still one thing after another: to make mixtures and mixtures again, and so to sophisticate the sophistications of Nature: as namely to paint and die their seelings, even the very embowed roofs and arches in building,[3] to mix and temper gold and silver together, therewith to make an artificiall metall Electrum: and by adding brasse or copper thereto, to have another metall, counterfeiting the Corinthian vessels.

It would not suffice our prodigal spendthrifts to rob the precious stone Amethyst of his name, and to apply it to a colour; but when they had a perfect Amethyst[4] die, they must have it to be drunken againe with the Tyrean purple, that they might have a superfluous and double name compounded of both (Tyriamethistus) correspondent to their two-fold cost and duple superfluitie. Moreover, after they have accomplished fully the colour of the Conchylium, they are not content untill they have a second die in the Tyrian

---

[1] The two possible translations have opposite meanings. *Praeterque jus temperatur aqua et pro indiviso humani potus excremento* can be read, 'the juice is tempered with water and in like manner (*pro indiviso*) with excrement of human urine'; or as Holland takes it,—with water instead of the excrement commonly used (*pro excremento indiviso*). It is little wonder if techniques described by Pliny are difficult to repeat now (see note on p. 99 and p. 158).
[2] Woollen cloth or table cover of red colour.
[3] *testudines tingere*. This has been translated as staining tortoise-shells, but Holland prefers the derived meanings of *testudo*, arches or vaults in buildings.
[4] Amethystos was a herb used to prevent drunkenness.

purple lead. It should seeme, that these double dies and compounded colours, came first from the errour and repentance of the
workeman when his hand missed: and so was forced to change
and alter that which he had done before, and utterly misliked. And
hereof forsooth is come now a pretty cunning and art thereof: and
the monstrous spirits of our wastfull persons are grown to wish
and desire that, which was a fault amended first: and seeing the
two-fold way of a double charge and expence troden before them
by the diers, have found the meanes to lay colour upon colour, and
to overcast and strike a rich die with a weaker, so that it might be
called a more pleasant and delicate colour. Nay it will not serve
their turn to mingle the above-said tinctures of sea fishes, but
they must also do the like by the die of land-colours: for when
a wooll or cloth hath taken a crimson or skarlet in graine, it must
be died againe in the Tyrian purple, to make (I would not else) the
light, red, and fresh Lustie-gallant.[1]

§ 46

Of the Nacre

(Chap. 42)

THE Nacre also called Pinna, is of the kind of shell-fishes. It is
alwaies found and caught in muddie places, but never without a
companion, which they cal Pinnoter, or Pinnophylax.[2] And it is no
other but a little shrimpe, or in some places, the smallest crab;
which beareth the Nacre companie, and waites upon him for to
get some victuals. The nature of the Nacre is to gape wide, and
sheweth unto the little fishes her seelie body, without any eie at
all.[3] They come leaping by and by close unto her: and seeing they
have good leave, grow so hardie and bold, as to skip into her shel

---

[1] A light red tint fashionable in Holland's day and named after a popular tune.
[2] Pinna is the sea-pen or fan-mussel. Pinnoter and Pinnophylax mean protector
of the sea-pen; they were probably hermit crabs.
[3] *corpus intus orbum luminibus.* Another translation suggests that the fishes see
her helpless body dark inside the shell, but the meaning could be that her body
was destitute (*orbum*) of eyes.

& fill it ful. The shrimp lying in spiall, seeing this good time and opportunitie, giveth token thereof to the Nacre, secretly with a little pinch. She hath no sooner this signall, but she shuts her mouth, and whatsoever was within, crushes and kils it presently: and then she devides the bootie with the little crab or shrimp, her sentinell and companion. I marvell therefore so much the more at them who are of opinion, that fishes and beasts in the water have no sence.

Why, the very Cramp-fish Torpedo, knowes her own force & power, and being her selfe not benummed, is able to astonish others. She lieth hid over head and eares within the mud unseen, ready to catch those fishes, which as they swim over her, be taken with a nummednesse, as if they were dead. There is no meat in delicate tendernesse, preferred before the liver of this fish. Also the fish called the sea-Frog,[1] (and of others the sea-Fisher) is as crafty every whit as the other: It puddereth in the mud, and troubleth the water, that it might not be seen: and when the little seely fishes come skipping about her, then she puts out her little hornes or Barbils which she hath bearing forth under her eies, and by little and little tilleth and tolleth them so neere, that she can easily seaze upon them. In like manner the Skate and the Turbot lie secret under the mud, putting out their finnes, which stir and crawle as if it were some little wormes; and all to draw them neer, that she might entrap them. Even so doth the Ray-fish or Thornback. As for the Puffen or Fork-fish, he lieth in await like a theefe in a corner, ready to strike the fishes that passe by with a sharpe rod or pricke that he hath, which is his weapon. In conclusion, that this fish is very subtill and crafty, this is a good proofe, That being of all others most heavie and slow, they are found to have in their bellie the Mullets, which of all others be the swiftest in swimming.[2]

[1] Diable de Mer (P. H.), Angler fish.

[2] The fishes mentioned here are:

cramp-fish torpedo	the electric ray (*torpedo*);
ray-fish, thornback	the sting ray (*pastinaca*);
puffen, fork-fish	unidentified but like a ray.

Holland's text differs from most which leave out the puffen and make the sting ray lie in wait.

§ 47

Of Sea-nettle fishes and other nastie and filthie creatures

(Chaps. 45, 47)

I VERILY for my part am of opinion, that those which properly are neither beasts nor plants, but of a third nature between or compounded of both (the sea-Nettles I mean, and Sponges) have yet a kinde of sense with them. As for those Nettles,[1] there be of them that in the night raunge too and fro, and likewise change their colour. Leaves they carry of a fleshie substance and of flesh they feed. Their qualitie is to raise an itching smart, like for all the world to the weed on the land so called. His manner is, when he would prey, to gather in his body as close, streight and stiffe as possibly may be. He spieth not so soon a silly little fish swimming before him, but he spreadeth and displaieth those leaves of his like wings; with them he claspeth the poore fish, and so devoures it. At other times, he lies as if he had no life at all in him, suffering himselfe to be tossed and cast too and fro among the weeds, with the waves of the sea: and look what fish soever he toucheth as he is thus floting, hee sets a smart itch upon them, and whiles they scratch and rub themselves against the rockes for this itch, hee sets upon them and eates them. In the night season he lieth for sea-Urchens and Scalops. When he feeleth ones hand to touch him, he changeth colour,[2] and draweth himselfe in close together on a heape: and no sooner toucheth he one, but the place will itch, sting, and be ready to blister: make not good hast to catch him quickly, he is hidden out of hand and gone. It is thought verily, that his mouth lyeth in his root, and that he voideth his excrements at a small pipe or issue above, where those fleshie leaves are. . . .

We must needs confesse, that fishes within stone shels, have small or no sense, as namely oisters. Many are of the nature of very Plants, to wit, those that they cal Holothuria: also Pulmones, resembling the lungs of a beast: and Star-fishes, made in forme of

---

[1] Jellyfish.
[2] Or, *locumque mutant*, they change their position and move away.

stars (such stars I meane as it pleaseth the Painter to draw.) In sum, what is there not bred within the sea? Even the very fleas that skip so merily in summer time within victualling houses and Ins, and bite so shroudly: as also lice that love best to lie close under the haire of our heads, are there engendred & to be found: for many a time the fishers twitch up their hooks, and see a number of these skippers and creepers setled thicke about their baits which they laied for fishes. And this vermine is thought to trouble the poore fishes in their sleep by night within the sea, as well as us on the land.

§ 48

Of the fish Anthias, and how he is taken

(Chap. 59)

I THINKE it not meet to conceale that, which I perceive many do beleeve & hold, as touching the fish Anthias.[1] We have in our Cosmographic made mention of the Isles Cheldoniae in Asia, scituate in a sea full of rocks under the promontory of Taurus; among which are found great store of these fishes: and much fishing there is for them, but they are suddenly taken, and ever after one sort.[2]

For when the time serveth, there goeth forth a fisher in a smal boat or barge for certain daies together, a pretty way into the sea, clad alwaies in apparel of one and the same colour, at one houre, and to the same place stil, where he casteth forth a bait for the fish: but the fish Anthias is so craftie and warie, that whatsoever is thrown forth, he suspecteth it evermore, that it is a means to surprise him. He feareth therefore and distrusteth: and as he feareth, so is he as warie: untill at length, after much practise & often using this devise of flinging meat into one place, one above the rest groweth so hardy and bold, as to bite at it, for now by this time he is grown acquainted with the maner thereof, and secure.

[1] Probably a wrasse.
[2] The area where wrasse were caught by this very remarkable method was around the Swallow Islands of Lycia, off Cape Gelidonya in modern Turkey.

The fisher takes good mark of this one fish, making sure reckoning that he wil bring more thither, and be the means that he shall speed his hand in the end. And that is no hard matter for him to do, because for certain daies together, that fish, & none but he, dare adventure to come alone unto the bait. At length this hardy captaine meets with some other companions, and by little & little he cometh every day better accompanied than other, until in the end he brings with him infinite troups and squadrons together, so as now the eldest of them all (as crafty as they be) be so well used to know the fisher, that they will snatch meat out of his hands.

Then hee espying his time, putteth forth an hook with the bait, somwhat beyond his fingers ends, flieth and siezeth upon them more truly; then catcheth them, and speedily with a quick & nimble hand whippes them out of the water within the shadow of the ship, for feare the rest should perceive, & giveth them one after another to his companion within; who, ever as they be snatcht up, latcheth them in a course twillie or covering, & keeps them sure enough from strugling or squeaking, that they should not drive the rest away. The speciall thing that helpeth this game and pretty sport, is to know the captain from the rest, who brought his fellows to this feast, & to take heed in any hand that he be not twitcht up and caught. And therfore the fisher spareth him, that he may flie and goe to some other flock for to train them to the like banket.[1] Thus you see the maner of fishing for these Anthae.

Now it is reported moreover, that one fisher upon a time (of spightfull minde to do his fellow a shrewd turn) laid wait for the said captain fish, the leader of the rest (for he was very wel known from all others) and so caught him: but when the foresaid fisher espied him in the market to be sold, and knew it was he: taking himself misused & wronged, brought his action of the case against the other, and sued him for the dammage, and in the end condemned him.

[1] Lead them to a similar feast.

In
THE TENTH BOOKE
are contained the natures and stories
of Fowles and flying creatures

§ 49
Of the Cuckow

(Chap. 9)

IN the spring, he commeth abroad, and by the beginning of the
dog-daies, hides himselfe. These lay alwaies in other birds neasts,
and most of all in the Stockdoves, commonly one egge and no
more (which no other bird doth besides) and seldom twain. The
reason why they would have other birds to sit upon their eggs
and hatch them, is because they know how all birds hate them:
for even the very little birds are readie to war with them: for feare
therefore that the whole race of them should be utterly destroied
by the furie of others of the same kind, they make no nest of their
owne (being otherwise timorous and fearefull naturally of themselves) and so are forced by this craftie shift to avoid the danger.
The Titling therefore that sitteth, being thus deceived, hatcheth
the egge & bringeth up the chick of another bird. And this yong
Cuckow being greedy by kind, beguiling the other yong birds
and intercepting the meat from them, groweth hereby fat and
faire-liking: whereby it comes into speciall grace and favour with
the dam of the rest, and nource to it. She joieth to see so goodly
a bird toward: and wonders at her selfe that she hath hatched &
reared so trim a chick. The rest, which are her owne indeed, she
sets no store by, as if they were changelings: but in regard of that
one, counteth them all bastards and misbegotten: yea, and suffereth
them to be eaten and devoured of the other even before her face:
and this she doth so long, untill the yong cuckow being once
fledge & readie to flie abroad, is so bold as to seize on the old

Titling, and to eat her up that hatched her. And by that time there is not another bird againe for goodnesse and sweetnesse of meat, comparable to the yong Cuckow.

§ 50

Of Peacocks and of Cocks

(Chaps. 20, 21)

THE Peacock far surpasses all the rest of this kind, as well for beauty, as also for the wit and understanding that he hath; but principally for the pride and glory he takes in himself. For perceiving at any time that he is praised and wel liked, he spreadeth his taile round, shewing and setting out his colours to the most, which shine againe like precious stones: and namely when he turnes them against the Sun, as his manner is, for so he giveth them a more radiant and glittering lustre. And for the same purpose also with his taile, representing fish shels,[1] he gives a certain shadow to the rest of his feathers, which seeme the brighter when they be a little shadowed: and withall, he sets all those eyes of his feathers together in a ranke and gathereth them round, knowing full well that hee is the more looked on for them; and therein he taketh no small joy and pleasure. On the other side, when he hath lost this taile, which usually he moulteth every yere when trees shed their leaves, until such time as trees blossom new, and his taile be grown again, he hath no delight to come abroad, but as if he were ashamed, or mourned, seeketh corners to hide himselfe in. The Peacocke ordinarily liveth 25 yeares. At 3 yeres of age he begins to put forth that varietie of colours in his feathers. Authors who have written of him say, that he is not only a proud and vainglorious creature, but also as malicious and spightfull, as the Goose is bashfull and modest: for so have some of them observed these properties and qualities in these birds. But I for my part like not to make such similitudes. . . .

Next to Peacocks, these birds about our houses which are our sentinels by night, & whom Nature hath created to breake men of

[1] Concave like a shell.

their sleepe, to awaken and call them up to their work, have also a sence and understanding of glory; they love (I say) to be praised, and are proud in their kind. Moreover, they are Astronomers, and know the course of the stars, they divide the day by their crowing, from 3 houres to 3 houres: when the Sun goeth to rest, they go to roost: and like sentinels they keepe the reliefe of the fourth watch in the camp: they cal men up to their carefull labour and travell: they will not suffer the Sun to rise and steale upon us, but they give us warning of it: by their crowing they tell us that the day is comming, and they foretell their crowing likewise, by clapping their sides with their wings. They are Commanders and rulers of their own kind, be they Hens or other Cocks; and in what house soever they be they will be masters and kings over them. This soveraignty is gootten by plain fight one with another, as if they knew, that naturally they had spurs, as weapons, given them about their heeles, to try the quarrell: and many times the combat is so sharp and hot, that they kill one another ere they give over. But if one of them happen to be conqueror, presently upon victorie he croweth, and himselfe soundeth the triumph. He that is beaten makes no words, nor croweth at all, but hideth his head in silence; and yet neverthelesse it goeth against his stomack to yeeld the gantlet and give the bucklers. Hardly can he brook to be under another: and not only these cocks of game, but the very common sort of the dunghill are as proud and high minded: ye shal see them to march stately, carying their neck bolt upright, with a combe on their head like the crest of a soldiers helmet.

§ 51

Of Cranes and Quailes

(Chap. 23)

THE nation of the prettie Pigmies enjoy a truce and cessation from armes, every yeare (as we have said before) when the Cranes, who use to wage war with them, be once departed and come into our countries.[1] And verily, if a man consider well how far it is

[1] See § 20.

from hence to the Levant sea, it is a mightie great journey that they take, and their flight exceeding long.

They put not themselves in their journey, nor set forward without a counsell called before, and a generall consent. They flie aloft, because they would have a better prospect to see before them: and for this purpose a captain they chuse to guide them, whom the rest follow. In the rereward behind there be certaine of them set and disposed to give signall by their manner of crie, for to raunge orderly in rankes, and keep close together in array: and this they doe by turnes each one in his course. They maintaine a set watch all the night long, and have their sentinels. These stand on one foot, and hold a little stone within the other, which by falling from it, if they should chance to sleepe, might awaken them, and reprove them for their negligence. Whiles these watch, all the rest sleep, couching their heads under their wings: and one while they rest on the one foot, and otherwhiles they shift to the other. The captaine beareth up his head aloft into the aire, and giveth signall to the rest what is to be done.

These Cranes if they be made tame and gentle, are very playfull and wanton birds: and they will one by one dance (as it were) and run the round with their long shankes stalking ful untowardly. This is surely known, that when they mind to take a flight over the sea Pontus, they will fly directly at the first to the narrow streights of the sayd sea, lying between the two capes Criumetopon and Carambis, and then presently they ballaise themselves with stones in their feet, and sand in their throats, that they flie more steadie and endure the wind. When they be halfe way over, down they fling these stones: but when they are come to the continent, the sand also they disgorge out of their craw. . . .

But since we are entred into this discourse of those foules that make voiages by whole flocks over sea and land to see strange countries, I canot put off to speak of lesser birds also, which are of the like nature. For those beforenamed may seeme in some sort to be induced to such great travell, so bigge they are of bodie, and so strong withall. As touching Quailes therefore, they alwaies come before the Cranes depart.

A little bird it is, and whiles she is among us here, mounteth not aloft in the aire, but rather flieth below neere the ground. The manner of their flying is like the former, in troupes: but not without some danger of the sailers when they approch neer to land. For oftentimes they settle in great number on their sailes, and there perch, which they doe evermore in the night, and with their poise beare downe barkes and small vessels, and finally sinke them. These Quailes have their set gists, to wit, ordinarie resting and baiting places. When the Southwind blowes, they never flie: for why? it is a moist, heavy, and cloggie wind, and that they know well ynough. And yet they willingly chuse a gale whensoever they flie, by reason that their bodies are too weightie (in comparison of their wings) to beare them up: and besides, their strength is but small. And hereupon it is, that as they flie, they seem by their manner of crie to complaine, as though they flew with paine. Commonly therefore they chuse a Northerne wind to flie with: and they have one mighty great Quaile called Ortygometra, to lead the way and conduct them, as their captain. The formost of them, as he approcheth neere to land, paieth toll for the rest unto the Hauke, who presently for his welcome preieth upon him.

Whensoever at any time they are upon their remoove and departure out of these parts, they persuade other birds[1] to beare them company: and by their inducements, there go in their train the Glottis, Otis,[2] and the Cychramus. As for the Glottis [a plover], he putteth forth a long tongue, whereupon he hath that name. This bird is very forward at the first setting out (as being desirous to be a traveller, to see far countries, and to change the aire:) and the first daies journy he undertaketh with pleasure: but soone finding the tediousnesse and paines in flying, he repents that ever he enterprised the voiage. To go backe again without company, hee is ashamed: and to come lag behind he is as loth: howbeit, for that day he holdeth out so so, and never goeth farther; for at the next resting place that they come unto, hee faire leaveth the company and staieth there; where lightly he meeteth with such

[1] The birds in this section are:
Ortygometra   the quail-mother, another
              name for the landrail;
Glottis   a kind of plover;
Otis   the great bustard;
Cychramus   probably the ortolan;
Like-owl   *bubo*, a horned owl;
Howlet   *noctua*, a night owl.
[2] The Bustard or Horn-owle (P. H.).

another as himselfe, who the yere before was left behind. And thus they do from time to time, yere by yere. As for the Cychramus [the ortolan], he is more staid and resolute to indure the travel: he maketh hast and hath an earnest longing to come into those parts which he so much desires: and therfore in the night season he is as good as a trumpet to awake the rest, and put them in mind of their journy. The Otis is a bird lesse than the Like-Owle, bigger than the Howlet, having two plumed ears standing up aloft, whereupon he took that name Otis in Greek. . . . This bird besides hath certain qualities by her self, and is skilful to counterfeit and make gestures like a flattering parasite: she can foot it, turn and trip, mount and capre, as if she were a professed dauncer: easie she is to be taken like as the Howlet, for whiles she is amused and looking wistly upon one that goeth about her, another commeth behind and soon catcheth her.

But to return to our Quailes aforesaid. If a contrarie wind should chance to arise and begin to drive against them, and hinder their flight: to prevent this inconvenience, they be well provided. For they flie well ballaised either with small weightie stones within their feet, or els with sand stuffed in their craw: the seed or grain of the white Elebore (a very poison) they love passing wel, and it is their best meat. But hereupon it is, that they are not served up as a dish to the table. Moreover, they are wont to fome and slaver at the mouth, by reason of the falling sicknesse, unto which they onely of all other creatures, but man again, are subject.[1]

§ 52

The nightingale

(Chap. 29)

THE Nightingale for fifteene daies and nights together, never giveth over but chaunteth continually, namely, at that time as the

---

[1] *veneni semen*, the seed of a poisonous plant, can be read *veratri semen*, hellebore seed. There may be other corruptions here for surely the Romans ate quails. The sentence about epilepsy in quails can also be translated, 'people are accustomed to spit at the sight of them as a charm against epilepsy, from which they only of all creatures except man can suffer'. No modern reference to epilepsy in quails has been found.

trees begin to put out their leaves thicke. And surely this bird is not to be set in the last place of those that deserve admiration: for is it not a wonder that so loud and cleare a voice should come from so little a body? Is it not as strange that shee should hold her wind so long, and continue with it as she doth?

Moreover, she alone in her song keepeth time and measure truly: she riseth and falleth in her note just with the rules of Musick and perfect harmony; for one while, in one entire breath she drawes out her tune at length treatable; another while she quavereth, and goeth away as fast in her running points: sometime she maketh stops and short cuts in her notes, another time she gathereth in her winde and singeth descant between the plain song: she fetcheth her breath againe, and then you shall have her in her catches and divisions: anon all on a sudden, before a man would thinke it, she drowneth her voice, that one can scarce heare her: now and then she seemeth to record to her selfe; and then she breaketh out to sing voluntarie. In sum, she varieth and altereth her voice to all keies: one while, ful of her largs, longs, briefs, semibriefs, and minims; another while in her crotchets, quavers, semiquavers, and double semiquavers: for at one time you shall heare her voice ful loud, another time as low; and anon shrill and on high: thick and short when she list; drawn out at leisure againe when she is disposed: and then (if she be so pleased) shee riseth and mounteth up aloft, as it were with a wind-organ. Thus she altereth from one to another, and sings all parts, the Treble, the Mean, and the Base. To conclude, there is not a pipe or instrument againe in the world (devised with all the art and cunning of man so exquisitely as possibly might be) that can affoord more musick than this pretty bird doth out of that little throat of hers.

So as no doubt there was fore-signified most excellent and melodious musicke, by an excellent presage of a nightingale which setled upon the mouth of *Stesichorus* the Poet, and there sung full sweetly: who afterwards proved to be one of the most rare and admirable musitians that ever was. And that no man should make a doubt that there is great Art and cunning herein, do but marke, how there is not one Nightingale but hath many notes and tunes. Againe, all of them have not the same, but every one a speciall kind of Musick by her selfe: nay, they strive who can do best, and one laboreth to excell another in varietie of song and long continuance: yea, and evident it is, that they contend in good earnest with all their will and power: for oftentimes shee that hath the worse and is not able to hold out with another, dieth for it, and sooner giveth she up her vitall breath, than giveth over her song.

Ye shall have the yong Nightingales studie and meditate how to sing, by themselves; ye shal have them listen attentively to the old birds when they sing, and to take out lessons as it were from them, whom they would seeme to imitate staffe by staffe. The scholler when she hath given good eare unto her mistresse, presently rehearseth what she hath heard; and both of them keep silence for a time in their turns. A man shall evidently perceive when the yong bird hath learned well, and when again it must be taught how to correct and amend wherein it did amisse; yea, and how the teacher will seeme to reprove and finde a fault; no marvell therfore if one of these Nightingales carrie the price (in the market) of a bond-slave; yea and a higher too, than a man might in old time have bought a good page and harnesse-bearer.

I my selfe have knowne one of them (mary it was white, which was a rare thing and not commonly seen) to have bin sold for 6000[1] Sesterces, for to be given as a Present unto the Empresse *Agrippina*, wife of *Claudius Caesar* late Emperor of Rome.

§ 53

Of House-Doves

(Chap. 34)

NEXT after Partridges, the nature of Doves would be considered, since that they have in a manner the same qualities . . . : howbeit, they be passing chaste, and neither male nor female change their mate, but keep together one true unto the other. They live (I say) as coupled by the bond of mariage: never play they false one by the other, but keep home still, and never visit the holes of others.

They abandon not their owne nests, unlesse they bee in state of single life or widdowhead by the death of their fellow. The

---

[1] Or 600,000.

females are very meek and patient; they will indure and abide their emperious males, notwithstanding otherwhiles they be very churlish unto them, offering them wrong and hard measure; so jealous be they of the hens, and suspicious, though without any cause and occasion given: for passing chaste and continent by nature they are. Then shall ye heare the cocks grumble in the throat, quarrell and complain, and all to rate the hens: then shall ye see them peck and job at them cruelly with their beakes; and yet soone after, by way of satisfaction, and to make amends again for their curst usage, they will fall to billing and kissing them lovingly, they will make court unto them and wooe them kindly, they will turne round about many times together by way of flatterie, and as it were by praiers seeke unto them for their love.

As well the male as the female be careful of their yong pigeons, and love them alike; nay ye shall have the cocke oftentimes to rebuke, yea chastise the hen, if she keep not the nest well; or having bin abroad, for comming no sooner home againe to her yong. And yet, kind they be to them, when they are about to build, lay, and sit. A man shall see how ready they be, to helpe, to comfort and minister unto them in this case. So soon as the egs be hatched, ye shall see them at the very first, spit into the mouths of the yong pigeons salt brackish earth, which they have gathered in their throat, thereby to prepare their appetite to meat, and to season their stomacks against the time that they should eat.

Doves and Turtles have this property, in their drinking not to hold up their bils between-whiles, and draw their necks backe, but to take a large draught at once, as horses and kine do.

§ 54

Of the Parrat and other birds that can speake

(Chaps. 42, 43)

BUT above all other birds of the aire, the Parrats passe, for counter-feiting a mans voice: insomuch, as they will seeme to parle and prate our very speech. This foule commeth out of the Indies. . . .

It is all the body over greene, onely it hath a collar about the necke of vermilion red, different from the rest of her feathers. The Parrat can skil to salute Emperors, and bid good morrow: yea, and to pronounce what words she heareth. She loveth wine well, and when shee hath drunk freely, is very pleasant, plaifull, and wanton. She hath an head as hard as is her beak: when she learns to speak, she must be beaten about the head with a rod of yron: for otherwise she careth for no blowes. When she taketh her flight down from any place, she lighteth upon her bil, and resteth therupon, and by that means favoreth her feet, which by nature are but weake and feeble, and so carrieth her owne weight more lightly.

There is a certain Pie, of nothing so great reckoning and account as the Parrat, because shee is not far set, but here-by neere at hand: howbeit, she pronounces that which is taught her more plainly and distinctly than the other. These take a love to the words that they speak: for they not only learn them as a lesson, but they learn them with a delight and pleasure. Insomuch that a man shall find them studying thereupon, and conning the said lesson: and by their carefull thinking upon that which they learn, they shew plainly how mindfull and intentive they be thereto. It is for certain knowne that they have died for very anger and griefe that they could not learn to pronounce some hard words: as also, unlesse they heare the same words repeated often unto them, their memory is so shittle, they will soone forget the same againe. If they misse a word, and have lost it, they wil seeke to call it againe to remembrance; and if they fortune to heare the same word in the mean time, they will wonderfully joy thereat. As for their beautie, it is not ordinary, although it be very lovely. But surely amiable enough they are in this, that they can so well resemble mans speech. It is said, that none of their kinde are good to bee made scholers, but such only as feed upon mast: and among them, those that have five toes to their feet. But even these also are not fit for that purpose, after the first two yeares of their age. And their tongue is broader than ordinarie: like as they be all that counterfeit mans voice, each one in their kind; although it be in maner general to all birds whatsoever to be broad tongued.

Agrippina the Empresse, wife to *Claudius Caesar*, had a Blackbird or a Throstle, at what time as I compiled this book, which could counterfeit mans speech; a thing never seen nor knowne before. The two *Caesars* also, the yong princes (to wit, *Germanicus* and *Drusus*) had one Stare,[1] and sundry Nightingales, taught to parle Greeke and Latine. Moreover, they would studie upon their lessons, and meditate all day long: and from day to day come out with new words still, yea, and were able to continue a long speech and discourse. Now for to teach them the better, these birds must be in a secret place apart by themselves, where they can heare no other voice: and one is to sit over them, who must repeat often that which he would have them to learn; yea, and please them also with giving them such meat as they best love.

Let us not defraud the Ravens also of their due praise in this behalfe, considering, that the whole people of Rome hath testified the same not only by taking knowledge, but also by a publick revenge and exemplarie punishment. And thus stood the case.

In the daies of *Tiberius* the emperor, there was a yong Raven hatched in a nest upon the church of *Castor* and *Pollux*; which, to make a triall how he could flie, took his first flight into a shoo-makers shop just over-against the said church. The master of the shop was well enough content to receive this bird, as commended to him from so sacred a place, and in that regard set great store by it. This Raven in short time being acquainted to mans speech, began to speak, and every morning would fly up to the top of the Rostra or publick pulpit for Orations, where, turning to the open Forum and market place, he would salute and bid good morrow to *Tiberius Caesar*, and after him, to *Germanicus* and *Drusus* the yong princes, both *Caesars*, every one by their names; and anon the people of Rome also that passed by. And when he had so don, afterwards would flie again to the shoomakers shop aforesaid. This duty [he] practised, yea and continued for many yeres together, to the great wonder and admiration of all men.

Now it fell out so, that another shoomaker who had taken the next . . . shop unto him, either upon a malicious envie that he occupied so neer him, or some sudden spleene and passion of choler (as he would seeme to plead for his excuse) for that the Raven chanced to meut a little, and set some spot upon a paire of his shooes, killed the said Raven. Whereat the people tooke such

[1] Starling.

indignation, that they rising in an uprore, first drove him out of that street, and made that quarter of the city too hot for him: and not long after murdered him for it. But contrariwise the carkasse of the dead Raven was solemnly enterred, and the funerals performed with all ceremoniall obsequies that could be devised. For the corps of this bird was bestowed in a coffin, couch or bed, and the same bedecked with chaplets and garlands of fresh floures of all sorts, carried upon the shoulders of two blacke-Mores, with minstrels before, sounding the Haut-boies, and playing on the Fife, as far as to the Funeral fire; which was piled and made in the right hand of the causey Appia, two miles without the city in a certain plain or open field called Rediculi. So highly reputed the people of Rome that ready wit and apt disposition in a bird, as they thought it a sufficient cause to ordaine a sumptuous buriall therefore: yea, and to revenge the death thereof, by murdering a citizen of Rome in that city, wherein many a brave man and noble person died, and no man ever solemnized their funerals: in that city I say which affoorded not one man to revenge the unworthy death of that renowned *Scipio Aemylianus*, after he had woon both Carthage and Numantia. This happened the fifth day before the Calends of Aprill, in the yeare when *M. Servilius*, and *C. Sestius* were Consuls of Rome.

Moreover, even at this very present, when I wrote this historie, I saw my selfe a Crow belonging to a certain knight of Rome, who brought him out of the realm of Grenado in Spaine, which was a very strange and admirable bird, not only for the exceeding blacke colour of his feathers, but also for that he could pronounce and expresse so perfectly many words and sentences together, and learned still new lessons every day more than other.

§ 55

Who first devised to cram Hens

(Chap. 50)

THEY of the Island Delos began the cramming of Hens and Pullein first. And from them arose that detestable gourmandise and gluttonie to eat Hens and Capons so fat and enterlarded with their owne grease. Among the old statutes ordained for to represse inordinate feasts, I find in one act made by *C. Fannius*, a Consul of Rome, eleven yeres before the third Punick war, an expresse prohibition and restraint, That no man should have his table served with any foule, unlesse it were one hen, and no more, and the same a runner only, and not fed up and crammed fat. The branch of this statute was afterwards taken forth and inserted in al other acts provided in that behalfe, and went currant thorough all. Howbeit, for all the law so well set down, there was a starting hole found to delude and escape the meaning therof, namely, to feed Cocks and Capons also with a past soked in milk and mead together, for to make their flesh more tender, delicate, and of sweeter tast: for that the letter of the statute reached no farther than to Hens or Pullets.

As for the Hens, they only be thought good and well ynough cramm'd, which are fat about the neck, and have their skin plumpe and soft there. Howbeit, afterwards our fine cookes began to looke to their hind-parts about the rumpe, and chuse them thereby. And that they should make a greater shew in the platter, they slit them along the chine: and lay their legs out at large, that they might take up the whole dresser bourd. The Parthians also have taught our cooks their own fashions. And yet for all this fine dressing and setting out of meat, there is nothing that pleaseth and contenteth the tooth of man in all respects; while one loves nothing but the leg, another likes and praises the white brawne alone, about the breast bone.

The first that devised a Barton & Mue[1] to keepe foule in, was *M. Laenius Strabo*, a gentleman of Rome, who made such an one at Brindisi, where he had enclosed birds of all kinds. And by his example we began to keepe foules within narrow coups and cages as prisoners, to which creatures Nature had allowed the wide aire for their scope and habitation.

[1] Aviary.

§ 56

The Auguries and presages of Egges

(Chap. 55)

LIVIA AUGUSTA the Empresse, wife somtime of *Nero*, when she was conceived by him, and went with that child (who afterwards proved to be *Tiberius Caesar*) being very desirous (like a yong fine lady as she was) to have a jolly boy, practised this girlish experiment to foreknow what she should have in the end: she tooke an egge, and ever carried it about her in her warme bosome; and if at any time she had occasion to lay it away, she would convey it closely out of her owne warme lap into her nurses, for feare it should chill. And verily this presage proved true, the egge became a cocke chicken, and she was delivered of a sonne.

And hereof it may well be came the device of late, to lay egges in some warme place, and to make a soft fire underneath of small straw or light chaffe to give a kinde of moderate heate: but evermore the eggs must be turned with a mans or womans hand, both night and day; and so at the set time they looked for chickens and had them. It is reported besides of a certaine Poulter, who had a secret by himselfe, whereby he could tell surely and never misse, which egge would be a cocke chicke, which a hen. . . . We have heard moreover, that when a brood hen chanced to die, the cocks that used to tread her, were seen to go about with the chickens one after another by turnes, and to do everie thing like to the very hen indeed that hatched them: and all that while to forbeare once to crow.

But above all it is sport alone to see the maner of an hen that hath sitten upon ducks egs and hatched them, how at the first she will wonder to have a teem of ducklings about her, and not acknowledge them for her owne; but soone after shee will clucke and call this doubtfull brood to her very carefully and diligently: but at the last, when she perceives them, according to their kind, to take the water and swim, how she will mourn and lament about the fish-poole, that it would pitty ones heart to see them what moane they will make.

§ 57

The sleepe of living creatures

(Chap. 75)

THE question, Whether living creatures sleep or no is not very difficult, but soon decided. For plain it is, that of land creatures, all that winke and close their eies doe sleepe. As for those in the water, that they also sleepe (though but a little) even they are of opinion who otherwise make doubt of the rest. And this they do not collect and gather by their eies (for lids they have none to shut) but because they are seene to lie so still and quiet, as fast and sound asleep, stirring no part, but a little wagging their tailes, and seeming to start and bee afright at any sudden noise made in the water. As for the Tunnies, we may avouch more confidently of their repose: for they come of purpose to sleep under the banks or rocks. And flat broad fishes lie so still sleeping among the shelves, that oftentimes a man may take them up with his hand. The Dolphins and Whales be heard to rout and snort again, they sleepe so soundly. Moreover, as touching Insects, no man need to doubt that they sleep, so quietly do they lie and make no noise: nay, if you bring a candle or other light, and set it even before their eies; you shall not have them to awake nor move.

An infant after it is borne, sleepeth for certaine moneths at the first, and in manner doth nothing els. But the elder hee waxeth, wakefull is he every day more than other. Babes at the very beginning do dreame. For they will waken and start suddenly in a fright; and as they lie asleep, keep a sucking of their lips, as if it were at the breast heads. Some never dream at all. And if such chance contrary to this custome, for to dreame once, it hath bin counted for a signe of death, as we have seene and prooved by many examples and experiments. And here in this place there offereth it selfe a great question,[1] and very disputable *pro et contra*, grounded upon many experiments of both sides: namely whether the soule of man while the body is at rest, foreseeth things to come? and how it should so do? or whether this be a thing of meere chance and altogether conjecturall, as many others be? And

[1] Argument.

surely if we go by histories, we may find as many of the one side as the other. Howbeit all men in manner agree in this, That dreames either immediately upon drinking wine and full stomacke, or els after the first sleep, are vaine and of no effect.

As for sleep it is nothing els but a retreat and withdrawing of the soule into the mids of it selfe. Evident it is, that Horses, Dogs, Kine, Oxen, sheep, and goats do dreame. Whereupon it is credibly also thought, that all creatures which bring forth their yong quicke and living, do the same. As for those that lay egges, it is not so certaine that they dreame: but resolved it is, that they all do sleep.

THE ELEVENTH BOOKE
telleth us of Insects

§ 58

Of the industrie and subtilitie of
Nature in framing Insects

(Chaps. 1, 2)

MANY and sundry sorts there be of Insects, as well among land creatures as those that fly in the aire. Some are winged, as bees: some have partly wings and partly feet, as Pismires: others want both, and neither flie nor go on their feet. And wel may they all be called *Insecta*: by reason of those cuts and divisions, which some have about the necke; others in the breast and belly; the which do go round and part the members of the body, hanging together onely by a little pipe and fistulous conveiance. There be of them, that have not the body divided entire, one part from the other by these incisures, cuts, and wrinckles; but they appeare only either under the belly, or upon the backe above, and go no deeper, neither yet round the whole compasse of the body. But a man shall perceive in them certaine rings or circles, apt to bend and wind to and fro, and those so plated and plaited one over another, that in nothing elswhere is more seen the workmanship of Nature, than in the artificiall composition of these little bodies.

In bodies of any bignes, or at least-wise in those of the greater sort, Nature had no hard piece of work to procreate, forme, and bring all parts to perfection; by reason that the matter wherof they be wrought, is pliable and will follow as she would have it. But in these so little bodies (nay pricks and specks rather than bodies indeed) how can one comprehend the reason, the power, and the inexplicable perfection that Nature hath therin shewed? How hath she bestowed all the five senses in a Gnat? and yet some there be, lesse creatures than they. But (I say) where hath she made the seat of her eies to see before it? where hath she set and disposed the tast? where hath she placed and inserted the instrument and organ of smelling? and above all, where hath she disposed that dreadful and terrible noise that it maketh, that wonderfull great sound (I say) in proportion of so little a body? can there be devised a thing more finely and cunningly wrought than the wings set to her body? Marke what long-shanked legs above ordinary she hath given unto them. See how she hath set that hungry hollow concavitie in stead of a belly: and hath made the same so thirstie and greedy after bloud, and mans especially.

Come to the weapon that it hath to pricke, pierce, and enter through the skinne, how artificially hath shee pointed and sharpened it? and being so little as it is (as hardly the finenesse thereof cannot be seen) yet as if it were of bignesse and capacity answerable, framed it she hath most cunningly for a twofold use: to wit, most sharpe pointed, to pricke and enter; and withall, hollow like a pipe for to sucke in and convey the bloud through it. Come to the Wood-worme, what manner of teeth hath Nature given it, to bore holes and eat into the very heart of hard Oke? who heareth not the sound that she makes whiles she is at her work? For in wood and timber is in manner all her feeding.

We make a wonder at the monstrous and mighty shoulders of Elephants, able to carry turrets upon them. We marvell at the strong and stiffe necks of buls, and to see how terribly they will take up things and tosse them aloft into the aire with their hornes. We keepe a wondering at the ravening of Tygres, and in the shag manes of Lions: and yet in comparison of these Insects there is nothing wherein Nature and her whole power is more seene, neither sheweth she her might more than in the least creatures of all. I would request therfore the Readers, that in perusing this treatise, they will not come with a prejudicate opinion, nor (because many of these silly flies and wormes be contemptible in their eies) disdaine, loath, and contemne the reports that I shall make thereof; seeing there is nothing either in Natures workes that may seeme superfluous, or in her order unworthy our speculation.

§ 59

The order that Bees keepe in their worke

(Chaps. 10, 11)

THE manner of their businesse is this. All the day time they have a standing watch and ward at their gates, much like to the *corps de guard* in a campe. In the night they rest untill the morning: by which time, one of them awaketh and raiseth all the rest with two or three big hums or buzzes that it gives, to warn them as it were with sound of trumpet. At which signall given, the whole troupe prepares to flie forth, if it be a faire and calme day toward, for they doe both foresee, and also foreshew when it will bee either windie or rainie, and then will they keepe within their strength and fort.

Now when the weather is temperate (which they foreknow well enough) and that the whole armie is on foot and marched abroad, some gather together the vertue of the floures within their feet and legges: others fil their gorge with water, and charge the downe of their whole body with drops of such liquor. The yonger sort of them go forth to worke, and carry such stuffe as is beforenamed, whiles the elder labor and build within the hive. Such as carry the floures abovesaid, stuffe the inner parts of their legs behind (and those Nature for that purpose hath made rough) with the help of their forefeet; and those again are charged full by the means of their muffle.[1] Thus being full laden with their provision, they return home to the hive, drawne even together round as it were in a heap, with their burden: by which time, there be three or foure ready to receive them, and those ease and discharge them of their lode. For this you must thinke, that they have their severall offices within. Some are busie in building, other in plaistering and overcasting, to make all smooth and fine: some be at hand to serve the workemen with stuffe that they need; others are occupied in getting ready meat and victuals out of that provision which is brought in: for they feed not by themselves, but take their repast together, because they should both labour and eat alike, and at the same houre.

As touching the maner of their building, they begin first above

---

[1] Muzzle, or nose.

to make arch-work embowed, in their combs, and draw the frame of their work downward; where they make two little allies for every arch or vault, the one to enter in by, the other to go forth at. The combs that are fastened together in the upper part, yea and on the sides, are united a little, and hang all together. They touch not the hive at all, nor join to it. Sometime they are built round, otherwhiles winding bias, according to the proportion of the hive. A man shall find in one hive hony combs somtime of two sorts: namely, when two swarms of bees accord together: and yet each one have their rites and fashions by themselves. For feare lest their combs of wax should be ready to fal, they uphold them with partition wals, arched hollow from the bottom upward, to the end that they might have passage every way to repair them. The formost ranks of their combes in the forefront, commonly are built void and with nothing in them, because they should give no occasion for a theefe to enter upon their labours. Those in the backe part of the hive, are ever fullest of hony: and therefore when men would take out any combes, they turne up the hives behind.

Bees that are emploied in carrying of hony, chuse alwaies to have the wind with them, if they can. If haply there do arise a tempest or a storm whiles they be abroad, they catch up some little stony greet to ballance and poise themselves against the wind. Some say, that they take it and lay it upon their shoulders. And withall, they flie low by the ground under the wind when it is against them, and keep along the bushes, to breake the force thereof. A wonder it is to see and observe the manner of their worke. They mark and note the slow-backs, they chastise them anon, yea, and afterwards punish them with death. No lesse wonderful also it is to consider how neat and clean they be. All filth and trumperie they remove out of the way: no foule thing, no ordure lieth in the hive to hinder their businesse. As for the doung and excrements of such as are working within, they be laid all on a heap in some by-corner, because they should not goe far from their worke: and in foule weather (when otherwise they have nought to do) they turn it forth.

Toward evening, their noise beginneth to slacke and grow lesse and lesse: untill such time as one of them flieth about with the same loud humming, wherewith she waked them in the morning, and thereby giveth a signal (as it were) and commandement for to go to rest: much after the order in a camp. And then of a sudden they are all husht and silent.

The houses and habitations that Bees build first, are for the Commons: which being finished, they set in hand with a pallace for their king. If they foresee that it will be a good season, and that they are like to gather store of provision, they make pavilions also for the Drones. And albeit they be of themselves bigger than the very bees, yet take they up the least lodgings. Now these drones be without any sting at all, as one would say unperfect bees, and the last fruit of such old ones as are weary and able to do no more good; the very later brood and increase, and to say a truth, no better than slaves to the right bees indeed. And therefore the others as master Bees over them, have them at their commandment: if any drudgery or such like businesse is to be don, out are they sent first: make they but slow hast in that they are set about, sure they are to pay for it, and to be punished without mercy. And not only in their ordinarie worke they serve them in good stead, but also they help them to multiply: for the hotter that the place is, the more hope there is of a greater increase. Certes, this is found by experience, That the better the hive is peopled with a number of bees, the Cast when time comes will bee the greater, and the oftner will they swarme. But after the hony is growing once to maturitie and perfection, then begin they to drive these drones out of dores: nay, ye shall have many bees set upon one poore drone, and kill him outright. So that a man shall not lightly see any of that kind but in the Spring-time.

If one pluck off the wings from a drone, and put him again within the hive, he will never lin[1] untill he have done the like by all the rest of the same kind. As touching the roiall pallaces for the kings and captaines that shall be, built they are all most stately, great of receit, in shew magnificent, seated by themselves apart, and like citadels raised upon some high knap or tuft of a mountaine. If one of these castles chance to be pressed or crushed, there will no more come of that princely race. All the lodgings and roomes where the bees abode is, are six cornered, according to the number of feet emploied in that worke. None of all this is done at any set time or day appointed: but they take the opportunity when they

---

[1] Give over.

can espie faire weather to fit their businesse, and so do these things by snatches.

§ 60

What things be contrarie and hurtfull unto Bees

(Chap. 18)

FILTHIE stinking savors they cannot abide, and namely, such as be contagious; and from them will they flie farre enough. Nay more than that, sure they will be to haunt and sting them that smell as they go of sweet pomanders and odoriferous ointments, notwithstanding they be otherwise themselves subject to the injuries of most living creatures. For first and foremost, they are molested and assailed by those of their owne nature, but yet degenerate and of bastard breed, to wit, Waspes and Hornets: also by a kind of Gnats called Muliones, Swallowes, Martins, and some other birds, make foule worke among them, and are their mortall enemies. The Frogs lie in wait for them as they come to drink: which is the principall worke they have to doe, when they be about to multiply and breed yong. And not those Frogs only which keep in standing pooles and running rivers, but those land-Frogs of a Todes kind will come of their owne accord from out of the brambles and briers where they keep, and leap up to the very dore and entrance of the hive; where they wil blow and breath in unto them: and when the Bees come flying forth thither, to see what the matter is, soone are they snapt up and devoured. And as for Frogs, all the sort of them are supposed not to feele the pricke of their sting. Sheep also are no friends of theirs: for if they be once intangled within their wool, hardly can they get out again. . . .

Over and besides, Bees naturally are many times sick; and that do they shew most evidently: a man shall see it in them by their heavie looks, and by their faintnesse in their busines: ye shall mark how some will bring forth others that be sicke and diseased, into the warme sun, and be readie to minister unto them and give them meat. Nay, ye shall have them to carie forth their dead, and to accompanie the corps full decently, as in a solemne funerall. If it

chance that the king be dead of some pestilent malady, the commons and subjects mourn, they take thought and grieve with
heavy cheere and sad countenance: idle they be, and take no joy
to doe any thing: they gather in no provision, they march not
forth; onely with a certaine dolefull humming they gather round
about his corps, and will not away. Then requisite it is and necessarie to sever and part the multitude, and so to take away the
body from them, otherwise they would keep a looking at the
breathlesse carcasse, and never go from it, but stil moan and mourn
without end. And even then also they had need be cherished and
comforted with good victuals, otherwise they would pine away
and die with hunger. To conclude, a man may soon know when
Bees be well in health, by their cheerfulnesse and fresh hue that
they carry.

§ 61

Of Indian Pismires

(Chap. 31)

IN the temple of *Hercules* at Erythrae, there were to be seen the
horns of a certain Indian Ant, which were there set up and fastned
for a wonder to posteritie. In the countrey of the Northerne
Indians, named Dardae, the Ants do cast up gold above ground
from out of the holes and mines within the earth: these are in
colour like to cats, and as big as the wolves of Aegypt. This gold
beforesaid, which they worke up in the winter time, the Indians
do steale from them in the extreme heate of Summer, waiting their
opportunitie when the Pismires lie close within their caves under
the ground, from the parching Sun. Yet not without great danger:
for if they happen to wind them and catch their sent, out they go,
and follow after them in great hast, and with such fury they fly
upon them, that oftentimes they teare them in pieces; let them
make way as fast as they can upon their most swift camels, yet
they are not able to save them. So fleet of pace, so fierce of courage
are they, to recover gold that they love so well.[1]

---

[1] Many explanations of these ants have been put forward; e.g. the horns of

§ 62

Of Mans eares and eies

(Chap. 37)

M A N alone hath not the power to shake his eares. Of flaggie, long, and hanging eares, came the syrnames first of the *Flacci* (families and houses in Rome). There is no one part of the bodie costeth our dames more than this, by reason of their precious stones and pendant pearls thereat. In the East countries, men also as wel as women, think it a great grace and bravery to weare earings of gold. . . .

Man only of all creatures hath a Face and Visage: the rest have either muzles and snouts, or else bils and beakes.

Other creatures have Foreheads also as well as men: but in mans alone we may see and reade sorrow and heavinesse, mirth and joy, clemencie and mildnesse, cruelty, and severity; and in one word, guesse by it, whether one be of a good nature or no?

In the ascent or rising of the forehead, man hath Eie-brows set, like to the eaves of an house; which he can move as he list, either both at once, or one after another: and in them is shewed part of the mind within. By them we denie, by them wee grant. These shew most of all others, pride and arrogancie. Wel may it be that pride doth appeare and settle in some other part, yet here is the seat and place of residence. True it is, that in the heart it beginnes, but hither it mounteth and ascendeth, here it resteth and re-maineth. No part can it find in the whole body more eminent and hauty, and withall more steepe than the browes, wherein it might rule and raigne alone without controlment. . . .

Men alone of all living creatures have eies of divers colours, some of one, and some of another. For all other creatures of one and the same kind, are eied alike. Howbeit, some horses there be that extraordinarily have red eies. But in men it is hard to set down the infinit variety and difference in them: for some have great glaring eies: others againe as little and as pinking. Others also there be

the ants in the temple of Hercules may have been the picks of Tibetan gold miners, and the ants themselves their dogs.

that have them of a moderate and reasonable bignes. Some be goggle eied, as if they would start out of their heads, and those are supported to be dim-sighted: others be hollow eied, and they are thought to have the best and clearest sight: like as they who for colour have goats eien. Moreover, ye shall have some men, who can discern a far off: others againe that see not but neere at hand. Many there are, whose eiesight dependeth of the Sunnes light: for let the day be overcast and cloudy, or the Sun gon downe, they see just nothing: and others contrariwise there be, that all the day time have but a bad sight; yet in the night season they see better than any others. . . . Grey eies commonly in the dark see more cleare than others.

It is reported of *Tiberius Caesar* the Emperor to have had this property by himself, that if he were awakened in the night, for a while he could see every thing as well as in the cleare day light; but soon after, by little and little, the darknesse would overcast and shadow all again: a gift that no man in the world was ever known to have but himselfe. *Augustus Caesar* of famous memory, had red eies like to some horses: and indeed wall eied he was, for the white thereof was much bigger than in other men: which also was the cause, that if a man looked earnestly upon him, and beheld him wistly (and a man could not anger him worse) he would be displeased, and highly offended. *Claudius Caesar* had a fleshy substance about the corners of his eies, that tooke up a good part of the white, and many times they were very red and bloud shotten. *C. Caligula* the Emperor, his eies were ever set in his head, and stiffe again. *Nero* had a very short sight; for unlesse he winked (as it were) and looked narrow with his eies, he could not well see ought, were it never so neere. Twentie couple of professed masters of fence and sword plaiers there were in the fence-schoole, that *C. Caligula* the Emperor maintained: and among the rest two there were and no more, whom a man could not make to winke, or once to twinckle with their eies: present before them what weapon he would, or make offer to strike, so steady and firm were they: and therfore they evermore carried the prize, and were invincible. So hard a matter is it for a man to keep his eies from twirling: and many men naturally cannot chuse but be evermore winking and twinckling with their eies: but such are holden for fearful and timorous persons.

§ 63

The resemblance that Apes have to men

(Chap. 44)

As for all the race and kind of Apes, they resemble the proportion of men perfectly in the face, nose, eares, and eye-lids; which eye-lids these creatures alone (of all foure-footed) have under their eyes as well as above: nay, they have paps and nipples in their brests, as women: armes also and legs bending contrarie waies, even as ours doe. Nailes they have also and fingers like to us, with the middle finger longer than the rest, as ours be. A little they differ from us in the feet, for somewhat long they are, like as their hands be; and the sole of their foot is answerable to the palm of their hand. Thumbs and great toes they have moreover, with joints directly like a man. And setting aside the member of generation, and that only in the he Ape, all inward parts are the very same that ours, as if they were made just by one patterne.

§ 64

Of Voices

(Chap. 51)

As an infant is comming into the world, it is not heard to crie all the while that it is in the birth, before it be fully born. When it is a yeare old, it begins to prattle and talke, but not before. King *Croesus* had a sonne, who lying swoddled in his cradle, spake by that time he was 6 months old: but this was a prodigious signe, and presaged the finall ruine of that kingdome. Those children that begin with their tongue betime, are later ere they find their feet. The voice in man or woman beginneth to change and waxe greater at 14 yeares old. The same in old age growes again to be smaller: and in no other creature doth it more often alter.

Moreover, as touching the Voice, there be strange and wonder-full matters reported, and those worth the rehearsal in this place.

For first and foremost, we do see, That upon the skaffold or stage in publick Theatres, if the floore be strowed over well and thicke with saw-dust or sand, the voice of the actors will be drowned and lost, yea, and remain stil above the skaffold, as if it were there buried: also where there be hollow and uneven wals round about or emptie drie-vats and tuns set, the voice will be taken up in them, and passe no farther. But the same voice, betweene two wals directly set one by another, runs apace: yea, and through a vault it may be heard from the one end to the other, be the sound never so low; provided, that all be smooth and even between, and nothing to hinder the passage thereof.

To speake yet somwhat more of the Voice: In it doth rest a great part of the countenance and visage of man, wherby he is discerned and knowne. For we know a man by hearing his voice before we see him, even as well as if our eies were fixed upon him. And see how many men and women there are in the world, so many sundrie voices there be, for each one hath a severall voice, as well as a face, by himself. And hereof arises that varietie of nations, that diversitie of languages all the world through. From hence come so many tunes in song, so many notes in Musick, as there bee. But above all, the greatest thing to be noted in Voice, is this, That wheras the utterance of our mind, therby doth distinguish us from brute and wild beasts: the same even among men maketh as great a difference betweene one and another, as the other is betweene man and beast.

IN THE TWELFTH BOOKE
are contained discourses of Trees

§ 65

Of the Woods and Trees

(Proeme)

THUS you see by that which hath bin written before, what are the natures as well in generall, as particularly in parts, of all living and sensitive creatures within the compasse of our knowledge. It remaineth now to discourse of those which the earth yeeldeth: and even they likewise are not without a soule in their kind (for nothing lives which wanteth it:) that from thence we may passe to those things that lie hidden within the earth, and are to be digged out of it: to the end, that no worke and benefit of Nature might overpasse our hands, and be omitted.

And in truth, these treasures of hers lay long covered under the ground, insomuch as men were persuaded, that Woods and Trees were the last and only goods[1] left unto us and bestowed upon us by Nature. For of the fruit of trees had wee our first food: their leaves and branches served to make us soft pallats and couches within the caves: and with their rinds and bark we clad and covered our nakednesse. And even at this day, some Nations there be that live still in that sort, and no otherwise. A wonderfull thing therefore it is, that from so small and base beginnings wee should grow to that passe in pride, that wee must needs cut through great mountaines for to meet with marble; send out as far as to the Seres[2] for silk stuffe to apparell us: dive downe into the bottome of the red sea for pearls: and last of all sinke deepe pits even to the bottom of the earth, for the precious Hemerauld. For this pride and vanitie of ours, we have devised means to pierce and wound our eares: because, for sooth it would not serve our

---

[1] *summum munus*, the best or supreme gift.
[2] Chinese.

turns to weare costly pearles and rich stones in carkanets about our necke, borders upon the haire of our head, bracelets about our arms, and rings on our fingers; unless they were ingraven also, and cut into the very flesh of our bodies.

Well then, to follow the course of Nature, and the order of our life (as meet it is we should) wee will treat in the first place of Trees, and lay before mens faces the life of the old world, and what was their behaviour and demeanure at the first, in their maner of living.

§ 66

Of great Plane trees

(Chap. 1)

T H E Plane trees of any great name at first, were those that grew in the walking place of the Academia in Athens; where the root of one outwent the boughs 36 cubits in length.[1] Now in this age there grows a famous one in Lycia, neer to the high way where men passe too and fro, and it hath a pleasant cold fountain adjoining to it: the same is hollow within like to a house, and yeelds a cave of 81 foot in compasse: but it caries such an head withal like a grove, so large, so broad, and so branched, that every arm resembles one entire tree: insomuch, as the shade therof takes up and spreadeth a great way into the fields. And because in every respect, it might resemble a very cabbin and cave indeed, there are stony banks and seats within, in form of an arbor round about, made as it were of pumish stone overgrown with mosse.

And in truth, this tree, and the scituation therof is so admirable, that *Licinius Mutianus* thrice Consull, and lately Lieutenant generall and Governor of that Province, thought this one thing worthy to be recorded as a memoriall to posterity, That he and 18 more persons of his company, used to dine and sup within the hollownesse of that tree: where the very leaves yeelded of their own sufficient bed and bench-room to rest and repose themselves:

[1] As it is unlikely that the roots would have been 50 feet longer than the branches, this has been translated that the branches were 50 feet long, longer than the roots.

where they might sit secured from danger of wind to blow upon them: where whiles he sat at meat, he wished nothing more than the pleasure to heare the showers of rain to pat drop by drop, and rattle over his head upon the leaves: and finally, that he tooke much more delight to lie within the said cabbin, than in a stately chamber built of fine marble, all glorious within with hangings of tapistrie and needleworke of sundry colours, and the same seeled over head with an embowed roofe laid with beaten gold.

Moreover, *Caligula* the Emperor had such another Plane tree growing in the country about Velitrae, most artificially: wherein he used to take great pleasure, with admiration of the sundry lofts and planks one over another, the large settles also and spacious branches that the boughs yeelded, where he was wont to sit at repast, making one of the 15 guests. For the room was of that capacity, that it would not only receive so many to sit with ease at the table, but also the gentlemen and servitors that waited and ministred unto them: and he termed this supping place by the name of, His nest: because it seemed like a birds nest in a tree. There is to be seen at Gortyna, within the Island Candy, one Plane tree neere unto a faire fountain: recorded it is as well by Greekes as Latines in their writings, and by the testimony of them both, never sheds the leaves, but remains alwaies green, as well in Winter as Summer: by occasion whereof arose the tale (so much given is Greece to devise fables by and by of every small matter) That *Jupiter* under that tree defloured the yong lady *Europa*: as if (forsooth) there were no other tree but it of the same kind and nature, in Cyprus. But as the nature of man is evermore curious, and seeketh after novelties the Candiotes desirous to have of the same race within Creet, set many slips thereof in sundry places, as if they longed to have more such vicious fruit. . . .

§ 67

The harvesting of Frankincense

(Chap. 14)

THEY used in old time to gather the Incense but once a yere; as having little vent, and small returne, and lesse occasion to sell than now adaies: but now, since every man calleth for it, they feeling the sweetnesse of the gaine, make a double vintage (as it were) of it in one yere.

The first, and indeed the kindly[1] season, falls about the hottest daies of the Summer, at what time as the Dog daies begin: for then they cut the Tree where they see the bark to be fullest of liquor, and wheras they perceive it to be thinnest and strut out most. They make a gash or slit only to give more libertie: but nothing do they pare or cut cleane away. The wound or incision is no sooner made, but out there gusheth a fat fome or froth: this soone congeales and growes to be hard: and where the place will give them leave, they receive it in a quilt or mat made of Date tree twigs, plaited and wound one within another wicker-wise. For elsewhere, the floore all about is paved smooth, and rammed downe hard. The former way is the better to gather the purer and clearer Frankincense: but that which falleth upon the bare ground, prooves the weightier. That which remaines behind, and stickes to the Tree, is parted and scraped off with knives, or such like yron tooles; and therefore no marvell if it be ful of shavings of the bark.

The whole wood or forrest is divided into certaine portions: and every man knowes his owne part: nay, there is not one of them will offer wrong unto another, and encroch upon his neighbors. They need not to set any keepers to look unto those Trees that be cut, for no man will rob from his fellow if he might, so just and true they be in Arabia. But beleeve me, at Alexandria where Frankincense is tried, refined, and made for sale, men canot look surely ynough to their shops and work-houses, but they will be robbed. The workeman that is emploied about it, is all naked, save that he hath a paire of trouses or breeches to cover his shame, and those are sowed up and sealed too, for feare of thrusting any into them. Hood-winked he is sure ynough for seeing the way to and fro, and hath a thicke coife or maske about his head, for doubt that he should bestow any in mouth or eares. And when these workmen be let forth againe, they be stripped starke naked, as ever they were borne, and sent away. Whereby we may see, that the rigor of justice canot strike so great feare into our theeves here, and make us so secure to keepe our owne, as among the Sabaeans,

[1] Natural.

the bare reverence and religion of those woods. But to returne againe to our former cuts. That Incense which was let out in Summer, they leave there under the Tree until the Autumne, and then they come and gather it. And this is most pure, cleane, and white.

A second Vintage and gathering there is in the Spring: against which time, they cut the bark before in the Winter, and suffer it to run out until the Spring. This comes forth red, and is nothing comparable to the former. . . .

That which is round like unto a drop, and so hangeth, we call the male Incense; wheras in other things lightly we name the male, but where there is a female. But folk have a religious ceremonie in it, not to use so much as the tearme of the other sexe, in giving denomination to Frankincense. Howbeit, some say, that it was called the Male, for a resemblance that it hath to cullions or stones. In very truth, that is held for the chiefe and best simply, which is fashioned like to the nipples or teats that give milk, standing thick one by another: to wit, when the former drop that distilled, hath another presently followeth after, and so consequently more unto them, and they all seeme to hang together like bigs.[1] I read, that every one of these were wont to make a good handfull, namely, when men were not so hasty and eager to carry it away, but would give it time and leisure to drop softly.

[1] Boils.

THIRTEENTH BOOKE
are contained Treatises of Ointments
and of Trees by the seaside

§ 68

Of Ointments and Perfumes

(Chaps. 1, 3)

BUT the truth is, The Persians and none but they ought to be reputed the inventors of precious perfumes and odoriferous ointments. For they to palliate and hide the ranke and stinking breath which commeth by their surfet and excesse of meats[1] and drinkes, are forced to helpe themselves by some artificiall meanes, and therefore goe evermore all to be perfumed and greased with sweet ointments. And verily, so farre as ever I could finde by reading histories; the first prince that set such store by costly perfumes, was King *Darius*, among whose coffers (after that *Alexander* the Great had defeated him and woon his campe) there was found with other roiall furniture of his, a fine casket full of perfumes and costly ointments. But afterwards they grew into so good credit even among us, that they were admitted into the ranke of the principal pleasures, the most commendable delights, and the honestest comforts of this life. And more than that, men proceeded so far, as therewith to honour the dead: as if by right that duty belonged to them. . . .

At this day there is not in Rome any thing wherein men more exceed, than in these costly and precious ointments: and yet of all other, they are most superfluous and may be best spared. True it is, that much money is laid out upon pearles and precious stones; but these are in the nature of a domaine and inheritance, and fall to the next heire in succession. Againe, rich and costly apparell

[1] Or, *illuvie*, from their filth.

stand us in a great deale of coine; howbeit they are dureable and last a long time: but Perfumes and ointments, are soone done and gone; they exhale and breath away quickly; they are momentarie, they serve but for the present, and die suddenly. The greatest matter in them, and their commendation is this, To cause a man (what businesse soever he hath otherwise) to cast his eie and looke after a gentlewoman as she passes by perfumed in the streets, and sendeth a smell from her as she goes. This is all the good they do: and yet forsooth a pound of this ware must cost 400 deniers: so deare is the pleasure that passes from our selves and goes to another: for the party himselfe that carrieth the perfume about him, hath little or no delight at all in it: others they be that reap the benefit and pleasure thereof.

And yet among these odoriferous compositions, there is choise and difference betweene one and another. We finde in the writings of *M. Cicero*, that he made more account of those ointments that savored of the earth, than those which smelled all strong of Saffron: as if he meant thereby, That in this excessive disorder and most corrupt enormitie of all others, a certaine moderation yet and sad delay would do wel; and that a severity (if I may so say) in the vice it self, were better to be liked. But some take delight especially in thick and grosse ointments, and are not content to be perfumed yea and bathed all over, unlesse they be besmeared, greased and daubed also therewith. I have my selfe seen some of them to annoint the very soles of their feet with these precious Baulms: and (by report) it was *M. Otho* that first taught the Emperor *Nero* this wanton delicacie. But I would gladly know, and some good body tell me, I pray, how he could feele the smell thereof, and what delight or contentment it might yeeld from that part of the body? I have heard say besides, by some of the inward familiars and speciall favorits of this prince, That he commanded the very walls of his baines and stouves to be perfumed with precious ointments: and that *C. Caligula* the Emperor, caused the very vessels and seats wherein he used to sit when he bathed or swet in his hot house, to be in that manner annointed. And because this might not seeme to be a speciall pleasure fit for an Emperor onely, I knew one of *Neroes* servants afterwards, who used so to do as well as his lord and master.

But I muse and marvell at nothing so much, as that this wanton delight should find the way and enter so far as into the mids of the camp. For wot ye what? I assure you the very standards and ensignes, the Aegles (I say) and Minotaures, so dusty as they be otherwise, so foule and ill-favored, as being kept so long, and standing by unoccupied, are wont forsooth to be annointed and perfumed upon high and festivall daies. And, so god helpe me, I would I knew who it was that first brought up this fashion and needlesse superfluitie: Certes, I would not defraud him of his due honor: I would (I say) recommend his name unto all posterity. But thus it is (no doubt) and it cannot otherwise be; Our Aegles and standerds (bribed, hired, and corrupted with this so good a reward) have therefore in recompense conquered the whole world. Under such colors and pretences (indeed) we deceive our selves, and cloak the vice and ryot of our times: and thus having so good a reason as this, to induce and draw us on, we may not sticke to have precious baulmes upon our heads, so it be under our sallats and mourrons.[1]

§ 69

Of the nature of Dates

(Chap. 4)

MOREOVER, it is constantly affirmed, That the females be naturally barren, and will not beare fruit without the company of the males among them to make them for to conceive: yet grow they wil neverthelesse and come up of themselves, yea and become tall woods: and verily a man shall see many of the females stand about one male, bending and leaning in the head full kindly toward him, yeelding their branches that way as if they courted him for to win his love.

But contrariwise, he a grim sir and a coy, carries his head aloft, bears his bristled and rough arms upright on high: and yet what with his very lookes, what with his breathing and exhalations upon them, or else with a certain dust that passes from him, he doth the part of an husband, insomuch as all the females about

[1] Helmets.

him, conceive and are fruitfull with his only presence. It is said moreover, that if this male tree be cut downe, his wives wil afterwards become barren and beare no more Dates, as if they were widows. Finally, so evident is the copulation of these sexes in the Date trees, and knowne to be so effectuall, that men have devised also to make the females fruitful, by casting upon them the blooms and down that the male bears, yea, and otherwhiles by strewing the pouder which he yeelds upon them. . . .

Now to conclude this treatise, I thinke it not amisse to set downe for an example, what did betide the souldiers that were of *Alexanders* army, who with eating of green dates new ripe, were choked and so died. In the Gedrosians country, this accident befell unto them, onely by the nature of the fruit itselfe, eat they of it as moderately as they could: but in other parts, their greedy and over liberall feeding upon them, was their bane. For surely new dates as they come from the tree, are so exceeding pleasant and delicious, that a man can hardly forbeare and make an end in good time, before hee surfet of them and catch a shrewd turne.

FOURTEENTH BOOKE
shewth of vine plants

§ 70

The Decay of ancient knowledge

(Proeme)

AND verily, I cannot chuse but marvell still and never give over, how it comes to passe, that the remembrance, yea, and the verie names of some trees which ancient Writers have delivered in their bookes, should be quite gone and abolished. For who would not thinke, that our life should ere this have gained much by the Majestie of the Romane Empire; have discovered all things by the meanes of the commerce we have had with the universall world, by the traffick, negotiation, and societie I say that we have entered into during the blessed time of peace which we have injoyed? considering that by such trade and entercourse, all things heretofore unknowne, might have come to light.

And yet for all this, few or none (beleeve me) there are who have attained to the knowledge of many matters which the old writers in times past have taught and put in writing. Whereby wee may easily see, that our ancestours were either far more carefull and industrious, or in their industrie more happie and fortunate. Considering withall, that above two hundred[1] yeares past *Hesiodus* (who lived in the very infancie of Learning and good letters) began his worke of Agriculture, and set downe rules and precepts for husbandmen to follow. After whose good example, many others having travelled and taken like paines, yet have put us now to greater labour. For by this means we are not onely to search into the last inventions of later writers, but also to those of antient time which are forgotten and covered with oblivion,

[1] Or 1,000.

through the supine negligence and general idlenesse of all mankind. And what reasons may a man alledge of this drowsinesse, but that which hath lulled the world asleepe? the cause in good faith of all, is this and no other, Wee are readie to forgoe all good customes of old, and to embrace novelties and change of fashions: mens minds now adaies are amused and occupied about new fangles, and their thoughts be rolling; they wander and rove at random; their heads be ever running; and no arts and professions are now set by and in request, but such as bring pence into our purses.

Heretofore whilest Kings and Potentates contained themselves within the Dominion of their owne Nations, and were not so ambitious as now they bee, no marvell if their wits and spirits kept still at home: and so for want of wealth and riches of Fortune, were forced to employ and exercise the gifts of their minde: in such sort as an infinite number of Princes were honoured and renowned for their singular knowledge and learning. Yea, they were more brave in port, and carried a goodlier shew in the World for their skill in Liberall Sciences, than others with all their pomp or riches; beeing fully persuaded and assured, that the way to attaine unto immortalitie and everlasting Fame, was by literature and not by great possessions and large seignories. And therefore as learning was much honoured and rewarded in those daies, so arts and sciences tending to the common good of this life daily increased. But afterwards when the way was once made to inlarge their territories farther in the world, when princes and states beganne to make conquests and grow rich and mighty, the posterity felt the smart and losse thereby. Then began men to chuse a Senator for his wealth; to make a judge for his riches; and the election of a civill magistrate and martiall captain, to have an eie and regard only to goods and substance, to land and living: when rents and revenues were the chiefe and onely ornaments that made men seeme wise, just, politicke, and valiant. Sincetime that childlesse estate was a point looked into, and advanced men into high place of authoritie and power, procuring them many favorites in hope of succession, since time I say that every man aimed and reached at the readiest meanes of greatest lucre and gaine, setting their whole mind, and reposing their full content and joy in laying land to land, and heaping together possessions; downe went the most precious things of this life, and lost their reputation: all those liberall arts which tooke their name of liberty and freedome (the soveraigne good in this world which were meet for princes, nobles, gentlemen and persons of great state) forwent that prerogative, and fell a contrarie way, yea, and ran quite to wracke and ruine: so as in stead thereof, base slaverie and servitude be the only waies to arise and thrive by: whiles some practise it one way, some another, by flattering, admiring, courting, crouching, and adoring: and all, to gather good and get mony. This is the onely marke they shoot at, this is the end and accomplishment of all their vowes, praiers and desires. Insomuch, as we may perceive every where, how men of high spirit and great conceit are given rather to honor the vices and imperfections of others, than to make the best of their owne vertues and commendable parts. And therefore we may full truly say, that life indeed is dead; Voluptuousnesse and Pleasure alone is alive, yea and beginneth to beare all the sway.

Neverthelesse, for all these enormities and hinderances, give over will not I to search into those things that be perished and utterly forgotten, how small and base soever some of them be; no more than I was affrighted in that regard, from the treatise and discourse of living creatures. Notwithstanding that I see *Virgil* (a most excellent Poet) for that cause only forbare to write of gardens and hortyards, because he would not enter into such petty matters; and of those so important things that he handled, he gathered only the principal floures, and put them downe in writing. Who albeit that he hath made mention of no more than 15 sorts of grapes, three kinds of Olives, and as many of Peares, and setting aside the Citrons and Limons, hath not said a word of any apples; yet in this one thing happy and fortunate hee was. For that his worke is highly esteemed, and no imputation of negligence charged upon him.[1]

[1] Irony perhaps. The excellence of Vergil's poetry and character has been challenged by Robert Graves in his *Oxford Addresses on Poetry* (Cassell, London, 1962), and Pliny may have felt that Vergil merited the imputation of negligence.

§ 71

Of Vines

(Chap. 1)

BUT where now shall we begin this treatise of ours? What de-serveth the chiefe and principall place, but the vine? in which respect Italy hath the name for the very soveraignty of Vine-yards: insomuch, that therein alone, if there were nothing els, it may well seeme to surpasse all other lands, even those that bring forth odoriferous spices and aromaticall drugs. And yet to say a truth, there is no smell so pleasant whatsoever, that out-goeth Vines when they be in their fresh and flouring time.

Vines in old time were by good reason for their bignesse reckoned among trees. For in Populonium, a citie of Tuscan, we see a statue of *Jupiter* made of the wood of one entire Vine, and yet continued it hath a world of yeares uncorrupt, and without worme. Likewise at Massilia there is a great standing cup or boll to be seene of Vine-wood. At Metapontum there stood a temple of *Juno*, bearing upon pillars of Vine wood. And even at this day there is a ladder or paire of staires up to the temple of *Diana* in Ephesus, framed of one Vine-tree, brought (by report) out of the Island Cypres, for there indeed vines grow to an exceeding bignesse. And to speake a truth, there is no wood more dureable and lasting than is the vine. Howbeit, for my part I would thinke that these singular pieces of worke before-named, were made of wild and savage Vines: for that these our tame and gentle vines here planted among us, are by cutting and pruning every yere kept downe: so as all their whole strength is either drawne without-forth into branches, or els downward into the root for to put out new shoots ever fresh out of the ground: and regard is only had of the fruit and juice that they do yeeld divers waies, according to the temperature of the aire and climat, or the nature of the soile wherin they be planted.

In the countrey of Campaine about Capua, they be set at the roots of Poplars, and (as it were) wedded unto them: and so being suffered to wind and claspe about them as their husbands, yea, and with their wanton armes or tendrils to climbe aloft, and with their joints to run up their boughes, they reach up to their head, yea, and overtop them: insomuch as the grape-gatherer in time of Vintage, puts in a clause in the covenants of his bargaine when he is hired, that in case his foot should faile him, and he breake his neck, his master who sets him a worke should give order for his funerall fire and tombe at his owne proper cost and charges. And in truth Vines will grow infinitly: and unpossible it is to part them, or rather to pluck them from the trees which they be joined and coupled unto. *Valerianus Cornelius* making mention of many properties and singularities of a vine, thought this among the rest worthie of especiall note and remembrance, that one onely stocke of a vine was sufficient to compasse and inviron round about a good ferme-house or country messuage, with the branches and pliable shoots that it did put forth.

At Rome there is one vine growing within the cloistures of the Portches and galleries built by the Empresse *Livia*, which running and trailing upon an open frame of railes, covereth and shadoweth the ouvert allies made for to walke in: and the same Vine yeeldeth one yeare with another a dozen Amphores of good new wine yearely.

§ 72

Of avoiding Drunkenesse

(Chap. 22)

IF a man marke and consider well the course of our life, we are in nothing more busie and curious, nor take greater paines, than about wine: as if Nature had not given to man the liquor of water, which of all others is the most wholsom drink, and wherwith all other creatures are wel contented. But we thinking it not sufficient to take wine our selves, give it also to our Horses, Mules, and labouring beasts, and force them against Nature to drink it. Besides, such pains, so much labor, so great cost and charges we are at, to have it, such delight and pleasure we take in it; that many of us think, they are borne to nothing else, and can skill of no other contentment in this life: notwithstanding, when all is don, it transports and carries away the right wit and mind of man, it causes fury and rage, and induces, nay, it casts headlong as many as are given thereto, into a thousand vices and misdemeanors.

And yet forsooth, to the end that we might take the more cups, and poure it downe the throat more lustily, we let it run thorough a strainer, for to abate and gueld (as it were) the force thereof: yea, and other devises there be to whet our appetite thereto, and cause us to quaffe more freely. Nay, to draw on their drinke,[1] men are not afraid to take poisons, whiles some take hemlocke before they sit downe, because they must drinke perforce then, or els die for it; others, the powder of the pumish stone, and such like stuff, which I am abashed to rehearse and teach those that be ignorant of such leaudnesse. And yet wee see these that be stoutest and most redoubted drinkers, even those that take themselves most secured of danger, to lie sweating so long in the baines and brothel-houses for to concoct their surfet of wine, that otherwhiles they are carried forth dead for their labour. Ye shall have some of them again when they have been in the hot house, not to stay so long as they may recover their beds, no not so much as to put on their shirts: but presently in the place, all naked as they are, puffing and laboring still for wind, catch up great cans and huge tankards of wine (to shew what lustie and valiant champions they be) set them one after another to their mouth, pour the wine downe the throat without more adoe, that they might cast it up againe, and so take more in the place; vomiting or revomiting twice or thrice together that which they have drunke, and still make quarrell to the pot: as if they had been borne into this world for no other end but to spill and mar good wine: or, as if there were no way els to spend and wast the same, but thorow mans body.

And to this purpose, were taken up at Rome these forreine exercises, of vaulting and dancing the Morisk; from hence came the tumbling of wrastlers in the dust and mire together; for this, they shew their broad breasts, beare up their heads, and carrie their neckes far backe. In all which gesticulations, what do they else but professe that they seek means to procure thirst and take occasion to drink? But come now to their pots that they use to quaffe and drink out of: are there not graven in them faire pourtrais think you of adulteries? as if drunkenesse it self were not

[1] To bring on a thirst.

sufficient to kindle the heart of lust, to pricke the flesh, and to teach them wantonnes. Thus is wine drunke out of libidinous cups: and more than that, he that can quaffe best and play the drunkard most, shal have the greatest reward. But what shal we say to those (would a man think it?) that hire one to eat also as much as he can drink, and upon that condition covenant to yeeld him the price for his wine drinking, and not otherwise. Ye shall have another that will injoine himselfe to drinke every denier that he hath won at dice. Now when they are come to that once and be throughly whitled, then shall yee have them cast their wanton eies upon mens wives; then fall they to court faire dames and ladies, and openly bewray their folly even before their jealous and sterne husbands; then (I say) the secrets of the heart are opened and layed abroad.

Some ye shal have in the mids of their cups, make their wils, even at the very board as they sit: others againe cast out bloudy and deadly speeches at randon, and cannot hold but blurt out those words which afterwards they eat againe with the swords point: for thus many a man by a lavish tongue in his wine, hath come by his death and had his throat cut. And verily the world is now growne to this passe, That whatsoever a man saith in his cups, it is held for sooth; as if Truth were the daughter of Wine. But say they escape these dangers: certes speed they never so well, the best of them all never seeth the Sun-rising, so drowsie and sleepy they are in bed every morning, neither live they to bee old men, but die in the strength of their youth. Hence comes it, that some of them looke pale, with a paire of flaggie blabd-cheekes; others have bleared and sore eies: and there be of them that shake so with their hands, that they cannot hold a full cup, but shed and poure it downe the floore. Generally they all dreame fearfully (which is the very beginning of their hell in this life) or els have restlesse nights. . . .

Well, what becomes of them the morrow after? they belch soure, their breath stinketh of the barrell, and telleth them what they did over night; otherwise they forget what either they did or said, they remember no more, than if their memory were utterly extinct and dead. And yet our jolly drunkards give out and say, That they alone injoy this life, and rob other men of it. But who seeth not, that ordinarily they lose not onely the yesterday past, but the morrow to come?

THE
FIFTEENTH BOOKE
comprehendeth all fruitfull trees

§ 73
Cato's Fig

(Chap. 18)

N o w forasmuch as we are fallen to mention the figs in Africk, which were in so great request in the time of *Cato*, I am put in mind to speake somewhat of that notable opportunity and occasion which by the means of that fruit he took for to root out the Carthaginians, and rase their very city.

For as he was a man who hated deadly that city, and was otherwise carefull to provide for the quiet and securitie of his posteritie, he gave not over at every sitting of the Senat, to importune the Senators of Rome, and to cry out in their eares, That they would resolve and take order to destroy Carthage: and in very truth one day above the rest, he brought with him into the Senat house an early or hasty fig which came out of that country, and shewing it before all the lords of the Senat, I would demand of you (quoth he) how long ago it is (as you think) since this fig was gathered from the tree? And when none of them could deny but that it was fresh and new gotten: Lo (quoth he) my masters all, this I do you to wit, It is not yet ful three daies past since this fig was gathered at Carthage: see how neere to the walls of our citie we have a mortall enemie. Upon which remonstrance of his, presently they concluded to begin the third and last Punick war, wherein Carthage was utterly subverted and overthrown. Howbeit *Cato* survived not the rasing and saccage of Carthage, for he died the yeare immediately following this resolution.

But what shall we say of this man? whether was more admirable in this act, his provident care and promptnesse of spirit; or the occasion presented by the sudden object of the fig? Was the present resolution and forward expedition of the Senat, or the vehement earnestnesse of *Cato*, more effectuall to this enterprise? Certes, somewhat there is above all, and nothing in mine opinion more wonderful, that so great a signiory and state as Carthage, which had contended for the Empire of the world for the space of 120 yeres, and that with the great conquerours the Romanes, should thus be ruined and brought utterly to nought, by occasion of one fig. A designe that neither the fields lost at Trebia and Thrasymenus, nor the disgrace received at the battell of Cannae, wherein so many brave Romans lost their lives, and left their dead bodies on the ground to be interred, could effect: nay not the disdain that they took to see the Carthaginians incamped and fortified within 3 miles of Rome, ne yet the bravadoes of *Annibal* in person, riding before the gate Collina, even to dare them, could ever bring to passe. See how *Cato* by the means of one poore fig, prevailed to bring and present the forces of Rome to the very walls of Carthage.

THE
SIXTEENTH BOOKE
describeth all wild trees

§ 74

Of Zeland and wonderful trees in the Northerly regions

(Chap. 1)

WEE have shewed heretofore, that in the East parts verily toward the maine Ocean, there be many countries in that estate, to wit, altogether destitute of trees. In the North also I my selfe have seene the people called Chauci,[1] as well the greater as the lesse, (for so they be distinguished) where there is no shew or mention at all of any tree whatsoever. For a mightie great compasse, their Country lieth so under the Ocean, and subject to the tide, that twice in a day and night by turns, the sea over floweth a mighty deale of ground when it is floud, and leaves all dry again at the ebbe and return of the water: insomuch, as a man can hardly tell what to make of the outward face of the earth in those parts, so doubtfull it is between sea and land.

The poore silly people that inhabit those parts, either keep together on such high hils as Nature hath afforded here and there in the plain: or els raise mounts with their own labor and handy work (like to Tribunals cast up and reared with turf, in a camp) above the height of the sea, at any spring tide when the floud is highest; and thereupon they set their cabbins and cottages. Thus dwelling as they do, they seeme (when it is high water, and that all the plain is overspread with the sea round about) as if they were in little barks floting in the midst of the sea: againe, at a low water when the sea is gone, looke upon them, you would take them for such as had suffered shipwracke, having their vessels cast away,

---

[1] The Low countries of Zeland, etc. (P. H.).

and left lying ato-side amid the sands: for ye shall see the poore wretches fishing about their cottages, and following after the fishes as they go away with the water: they have not a four-footed beast among them; neither injoy they any benefit of milk, as their neighbour nations do: nay, they are destitute of all means to chase wild beasts, and hunt for venison; in as much as there is neither tree nor bush to give them harbor, nor any neare unto them by a great way. Sea-weeds or wrack, rushes and reeds growing upon the washes and meers, serve them to twist for cords to make their fishing nets with.

These poore souls and silly creatures are faine to gather a slimy kinde of fatty mud or oase,[1] with their very hands, which they drie against the wind rather than the Sun: and with that earth, for want of other fuell, they make fire to seeth their meat (such as it is) and heat the inward parts of their body, ready to be starke and stiffe againe with the chilling North winde. No other drink have they but rain water, which they save in certain ditches after a shower, and those they dig at the very entry of their cottages. And yet see! this people (as wretched and miserable a case as they be in) if they were subdued at this day by the people of Rome, would say (and none sooner than they) that they lived in slaverie. But true it is, that Fortune spareth many men, to let them live still in paine and misery. Thus much as touching want of woods and trees.

On the other side, as wonderfull it is to see the mighty forrests at hand thereby, which overspread all the rest of Germany: and are so big, that they yeeld both cooling and shade to the whole countrey; yea, the very tallest woods of all the rest are a little way up higher in the countrey, and not farre from the Chauci above-said: and especially those that grow about the two great loughes or lakes in that tract. Upon the banks whereof, as also upon the sea-coasts, there are to be seene thick rows of big Okes, that love their seat passing wel, and thrive upon it in growth exceeding much: which trees happening to be either undermined by the waves and billowes of the sea under them, eating within their roots, or chased with tempestuous winds beating from above, carry away with them into the sea (in manner of Islands) a great part of the Continent, which their roots doe claspe and embrace:

[1] Thought to be peat.

wherewith being counterpoised and ballaised, they stand upright, floting and making saile (as it were) amid the waves, by the means of their mighty armes which serve in stead of tackling.

And many a time verily, such Okes have frighted our fleets and armadoes at sea, and especially in the night season, when as they seemed to come directly against their prowes standing at anker, as if of purpose they were driven upon them by the waves of the sea: insomuch, as the sailers and passengers within, having no other means to escape them, were put to their shifts, and forced for to addresse themselves, and range a navall battell in order, and all against trees, as their very enemies.

§ 75

The juice in trees and the nature of their timber

(Chap. 38)

TREES have a certaine moisture in their barkes, which we must understand to be their very bloud, yet is it not the same nor alike in all: for that of the Fig trees is as white as milke, and as good as rendles to give the forme to cheese. Cherry trees yeeld a glutinous and clammy humor, but Elmes a thin liquor in manner of spittle. In Apple trees the same is fattie and viscous; in Vines and Pyrries[1] waterish. And generally, those trees continue and live longest, that have such a glewy moisture in them.

In summe, there are to be considered in the substance and body of trees, like as of all other living creatures, their skin, their bloud, flesh, sinues, veins, bones, and marrow. For in lieu of their hide is the barke. And I assure you, a strange and marvellous thing it is to be observed here in the Mulberry, that when Physitians seek to draw the foresaid liquor out of it, at seven or eight a clocke in a morning, if they scarifie or lightly cut the bark with a stone, it issueth forth, and they have their desire: but if they crush or cut it deeper in, they meet with no more moisture than if it were stark

[1] Pears.

dry.[1] In most trees next to the skin lieth the fat: this is nought else but that white sap which of the colour is called in Latin Alburnum. As it is soft in substance, so is it the worst part of the wood; and even in the strong oke, as hard as otherwise it is, ye shal have it soon to putrifie and rot, yea and quickly be worm-eaten. And therefore if a man would have sound and good timber, this white must be alwaies cut away in the squaring. After it followeth the flesh of the tree; and so the bone, which is the very heart and best of the wood.

All trees whereof the wood is over dry, beare fruit but each other yeare, or at leastwise more in one yere than another, as namely the Olive tree: a thing observed more in them than in those that have a pulpous and fleshie substance, as the Cherry tree. Neither are all trees indifferently furnished with store of the said fat or flesh, no more than the most fierce and furious beasts. As for the Box, Cornel, and Olive trees, they have neither the one nor the other, ne yet any marrow at all, and but very little bloud. Semblably, the Servis tree hath no heart, the Elder no carnositie, (and yet both of them are stored wel enough with marrow, which is their pith) no more than canes or reeds for the most part.[2] In the fleshy substance or wood of some trees there are to be found graine and veine both. And easie it is to distinguish the one from the other: for commonly the veins be larger and whiter; contrariwise the grain, which the Latines cal Pulpa, runneth streit and direct in length, and is to be found ordinarily in trees that wil easily cleave. And hereupon it commeth, that if a man lay his eare close to one end of a beame or piece of timber, he shall heare the knocke or pricke that is made but with a pen-knife at the other end, be the piece never so long, by reason that the sound goeth along the streit grain of the wood. By this means also a man shall find when the timber doth twine, and whether it run not even, but be interrupted with knots in the way.

[1] In Book 23 Pliny records many medicines made from the mulberry, the most interesting being the extract of bark used as a vermifuge. The juice from incisions through the bark was good for toothache and abscesses.

[2] The meaning is that the Service and Elder have no heart wood; it is replaced by pith as in most canes and reeds.

§ 76

What wood doth endure and continue always good

(Chap. 40)

IT is commonly thought, that the Box, the Ebene, the Cypresse, and the Cedar wood, is everlasting, and will never be done. An evident proofe thereof as touching all these sorts of timber, by the judgment and choise of so many men, was to be seene in that famous temple of *Diana* in Ephesus: for al Asia set to their helping hand and contributed toward that work, which in foure hundred yeres[1] and not before, they brought to an end and finished. The beames, rafters, and spars that went to the making of the roufe, were by the generall voice of the whole world, of Cedar timber. As touching the statue or image itselfe of the goddesse *Diana*, it is not certainly known of what wood it was: all writers, save only *Mutianus*, report that it was of Ebene. As for him, a man who had been thrice Consull of Rome, and one of the last who upon their owne sight of the said thing, wrate thereof, avoucheth that it was made of Vine wood; and that, howsoever the temple was ruined and rebuilt againe no lesse than seven times, yet the foresaid image was never altered nor changed. Who saith moreover, that *Endoeus* chose that wood for the best (for so he named the workman that cut and carved it.) And I much marvel therat, considering that by his saying this image was of greater antiquity than that of lady *Minerva*, much more than of prince *Bacchus*. He addes moreover and saith, that this statue was embaulmed within, by reason of the precious oile of Spiknard, which was distilled into it at many holes: by means of which medicinable liquor, the wood was nourished, and the joints held close and fast together: whereat I canot chuse but marvell again very much, that considering the statue was so small, it should have any peece or joint at all.

Now as touching the leaves of the dores belonging to this temple, they were by his report, of Cypresse wood: and continued still fresh and new to the eye, notwithstanding it is foure hundred yeares well neare since they were made. Where, by the way this is to be noted, that these dores stood foure yeres glewed in the clave.

[1] Or 120 years.

And verily, this wood was chosen for that purpose, because among other properties, the Cypresse alone hath the gift, to look alwaies shining and polished, and never loseth the glosse and beauty. And for to prove this, we need not to goe farre: Looke but upon the image of *Jupiter*, in the Capitol, made of Cypresse wood, doth it not endure still faire and trim? and yet was it dedicated and consecrated in that temple, in the yeare after the foundation of Rome, 551.[1]

A famous and memorable temple there is of *Apollo* at Utica,[2] where the beames and maine peeces of timber, made of Numidian Cedars, remaine as whole and entire as at the first day when they were set up, which was when the citie was first founded: by which computation, they have continued alreadie 1188 yeares.

§ 77

Of Misselto and the priests called Druidae

(Chap. 44)

AND this you must thinke, that this Misselto is not to be taken for the fruit of a tree, and therfore as great a wonder it is in nature, as any other: for some things there be, that not willing to grow out of the earth, engender in trees; and having no proper place of their own habitation to seat themselves in, sojourn as it were and make their abode with others, and of this nature is the Misselto. . . .

Moreover, set or sow this Misselto what way soever you will, it will never take and grow: it comes onely by the mewting of birds, especially of the Stockedove or Quoist, and the Blackbird, which feed thereupon, and let it passe thorough their body. And this is the nature of it, unlesse it bee mortified, altered and digested in the stomacke and belly of birds, it will never grow. It exceedeth not at any time a cubit in heighth, notwithstanding it be alwaies

[1] 202 B.C. The statue was about 270 years old when Pliny wrote.

[2] Utica, now Bou-shatter just north of Tunis, was founded 287 years before Carthage which, according to Josephus who inspected old Phoenician documents in Tyre, may have been founded in 862 B.C. There are, however, many other opinions on the age of Carthage.

greene and full of branches. The male beareth a certaine graine or
berry: the female is barren and fruitlesse. But sometimes neither
the one nor the other beareth at all.

Now as touching Birdlime, it is made of the berries of Misseltoe,
gathered in harvest time before they are ripe; for if they should
tarry stil to take showres of rain, wel might they thrive and
increase in bignesse, but their strength and vertue would be gon
clean, for ever making any such glew or birdlime aforesaid. Being
so gathered, . . . they must be laid abroad a drying, and when they
be once dry, they are braied or stamped, and so put in water to
steepe, and let to putrifie for the space of 12 daies or thereabout.
This one thing yet in the whole world is the better for putrefac-
tion, and serveth to good purpose. When this is done, the said
berries thus putrified and corrupt, are beaten or punned once
again with mallets, in running water; by which means when they
are husked and turned out of their skins, the fleshy substance
within, becommeth glutinous, and will stick too, in manner of
glew. This is the way to make birdlime for to catch poore birds
by their wings, entangled therewith; which foulers use to temper
and incorporate with the oile of Walnuts,[1] when they list to set
limetwigs to take foule.

And forasmuch as we are entred into a discourse as touching
Messelto, I cannot overpasse one strange thing thereof used in
France: The Druidae (for so they call their Divinors, Wisemen,
and the state of their Clergy) esteeme nothing more sacred in the
world than Misselto, and the tree whereupon it breeds, so it be on
Oke. Now this you must take by the way,[2] These priests or
Clergy men chose of purpose such groves for their divine service, as stood only upon Okes; nay, they solemnise no sacrifice,
nor perform any sacred ceremonies without branches and leaves
thereof, so as they may seem well enough to be named thereupon
Dryidae in Greek, which signifieth as much as the Oke priests.
Certes, to say a truth, whatsoever they find growing upon that
tree over and besides the own fruit, be it Misselto or any thing
else, they esteem it as a gift sent from heaven, and a sure signe

---

[1] *Oleo* in most texts, but Holland again follows Dalechamp, who quotes MS.
readings of *iuglandis oleo* and *glandis oleo*, and specifies, alone among the translators,
walnut oil. This passage, and that on the Tyrian purple (p. 99), both show the
near-impossibility of successfully copying the recipes reported in translations of
early writers.   [2] As a digression.

by which that very god whom they serve giveth them to under-stand, that he hath chosen that peculiar tree. And no marvel, for in very deed Misselto is passing geason[1] and hard to be found upon the oke; but when they meet with it, they gather it very devoutly and with many ceremonies: for first and formost, they observe principally, that the Moon be just six daies old (for upon that day they begin their months and new yeares, yea and their several ages, which have their revolutions every thirty yeres) because she is thought then to be of great power and force sufficient, and is not yet come to her halfe light and the end of her first quarter.

They call it in their language All-Heale, (for they have an opinion of it, that it cureth all maladies whatsoever) and when they are about to gather it, after they have well and duly prepared their sacrifices and festival cheare under the said tree, they bring thither two yong bullocks milk white, such as never drew in yoke at plough or wain, and whose heads were then and not before bound by the horn: which done, the priest araied in a surplesse or white vesture, climbeth up into the tree, and with a golden hooke or bill cutteth [the Misselto] off, and they beneath receive it in a white soldiers cassock or coat of armes: then fall they to kil the beasts aforesaid for sacrifice, mumbling many oraisons and praying devoutly: that it would please God to blesse this gift of his to the good and benefit of all those to whom he had vouchsafed to give it. Now this persuasion they have of Misselto thus gathered, That what living creatures soever (otherwise barren) do drink of it, will presently become fruitfull thereupon: also, that it is a soveraign countrepoison or singular remedie against all vermine. So vain and superstitious are many nations in the world, and oftentimes in such frivolous and foolish things as these.

[1] Rare.

THE
SEVENTEENTH BOOKE
containeth
tame trees within Hortyards

§ 78

Of the wonderfull prices of Some Trees

(Chap. 1)

I CANOT chuse but marvel how it is come to passe, That those trees which for necessity and need we have taken from the wilde and brute beasts, and possessed in common with them (considering that men maintaine fight and scramble with them for the fruits that fall, yea and otherwhiles with the fowles of the aire, about those which hang upon the tree) should grow to so excessive a price, as to be esteemed among the principall delights of this world? And that this is so, appeareth by that most notable example (in mine opinion) of *L. Crassus* and *Cn. Domitius Ahenobarbus.*

This *L. Crassus* (a right renowmed Orator of Rome as any one of his time) had a stately and sumptuous dwelling upon mount Palatine: howbeit that house of *Q. Catulus* (who defeated in battell the Cimbrians, together with *C. Marius*) went beyond it a faire deale in magnificence, and stood likewise within the pourprise of the same mount. But the goodliest and fairest Pallace knowne in that age, was that of *C. Aquilius* a Gentleman or Knight of Rome, scituate upon the hill of Osiers, called Viminalis: in regard whereof there went a greater name of him, than for all the skill he had in the Civill Law, which was his profession. Yet of all those three, *Crassus* onely was challenged and reproched for that foresaid house of his. And in this manner is the storie delivered.

Crassus and *Domitius* (great personages both, and descended from most noble Houses in Rome) after they had beene Consuls, happened also to be chosen Censors together: and this fell out to be in the six hundred sixty two yeare after the foundation of the city: but during this Magistracie of theirs there passed many a foule day and bitter fit betweene them; so dissonant were their natures, and their conditions so farre unlike. Now it fortuned upon a time, that *Cn. Domitius* (as he was [a] hot and hasty man by nature, and carried an inward hatred besides in his heart, which soone is kindled and set on fire, yea and most insatiable, upon emulation and envy betweene Concurrents, such as they two were) reprooved *Crassus* verie sharpely for his excesse in expence, and namely, That any Censor of Rome should dwell in so stately and sumptuous a Pallace as he did; and ever and anon made offer to buy the House, and pay him downe-right for it an hundred Millions of Sesterces:[1] whereat *Crassus* (being a man quicke of spirit, and of a prompt and present wit, finely conceited withall, and not to seeke for a ready answer) tooke him at his word, and accepted of the offer; reserving only six trees that grew about his house.

Tush (quoth *Domitius*, replying againe) take those Trees away, and take all; if they be gone, I will none of the house though I might have it for a single denier. Then *Crassus* having gotten the vantage and start of him, rejoyned and came upon him thus: Tell me now I pray you good *Domitius*, whether of us twaine giveth a scandalous example to the world? Whether am I myselfe (I say) offensive, and deserve to be taxed and noted by mine own Censorship, who can be contented to live quietly and lovingly among my neighbours in mine owne house, and that house which came to me by way of inheritance from my father; or you rather, that for six trees bid 100 millions of Sesterces? Now, if a man be desirous to know, what these trees might be? truly they were no other but six Lote[2] trees, very faire and beautifull indeed, but there was nothing in them commendable, save only their spreading and casting a goodly shade. And verily, *Caecina Largus*, a Nobleman and principal citizen of Rome, used many a time and often (I remember well) to shew me when I was a yong man, those trees about his house. And since our speech hath bin of such trees as live very long, these I wote wel, continued for the space of 180 yeres after *Crassus* death, to the great fire that *Nero* caused to bee

---

[1] *Millies Sestertium.* An incredible price for a dwelling house ... (P. H.). Another reading is one million sesterces.   [2] Nettle trees.

made for to burne Rome; fresh and green they were with good keeping, and looked yong still, like to have lived many a faire day more, had not that prince hastened the untimely death even of trees also (as well as of citizens).

Now lest any man should think, that all the sumptuositie of *Crassus* consisted only in those trees, and that the furniture otherwise of his house was but mean and simple, and could minister unto *Domitius* no matter of such contesting and reproofe, disposed as he was to quarrel and find fault: know he thus much, That the said *Crassus* had before that time set up in the open hall of that house, foure goodly pillars of Hymettian marble; which in the yere of his Edileship were brought abroad to rich and beautifie the Theatre, the Stage and Shew-place of the solemne plaies by him set out: for as yet there had not bin in publicke place at Rome any marble pillars seen:[1] lo how lately is come up this excessive expence in rich and glorious building, so common in these daies. See (I say) how in those times, faire trees beautified pallaces more than any thing els; insomuch, as *Domitius* for the want of six trees only would not stand to the price that himselfe first made, no not to buy his very enemy out of house and home with it.

§ 79

Of Trees in the winter

(Chap. 2)

As for the cold pinching black frosts and Northern winds, which blow out of season, come they early or come they late, they be hurtfull all. But if the wind stand Northeast in winter, there is nothing so good generally for all fruits of the earth. And verily, a good shower now and then during that time, wil do no harm; and that men wish for rain then, the reason is evident: for why? trees with bearing of fruit, are drawne dry and have lost their naturall moisture; with shedding their leaves they be poore and feeble; so that it is kind[2] for them to be hungry then, and to have a greedy appetite to new food; which is raine. Now if the winter be

---

[1] See § 152, p. 294, for more about these pillars.
[2] Natural.

open and warm withal, that so soone as the trees have don bearing, they rest not between, but conceive again presently upon it (that is to say, bud and spurt anew, yea, and fall afresh to blossome, whereby they have another evacuation that way also, to spend their sap and radicall moisture) we find by experience, that there is nothing in the world so bad for them. Nay, if many such yeres come together, immediatly one after another, the very trees themselves will die; for who can looke for better, when they are thus pined and famished?

He then[1] whosoever he was that said, Husbandmen were to wish for faire winters: surely he was no friend therein to trees, nor never praied for them: neither are wet Mid-summers good for Vines. But in truth, That winter dust should cause plentiful harvest, was a word spoken in a bravery, and proceeding from a pregnant wit and jolly spirit: for otherwise, who knoweth not, that every man (wishing well to trees and corn indifferently) praieth, that snow might lie long upon the ground? The reason is, for that not only it keepeth in and encloseth the vitall breath and soule (if I may so say) of the earth, ready to exhale out and vanish away, yea, and driveth it back again into the blade and root of corn, redoubling therby the force and vigor thereof: but also because it both yeeldeth moisture and liquor thereunto gently by little and little, and the same withall fine, pure, and passing light: considering, that snow is nothing els but the fome or froth of rainwater from heaven.

This humor therefore, not falling forcibly all at once to drown the root, ne yet washing away the earth from it (but distiling drop-meale a little at once, in that proportion and measure as thirst requireth and calleth for it) nourisheth all things, as from a teat or pap; nourisheth (I say) and neither drencheth nor over-floweth them. The earth also for her part, by this means wel soked, swelleth and hoveth as it were with a leaven, and lieth thereby more light and mellow: thus being full of juice and mois-ture it selfe, and not barren, but well replenisht with seeds sown, and plants suckled, thus continually in her womb; when the open time of the spring is once come to discharge her, she sheweth her selfe fresh and gay, and willingly entertaineth the warme weather of that season.

[1] Virgil (P. H.).

§ 80

Of the Smell of good ground

(Chap. 5)

WELL, to speake at a word, surely that ground is best of all other, which hath an aromaticall smell and tast with it. Now if we list moreover to be better instructed, what kind of savour and odour that should be, which we would so gladly find in the earth; we may oftentimes meet with that sent, even when she is not stirred with the plough, but lieth stil and quiet, namely, a little before the sun-setting, especially where a rainbow seemeth to settle and pitch her tips in the Horizon: also, when after some long and continuall drought, it beginneth to rain; for then being wet and drenched therwith, the earth will send up a vapor and exhalation (conceived from the Sun) so heavenly and divine, as no perfume (how pleasant soever it be) is comparable unto it.

This smell there must be in it when you ere it up with the plough: which if a man find once, he may be assured it is a right good ground; for this rule never faileth: so as (to say a truth) it is the very smel and nothing els, that will judge best of the earth: and such commonly are new broken grounds, where old woods were lately stocked up: for all men by a generall consent, do commend such for excellent. Moreover, the same ground for bearing is held to be far better, whensoever it hath rested between, and either lain ley or fallow; whereas for vineyards it is clean contrary: and therefore the more care and diligence is to be emploied in chusing such ground, least wee approove and verifie their opinion, who say, That the soile of all Italie is alreadie out of heart and weary with bearing fruit. This is certaine, that both there and elsewhere, the constitution of the aire and weather, both giveth and taketh away the opportunitie of good husbandrie, that a man cannot otherwhiles do what he would: for some kind of grounds there is so fat and ready to resolve into mire and dirt, that it is impossible to plough them and make good worke, after a shower of raine. Contrariwise, in Byzacium a territory of Africke, it is far otherwise: for there is not a better and more fruitfull piece of ground lieth without dore than it is, yeelding ordinarily 150 fold; let the season be dry, the strongest teeme of oxen that is, cannot plough it: fall there once a good ground shower, one poore asse, with the help of a silly old woman drawing the ploughshare at another side, will be able to go round away with it, as I my selfe have seen many a time and often.

And whereas some great husbands there be, that teach us to inrich and mend one ground with another, to wit, by spreading fat earth upon a lean and hungry soile; and likewise by casting drie, light, and thirstie mould, upon that which is moist and over-fat; it is a meere follie and wastfull expence both of time and travaile: for what fruit can he ever looke to reape from such a mingle mangle of ground?[1]

§ 81

Sundry sorts of Earth and Marle

(Chaps. 6, 7, 8)

T HE Britaines and Frenchmen have devised another meanes to manure their ground, by a kind of lime-stone or clay, which they call Marga (*i.* Marle). And verily they have a great opinion of the same, that it mightily inricheth it and maketh it more plentiful. This marle is a certaine fat of the ground, much like unto the glandulous kernels growing in the bodies of beasts, and it is thickned in manner of marrow or the kernell of fat about it.

The Greekes also have not overpassed this in silence: for what is it that they have not medled withall? The white clay or earth wherewith they use to marle their grounds in the territorie of Megara, those onely I meane which are moist and cold, they call Leucargillum. These marles (all the kind of them) do greatly inrich France and Britaine both, and therefore it would not be amisse to speak of them more exactly. In old time there were two sorts therof, and no more: but of late daies (as mens wits are

---

[1] We can go along with Pliny's joy in the scent of rich soil after rain, but the last sentence, which does not seem to be corrupt, would now be thought non-sense; and indeed he goes into much detail about marling, a method of mixing one soil with another, although he seems to regard it as a way of manuring.

inventive every day of one thing or other) they have begun to find out more kindes, and to use the same: for there are now divers marles, the white, the red, the Columbine, the clay soile, the stony, and the sandy: and all these are but two in nature, to wit, either hard and churlish, or else gentle and fat. The triall of both is knowne by the handling, and a twofold use they yeeld; either to beare corne onely, or els for grasse and pasture also. The stonie or gravelly soile is good only for to nourish corne; which if it be white withall, and the pit thereof found among springs or fountains, it wil cause the ground to be infinite fruitfull, but it is rough in handling, and if it be laid too thick upon the lands or leyes, it wil burn the very ground. The next to it is the red marle, called also Capnomargos,[1] which hath intermingled in it a certaine small stony grit full of sand: This stony marle the manner is to break and bruise upon the very lands; and for the first yeares, hardly can the straw be mowne or cut downe for the said stones. Lighter is this marle than the rest by the one halfe, and therefore the cariage thereof into the field is least chargeable. It ought to be spred and laid thin, and some thinke that it standeth somewhat upon salt. But both the one and the other will serve well for fifty yeares, and the ground inriched thereby, will (during that time) yeeld plenty as well of corne as grasse.

Of those marles which are found to be fat, the white is chiefe; and thereof be many sorts. The most mordant and sharpest of them all, is that whereof we spake before.[2] A second kind there is of chalkish clay, which our gold-smiths use (called Tripela): this lieth a great depth within the earth, insomuch as many times men are driven to sinke pits 100 foot deep, for it; and those have a small and narrow mouth above, but within-forth and under the ground they be digged wider, by reason that the veine thereof runneth many waies, in manner of other mettall mines. This is the marle so much used in Britain: the strength therof being cast upon a land, will last 80 yeres; and never yet was the man known that herewith marled the same ground twice in all his life time.

The third kind of white marle, is that which the Greekes call

---

[1] Smoke-coloured marl. The usual reading is *acaunumarga* or stony marl, a Celtic word from *agaunum*, stone.

[2] The lime marl, which roughens the hand and burns the ground. Johnson's Dictionary quotes Milton, 'Uneasy steps over the burning marl'.

Glischromargon: it is no other than the Fullers chalkie clay mixed with a viscous and fatty earth. The nature of it, is to breed grasse better than to beare corne: for after one crop of corne is taken off the ground in harvest, before seed time is come for winter grain, the grasse wil be so high growne, that a man may cut it down and have a plentiful after-math for hay: and yet al the while that it hath corn upon it, you shall not see it to beare any grasse besides. This marle continueth good 30 yeres: if it be laid over-thick upon a land, it choketh the ground. . . . . The Columbine marle, the Gauls call in their language, by a name borrowed of the Greeks, Pelias, (*i.* Dove or Pigeon marle):[1] it is fetched out of the ground in clots and lumpes, like as stones be hewed out of quarries: with Sunne and the frost together, it will resolve and cleave into most thin slates or flakes. This marle is as good for corne as for herbage. As for sandy marle, it will serve the turn for want of other: yea and if the ground be cold, moist, and weely, the husbandman will make choice thereof before other.

The Ubians, upon my knowledge, use to inrich their ground and make it more battle (though their territory otherwise be most fertile) with any earth whatsoever; provided alwaies that it be digged up three foot deep at least, and laid a foot thick; a devise that no other country doth practise: howbeit this soile and manner of manuring, continueth good not above ten yeres: the Aedui and Pictones, have forced their grounds and made them most plentifull, with limestone; which is found also by experience to be passing profitable for vines and olives.

To come now to the ordering of this piece of husbandry: the ground ought to be ploughed first, before marle of any sort be cast upon it; to the end that the medicinable vertue and substance thereof, might the sooner and more greedily be received into it. Now forasmuch as marle is at the first over-rough and hard, not so free in the beginning as to resolve and turne into blade or grasse, it had need of some compost or dung to be mingled with it: for otherwise, be it never so rich, it will rather do harm than good to the ground, by reason that it is yet strange and not acquainted

[1] Holland's reference to pigeon-marl could not be found in the Latin and the passage is, in any case, in some confusion with several readings other than Pelias. Holland took from Pinet's translation which notes, 'car les Grecques appellent les Pigeons, Pelas'.

therewith: and yet help it this way as wel as you can, it will not bring forth any plenty the first yere after it is laid on. Last of all, it skilleth much to consider the nature of the ground, which you mean to marle: for the dry marle, sorteth well with a moist soile; and the fatty, hitteth that which is dry and lean. But when the ground is of a middle temperature between both, it mattereth not whether you use the white gold-smiths chalke, or the Columbine marle, for either of them will serve well enough.

§ 82

Of the nource-garden

(Chap. 10)

FOR to make a good pepinnier or nource-garden, there would be chosen a principal and special peece of ground: for oftentimes it falleth out, yea and meet it is, that the nource which giveth sucke should be more tender over the infant, than the owne naturall mother that bare it. In the first place therefore, let it be sound and drie ground, howbeit furnished with a good and succulent elemental moisture, and the same broken up and after wel digged over and over with mattock and spade, and brought to temper and order, so as it be nothing coy but readie to receive al manner of plants that shall come, and to entertain them as welcome guests; and withall, as like as may be to that ground unto which they must be removed at last.

But before al things this would be looked to, that it be rid clean of all stones; surely fenced also and paled about, for to keep out cockes and hens and all pullen: it must not be full of chinkes and cranies, for feare that the heat of the sunne enter in and burne up the small filaments or strings and beard of the new roots: and last of all, these pepins or kernels ought to stand a foot and a halfe asunder: for in case they meet together and touch one another, besides other faults and inconveniences, they will be subject to wormes: and therefore I say there would be some distance between, that the ground about them may be often harrowed and raked, to kill the vermin, and the weeds pluckt up by the heeles that do

breed them. Moreover, it would not be forgotten to proin these
yong plants when they are but new come up: to cut away, I say,
the superfluous sprigs underneath, and use them betimes to the
hooke.[1] *Cato* giveth counsel to sticke forks about their beds a mans
height, and lay hurdles over them, so as the Sun may be let in
underneath: and those hurdles to cover and thatch over with
straw or holme, for to keepe out the cold in winter. Thus are yong
plants of Peare trees and Apple trees nourished: thus Pine nut trees,
thus Cypresses which do likewise come up of seed, are cherished.

As for the grains or seeds of the Cypres tree, they be exceeding
small, and so small indeed, that some of them can scarce be discerned well by the eye. Wherein the admirable worke of Nature
would be considered, to wit, that of so little seeds should grow
so great and mightie trees, considering how far bigger are the
cornes of Wheat and Barley (to make no reckoning nor speech of
Beans) in comparison of them. What should we say to Peare trees
and Apple trees? what proportion or likenesse is there between
them, and the pretty little pepins whereof they take their beginning? Marvell we not, that of so slender and small things at the
first, they should grow so hard, as to checke and turne again the
very edge of ax and hatchet? that frames and stocks of presses
should be made thereof so strong and tough, as will not shrinke
under the heaviest poise and weights that be? that Mast-poles
comming thereof should be able to beare saile in wind and weather?
and finally, that they should afford those huge and mightie Rams
and such like engins of batterie, sufficient to command towers and
bastils, yea, and beat downe strong walls of stone before them? Lo
what the force of Nature is! see how powerfull shee is in her works!

§ 83

Curious devises to plant vines

(Chap. 21)

BESIDES all this, there is another pretty and wanton devise,
more curious ywis than needfull, to plant Vines, and namely, after
this manner. Take foure branches of foure vines growing together,

---

[1] Accustom them early to the pruning knife.

and bearing sundry kindes of grapes; bind them wel and strongly together in that part where they are most ranke and best nourished: being thus bound fast together, let them passe along either through the concavitie of an Oxe shanke and maribone, or els an earthen pipe or tunnell made for the nonce. Thus couch them in the ground, and cover them with earth, so as two joints or buds be seen without. By this meanes they injoy the benefit of moisture, and take root together: and although they be cut from their owne stocke, yet they put out leaves and branches. After this, the pipe or bone aforesaid is broken, that the root may have libertie both to spread and also to gather more strength. And will you see the experience of a pretty secret? you shall have this one plant thus united of foure, to beare divers and sundry grapes, according to the bodies or stocks from whence they came.

Yet is there one fine cast more to plant a Vine, found out but of late, and this is the manner thereof: take a Vine-set or cutting, slit it along through the midst, and scrape out the marrow or pith very cleane; then set them together again wood to wood, as they were before, and bind them fast: but take heed in any case that the buds or oilets without-forth be not hurt, nor rased at all. This done, put the same cutting into the ground, interre it I say wel within earth and dung tempered together: when it begins to spread yong branches, cut them off; and oftentimes remember to dig about it, and lay the earth light: and certes, *Columella* holdeth it for certain, and assureth us upon his word, That the grapes comming of such a vine wil have no stones or kernels at all within them. A strange thing and passing wonderfull, that the very set it selfe should live; and that which more is, grow and beare, notwithstanding the pith or marrow is taken quite away.

§ 84
Of the play dayes of vines
(Chap. 23)

BUT throughout all Greece they tie their vines with Rushes, Cyperus, or Gladon, Reeke, and sea-grasse.[1] Over and besides, the

---

[1] *junco, cypero, ulva.* A long description of Cyperus is given in Book 21, immediately after § 109. It has been identified as the sweet rush. Reeke is seaweed.

maner is otherwhiles to untie the Vine, and for certain daies together to give it liberty for to wander loosely, and to spred it selfe out of order, yea, and to lie at ease along the ground, which all the yere besides it onely beheld on high: in which repose it seemeth to take no small contentment and refreshing: for like as draught horses, when they be out of their geeres, and haknies unsadled, like as Oxen when they have drawn in the yoke, yea, and greyhounds after they have run in chase, love to tumble themselves and wallow upon the earth: even so the Vine also, having bin long tied up, and restrained, liketh wel now to stretch out her lims and loins, and such easement and relaxation doth her much good. Nay, the tree[1] it selfe findes some comfort and joy therby, in being discharged of that burden which it carried continually as it were upon the shoulders, and seemeth now to take breath and heart again. And certes, go through the whole course and worke of Nature, there is nothing, but by imitation of day and night, desireth to have some alternative ease and play dayes between.

And it is by experience found very hurtfull, and therefore not allowed of, to prune and cut Vines presently upon the Vintage and grape-gathering, whiles they be still wearie and overtravelled with bearing their fruit so lately: ne yet to binde them, thus pruned, in the same place again where they were tied before: for surely vines do feel the very prints and marks which the bonds made, and no doubt are vexed and put to pain therewith, and the worse for them.

[1] The poplar trees up which the vines were trained; see § 71, p. 146.

EIGHTEENTH BOOKE
is a Treatise of
Agriculture or Husbandrie

§ 85

Of the venomes of man

(Chap. 1)

NOW followeth the treatise of corn, of Gardens, and Floures, and generally of al things else, that by the goodnesse of Nature the Earth bringeth forth bountifully, besides Trees and Shrubs. The speculation whereof verily is infinit, if a man do but consider the number and variety of Herbes and Floures, together with their odors and colors; the diversity also of their juices, their several vertues and properties, whether it be to cure men of their maladies, or to give them pleasure and contentment to their senses. But before that I enter into this discourse, very willing I am to take in hand the cause of Earth (the common mother of us all) and to assist her against all slanderous imputations, notwithstanding I have in the beginning of this my worke pleaded once already in her defence. For when we looke into the matter within her contained, we are set on fire inwardly to find fault with her for breeding and bearing noisome things, charging upon her our own faults, and imputing to her that, for which we of right ought to be blamed. Set case she hath brought forth poison and venom, Who hath searched them out but man? . . .

Moreover, setting man aside, there is no creature furnished or armed with any other venome, but their own. We cannot chuse therefore but confesse our great fault and deadly malice, in that we rest not contented with naturall poisons, but betake our selves to many mixtures and compositions artificiall, made even with our owne hands. But what say you to this? Are not some men themselves meere poisons by nature? for these slanderers and backbiters in the world, what doe they else but lance poison out of their black tongues, like hideous serpents? what doe these envious persons, but with their malicious and poisonfull breath sindge and burne all before them that they can reach or meet with, finding fault with every thing whatsoever? Are they not well and fitly compared to these cursed souls flying in the dark, which albeit they sequester themselves from birds of the day, yet they bewray their spight and envy even to the night and the quiet repose thereof, by their heavie grones (the only voice that they utter) disquieting and troubling those that be at rest: and finally, all one they be with those unluckie creatures, which if they happen either to meet or crosse the way upon a man, presage alwaies some il toward, opposing themselves (as it were) to all goodnesse, and hindering whatsoever is profitable for this life. Neither do these monstrous and abominable sprites know any other reward of this their deadly breath, their cursed and detestable malice, but to hate and abhor all things.

Howbeit, herein may wee acknowledge and see the wonderfull majestie of dame Nature: for like as she hath shewed her selfe more fruitfull and liberall in bringing forth profitable and holesome plants, in greater plenty than hurtfull and noisom; so surely hath she furnished the world better with good men and vertuous for the weale publick. In which regard and consideration, we also taking no small joy and contentment (leaving these troublesome spirits to themselves for to broile and frie in their owne greace) will go on forward and proceed to declare the rest of Natures workes; and with the better resolution, for that wee seeke more pleasure and contentment in the paines and travell that we take, than expect any fame or bruit of men afterwards. For why? we are in hand to speake of the countrey and countrie commodities, such as in old time like as they were most necessary for this life, so they were accounted and honoured most highly.

§ 86

What famous persons addicted themselves wholly to Husbandrie

(Chap. 3)

LIKEWISE, *M. Varro* hath left in writing, That when *L. Metellus* made shew of so many Elephants in his triumph at Rome, a Modius[1] of good red wheat, was worth no more than one Asse; also a gallon of wine cost no more. And as for drie figges, thirty pound weight carried no higher price: and a man might have bought a pound of Oile olive, and 12 pound of flesh at the very same reckoning. And yet all this plenty and cheapnesse proceeded not from the great domaines and large possessions of those private persons that incroched upon their neighbors, and hemmed them within narrow compasse. For by the law published by *Licinius Stolo,* provided it was, that no Roman citizen should hold in privat above five hundred acres. The rigor of which law or statute was extended and practised upon the Law-maker himselfe, and by vertue thereof he was condemned: who, for to possesse above that proportion, and to defraud the meaning of the said Act, purchased more lands in the name of his Son. Loe what might be the proportion and measure of possessions allowed even then, when as the State and Common-wealth of Rome was in the prime and began to flourish. And as for the Oration verily of *Manius Curius* after such triumphs of his, and when he had subdued and brought under the obeisance of the Roman Empire and laid to their dominion so many forrein nations; what it was, every man knoweth, wherin he delivered this speech, That he was not to be counted a good man, but a dangerous citizen, who could not content himselfe with a close of seven acres of ground.

And to say a truth, after that the kings were banished out of Rome, and their regiment abolished, this was the very proportion of land assigned to a Roman Commoner. If this be so, What might be the cause of so great plenty and abundance aforesaid in those daies? Certes, this and nothing els, great LL.[2] and generals of the

---

[1] A peck.   [2] Lords.

field (as it should seem) tilled themselves their ground with their own hands; and the Earth again for her part, taking no small pleasure (as it were) to be eared and broken up with ploughes Laureat, and ploughmen Triumphant, strained her selfe to yeeld increase to the uttermost. Like it is also, that these brave men and worthy personages were as curious in sowing a ground with corne, as in ordinance of a battell in array: as diligent (I say) in disposing and ordering of their lands, as in pitching of a field: and commonly every thing that commeth under good hands, the more neat and cleane that the usage thereof is, and the greater paines that is taken about it, the better it thriveth and prospereth afterwards.

What shall we say more? was not C. *Attilius Serranus* (when the honourable dignity of Consulship was presented unto him, with commission to conduct the Roman army) found sowing his own field and planting trees, whereupon he took that syrname *Serranus*? As for *Quintius Cincinnatus*, a pursevant or messenger of the Senat brought unto him the letters patents of his Dictatorship, at what time as he was in proper person ploughing a piece of ground of his owne, containing foure acres and no more, which are now called Prata Quintiana, (*i. Quintius* his medowes) lying within the Vaticane and (as it is reported) not onely bare-headed was hee and open breasted, but also all naked and full of dust. The fore said officer or sergeant taking him in this maner, Do on your cloths sir (quoth he) and cover your body, that I may deliver unto you the charge that I have from the Senate and people of Rome. Where, note by the way, that such Pursevants and Sergeants in those daies were named Viatores;[1] for that eftsoones they were sent to fetch both Senatours and Generall captaines out of the fields where they were at worke: but now, see how the times be changed!

They that doe this businesse in the field, what are they but bond-slaves fettered, condemned malefactors manacled, and in one word, noted persons, and such as are branded and marked in their visage with an hot yron? Howbeit the Earth, whom wee call our Mother, and whom wee would seem to worship, is not so deafe and sencelesse, but she knoweth well enough how shee is by them deprived of that honour which was done in old time unto her: insomuch, as wee may well weet, that against her will shee

---

[1] Wayfarers.

yeeldeth fruit as shee doth; howsoever wee would have it thought, by these glorious titles given unto her, that she is nothing displeased therewith, namely, to be labored and wrought by such vile and base hirelings. But we forsooth do marvell, that the labor of these contemptible bondslaves and abject villains doth not render the like profit, as that travell in former times of great captains and LL. Generalls. And in very truth, even among other forrein nations, it was counted a princelike profession indeed, to be able for to give rules and directions about Husbandry: for so we may see, that both kings have studied this argument, as namely, *Hiero*, *Attalus Philometor*, and *Archelaus*: and also martiall captaines; to wit, *Xenophon*, and *Mago* the Carthaginian. As for *Mago* verily, our Senate did him that honour after Carthage was woon, that in sacking it and giving away among divers LL. of Affricke, the Libraries there found; they thought good to reserve only 28 volumes of his, and penned by him as touching Agriculture, and to have them translated into the Latin tongue (notwithstanding that *M. Cato* had already beforetime put out in writing and set forth certaine rules and precepts therof:) giving order for this translation, to those that were well seene in the Punicke or Carthaginian language: in which businesse, *D. Silanus* a Romane gentleman of a right worshipfull house, went beyond all others.

As for great schollers and men of profound and deep learning, a number there were besides that travelled in this matter, whom wee have named already in the forefront; and eftsoones shall mention in the discourse of this volume. In which range we must nominate not unthankfully among the meanest writers, *M. Varro*, who beeing foure-score yeares old and one, thought it not amisse to compile a speciall booke and treatise of Husbandry.

§ 87

Of good Husbandrie

(Chap. 6)

AFTER what manner then shall we proceed in the husbandry of our land to most benefit and behoofe? Learn a rule out of the Oracle or sententious riddle, which goeth in this forme, *Malis bonis* (*i.* Cheapest, Best). But herein, me thinks, good reason it is, that our old great grandfathers should be defended and excused for holding these strange and obscure paradoxes; they (I say) who by such rules and precepts, tooke great care and paines to instruct us how to live.

Would you know then what they meant by this word *Malis?* surely they understood those that were cheapest and stood them in least. The chiefe point of all their providence and forecast, was to goe the nearest way to worke, and to be at the smallest cost: and no marvell; for who were they that gave out these thriftie precepts? even those, who reproched a victorious General (and one who triumphed over the enemy) for having a cupboord of silver plate weighing but ten pound: those (I say) who if their bayliffes of husbandrie chanced to die, whereby their lands in the countrey stood void, would make suit to be gone themselves thither, and to return to their own fermes; leaving behind them the glory of all their victories by them atchieved: and to conclude, even those who whiles they were imploied in the conduct of armies, had their grounds looked unto and tilled at the charges of the common weale, and had no other for their bayliffs than the noble Senators of Rome. From their mouths came these other oracles and wise sentences following: An ill husband is he, who is forced to buy that, which his ferme might affoord him. As bad is that housholder and master of a family, who doth that in the day which might be don by night, unlesse unseasonable weather drive him to it: worse than either of these is he, who doth that upon work-daies which should have bin done on play daies or idle holidaies: but the worst of all other is he, who when the weather is fair, wil chuse to work rather within close house than abroad in the open field: and here I cannot hold and rule my selfe, but I must needs alledge one example out of antient histories, whereby it may be understood, How it was an ordinary matter to commense actions and to maintaine pleas in open court before the body of the people in the case of Husbandry: as also in what sort those good Husbandmen of old time were wont to defend their owne cause when they were brought into question.

And this was the case. There was one *C. Furius Chresimus,* late a bond-slave, and newly infranchised, who after that hee was set at liberty, purchased a very little piece of ground, out of which he gathered much more commodity than all his neighbors about him out of their great and large possessions: whereupon he grew to be greatly envied and hated; insomuch, as they charged him with indirect means, as if he had used sorcery, and by charmes and witch-craft drawne into his owne ground that increase of fruits, which should otherwise have growne in his neighbors fields. Thus upon complaint and information given, he was presented and indited, by *Spurius Albinus*, an Aedile Curule for the time being: and a day was set him down peremptorily for his personal appearance to answer the matter. He therfore fearing the worst, and doubting that he should be cast to pay some grievous fine; at what time as the Tribes were ready to give their voices, either to acquit or condemne him, brought into the common place his plough, with other instruments and furniture belonging to husbandry: he presented likewise in the open face of the court, his owne daughter, a lusty strong lasse and big of bone; yea, and (as *Piso* telleth the tale) well fed, and as well clad: he shewed there (I say) his tooles and plough yrons of the best making, and kept in as good order; maine and heavy coulters, strong and tough spades, massie and weighty ploughshares, and withall his draught Oxen, ful and faire.

Now, when his course came to plead his own cause before the people, and to answer for himselfe, thus he began and said: My masters (quoth he) you that are citizens of Rome, behold, these are the sorceries, charms, and all the inchantments that I use (pointing to his daughter, his oxen and furniture abovenamed:) I might besides (quoth he) alledge mine owne travell and toile that I take, the early rising and late sitting up so ordinary with me, the carefull watching that I usually abide, and the painefull sweats which I daily indure; but I am not able to represent these to your view, nor to bring them hither with me into this assembly. The people no sooner heard this plea of his, but with one voice they all acquit him and declared him unguilty, without any contradiction. By which example verily, a man may soone see, that good husbandrie goeth not all by much expence: but it is pains taking and careful diligence that doth the deed. And hereupon came the old sayd saw, so rife in everie mans mouth, that the only thing to make ground most fertile and fruitfull, is the Masters eie.

§ 88

Of faults incident to corne, and their remedies

(Chap. 17)

MANY there be who practise other remedies: and namely for the Millet, they would have a toad to be caried round about the field before that it be harrowed: which done, to be put close within an earthen pot, and so buried in the middest of the said field: and by this meanes forsooth, neither Sparrows will lie upon the corn, nor any worm hurt it. Mary, in any case this same toad must be digged out of the ground againe before the field be mowed, els will the Millet prove bitter in tast. The like experiment they say is of a Moldwarps shoulder, for if any corn be sowed or touched therewith before, it will come up the better and bring more increase.

Democritus had a devise by himselfe for all seed and corn whatsoever, namely, to temper and soke the same corn in the juice of the herb housleeke or Sen-greene, growing upon houses either tiled or shindled; which in Greeke is called Aizoon, and in Latine Sedum or Digitellum; for this medicine will serve for all maladies. The common practise of our husbandmen is this: in case through the oversweet sap or juice in greene corne, wormes take to the roots: for to sprinkle them with simple oile lees pure and clean without any salt, and afterwards to rake it in. Also, when the corn begins to joint and gather into knots, then to clense the ground, and put off no longer, for feare least the weeds do get head and overgrow. This I am sure upon mine owne knowledge, that there is an herbe (but what proper name it hath I wote not) which if it be interred in the foure corners of a field that is sown with Millet, it wil drive away Stares and Sparrows, which otherwise would by whole flights and flocks lie thereupon and do much harme; nay I will speake a greater word which may seeme wonderfull, There is not a bird of the aire one or other, that dare enter or approch such a field. Field-mice and Rats are skared away and will not touch corne, which before the sowing was either bestrewed with the ashes of weasels or cats, or els drenched with the liquor and decoction of water wherein they were boiled; howbeit this inconvenience insueth hereupon, That bread made of such corn will have a smach, and sent strongly of such cats and Weasels: and therefore it is supposed a more expedient and safer way to medicine our seed corne with oxe gall, for to preserve it from the said Mice and Rats.

But what remedy against the blast and mildew, the greatest plague that can befall upon corn? Mary prick downe certaine Lawrell boughes here and there among the standing corne, all the said mists and mildewes will leave the corne and pass to the Bay leaves, and there settle. What shall we do then to corne when it is over-rank? Eat it me downe with sheep and spare not, whiles it is young and in the blade onely, before (I say) it be knotted: and never feare harm by the sheeps teeth as neere as they go to the ground: for let it be thus eaten many times, the corn will be the better, yea and the head will take no harme thereby but proove the fairer.

§ 89

Of Prevarication and Delirium in husbandrie

(Chap. 19)

To come now unto our draught oxen that must labour at the plough: they ought to be coupled in yoke, as close together and as streight as is possible, to the end that whilst they be at work and ploughing, they may beare up their heads; for by that means they least doe gall or bruise their necks. If they chance to goe to plough among trees and vines, they must be muzled with some frailes[1] or devises made of twigs, to the end they should not brouse and crop off the yong springs and soft tendrils. Moreover, there ought a little hatchet to hang evermore fast to the plough beame before, therewith to cut through roots within the ground, that might breake or stay the plough: for better is it so to do, than to put the plough to it, to keep a plucking at them or to force the poore oxen to lie tugging and wrestling with them.

Also in ploughing, this order is to be kept, That when the oxen are gone down with one furrow to the lands end, they turne and

[1] Rush baskets.

goe up againe with another; so that in ploughing of a land they rest betweene whiles as little as may be, but evermore go forward in their labour untill they have made an end of their halfe acre, or halfe daies worke: and verily it is thought sufficient for a teem of oxen to breake up (at the first tilth) in one day of restie or ley ground, one acre, taking a furrow or stitch of nine inches; but at the second tilth or stirring, an acre and a halfe; which is to be understood of an easie and mellow soile to be wrought; for if it be tough and churlish, it is wel if they eare up at the first, halfe an acre; and at the next time they may go through with one whole acre, how hard soever the ground be; for thus have poore beasts their taske set, and their labour limited by Natures lore and appointment. Every field to be sown must be eared at first with streight and direct furrows; but those that follow after, ought to go byas and winding. If a ground upon the pendant or hanging of the hil be to be broken up, the furrowes must go crosse and over-thwart: howbeit, the point and beak of the plough-share must be so guided, that one while it beare hard above on the one side, and another while beneath on the other side: and verily in this mountaine worke, the ploughman that holdeth the plough hath toile enough, and laboreth at it as hard as the oxen do. Certes, there be some mountaines that have no use at all of this beast, but they eare their ground with raking and scraping hooks only.

The ploughman, unlesse he bend and stoope forward with his body, must needs make sleight worke, and leave much undon as it ought to be; a fault which in Latine we call Prevarication: and this terme appropriate unto husbandrie, is borrowed from thence by Lawyers, and translated by them into their courts and halls of pleas: if it be then a reprochfull crime for Lawyers to abuse their clients by way of collusion, wee ought to take heed how we deceive and mocke the ground, where this fault was first found and discovered. To proceed, the plough-man ever and anone had need to cleanse the culter and the share with his staffe, tipped and pointed at the end like a thistle-spade: he must beware that between two furrowes, he leave no naked balks raw and untilled: also that the clots ride not one upon anothers back. Badly is that land ploughed, which after the corn is sowed, needs the great harrows and clotting, Contrariwise, a man may know where there is good worke; namely, if the turfe be so close couched that there be no seams to be seen where the plough-share went: finally, it is a profitable point of husbandry and much practised (where the ground doth both beare and require it) For to draw here and there broad gutters or furrows, to drain away the water into ditches and trenches cast for the nones betweene the lands, that otherwise would stand within and drowne the corne.

After the second fallow called Stirring,[1] done with crosse and overthwart furrow to the first; then followeth clodding, if need be, either with rakes or great harrowes: upon which insueth sowing: and when the seed is in the ground, harrowing a second time with the smal harrow. In some places, where the manner of the country doth so require, this is performed with a tined or toothed harrow, or els with a broad planke fastened unto the plough taile, which doth hide and cover the seed newly sown: and in this maner to rake or harrow, is called in Latine Lirare, from whence came first the word Delirare, which is to leave bare balks uncovered, and by a Metaphore and borrowed speech, to rave and speake idlely.

§ 90

Of the Astronomers

(Chap. 25)

BUT now to come more particularly to the signs which fore-token the Spring: some there be that goe by the Butterflie, and hold that their brood comming abroad, is an assured token that the Spring is come, for that these creatures so feeble, are not able to abide any cold: howbeit, this was checked that very yere, wherin I wrote this Book or History of Natures work: for seen it was and marked very well, that 3 flights of them one after another were killed with the cold weather that surprised them thrice, for that they were stirring too early, and came abroad over-soon. Yea, and the very birds who are our guests in warm weather, visited us five or six daies before Februarie, and made a goodly shew of a timely Spring, putting us in good hope, that al cold weather was gone:

---

[1] To fallow was to plough ready for a second ploughing.

howbeit, there ensued a most bitter after-winter streight upon it, that nipped and killed them in manner everie one.

Hard and doubtfull therefore is the case, that whereas first and principally we were to fetch our rule from the heavens to guide and direct us, then afterwards we should be driven to goe by other signes and arguments meere conjecturall. But above all, the cause of this incertitude and difficultie, is partly the convexity of the cope of heaven, and partly the diverse climats observed in the globe of the earth, by meanes whereof, one and the same star seemeth to rise at sundrie times in diverse countres, and appears sooner or later to some than to others: and therefore the cause depending thereupon, is not in all places of like validity, nor sheweth the same effects alwaies at the same times.

And yet there is one difficultie more, arising from those Authors who writing of one and the same thing, have delivered divers opinions, according to the sundry climates wherein they were, at what time as they observed the figure and constitution of the heavens. Now were there of these Astronomers three Sects, to wit, the Chaldaeans, the Aegyptians, and the Greekes. To which there may be added a fourth, which among us *Caesar* the Dictatour first erected: who observing the course of the Sun, and taking with him also the advise of *Sofigenes* (a learned Mathematitian and skilfull Astronomer in his time) reduced the yeare unto the said revolution. Howbeit, in this calculation of his, there was found an error, and short he came of the marke, which he aimed at, by reason that there was no Bissextile or leap yere by him inserted, but after 12 yeres. Now, when it was observed by this reckoning, that the sun had performed his revolution sooner than the yere turned about, which before was wont to prevent[1] the course of the Sun, this error was reformed: and after every fourth yeare expired, came about the Bissextile aforesaid, and made al streight. *Sofigenes* also himselfe, albeit he was reputed a more curious and exquisite Mathematician than the rest, yet in three severall treatises that he made, retracting or correcting that in one booke that he had set down in another, seemed evermore to write doubtfully, and left the thing in as great ambiguitie and undetermined as he found it.

As for these writers whose names I have alleadged and prefixed

[1] Precede; the year used to end before the sun completed its revolution.

in the front of this present volume now in hand, they have like-wise delivered their opinions as touching this point, but hardly shal you find two of them in one and the same mind. Lesse marvell then if the rest have varied one from another, who may pretend for their excuse the divers tracts and climates wherein they wrote. As for those who lived in the same region, and yet wrot contrarie, I canot tel what to make of them: howbeit, I care not much[1] to set downe one example of their discord and disagreement. *Hesiodus* the Poet (for under his name also there goeth a Treatise of Astro-logie) hath put down in writing the matutine setting of the star Vergiliae (which is the occultation thereof by the raies and beames of the Sunne toward morning) to begin ordinarily upon the day of the Aequinox in Autumne. *Thales* the Milesian saith, That it falleth out upon the five and twentieth after the said Aequinox. *Anaximander* writeth, That it is nine and twenty daies after: and finally, *Euctemon* hath noted the 48 day following the said Aequinox, for the retrait or occultation of the forenamed Brood-hen star Vergiliae. Loe what varietie there is among these deepe clearkes and great Astrologers.

§ 91

The Seednes of Corne

(Chap. 25)

XENOPHON would not have us begin to sow before that God give us some good signe and token so to do. And *Cicero*[2] our countryman expounding this saying of *Xenophon*, taketh the raines in November[3] to be that signe which God giveth: whereas in very deed the true and undoubted rule to goe by, is to make no great hast into the field for to sow, before the leaves begin to fall, and this every man holdeth to be at the very occultation or retrait of the star Vergiliae. Some, as we have before said, have observed

---

[1] I do not mind setting down.
[2] In his lost translation of Xenophon's *Oeconomicus*.
[3] Called by our Husbandmen Gore-moone (P. H.).

it about 3 daies before the Ides of November. And for that the said star is so evident in the heaven, and easiest to be known of all others, called it is by the name of a garment hanging out at a Brokers shop.[1]

And therefore by the fall or retrait thereof, as many men as have a care and forecast to prevent the covetous dealing of the merchant-Tailor (as commonly such occupiers lie in the wind for gain) guesse aforehand what winter will follow: for if it be a cloudie season when the star retireth, it threatens a rainy winter, and then these merchants presently raise the price of the clokes which they sel: but if the weather be faire and cleare at the setting or occulta-tion thereof, it sheweth a pinching and hard winter toward; and then they hold other garments also very deare. But this Husbandman of ours, who cannot skill at all to looke up and to learn the order and position of the heavens, must spy this signe of winter amongst his briers and brambles: he must find (I say) the time of Seednes as he looketh downe upon the ground, namely, when he sees the leaves fallen and lying under his feet.

§ 92

Of the glo-worms

(Chap. 26)

THUS you see how these fixed starres and signes above rehearsed do ordinarily keepe their courses, ruling and governing this time between, to wit, from the Spring Aequinox in March, unto the sixt day before the Ides of May, which is the ninth of the said moneth. During the first 15 daies of which halfe quarter, the husbandmen must make hast and take in hand that work that he was not able to go through with and dispatch before the Aequinox; knowing full well, that upon neglect of this businesse, arose first, the opprobrious reproches that vine-pruners and cutters doe heare on both sides of their eares, from passengers and waifaring men, by way of counterfeiting the song of that Summer-bird which

---

[1] Vergiliae are the Pleiades. The constellation was called by the name of a garment for the reasons given in the next paragraph.

they call the Cuckow: for it is counted so foule a shame, worthie a checke and rebuke, that the said bird should come and find a pruning hooke or bill in a vine at that time of the yere; that folk therefore stick not to let flie at them bold taunts, and broad biting scofs even in the first beginning of the spring, And verily as these birds, so their song counterfeited in this sort, seemeth to carrie an ominous and cursed presage with them. See how the least things belonging to Agriculture, are guided and carried by naturall reasons!

As for the later end of this foresaid time, it must be employed in the sowing of Panicke and Millet; for it is ordinarie and usual to sow this kind of graine after that hastie Barley is ripe, and also upon the very same lands where it grew. Now the signe common to them both, testifying as wel the ripenes of one, as the Seednes of the other, are the glo-birds or glo-worms Cicindelae, shining in the evening over the corne-fields, for so the rustical paisants and country clowns cal certain flies or worms glowing and glittering star-like; and the Greeks name them Lampyrides: wherein we may see the wonderfull bounty and incredible goodnes of Nature, in teaching us by that silly creature.

·

§ 93

Democritus and the dearth of olives

(Chap. 28)

It is reported of *Democritus*, the first Philosopher who understood himselfe, and afterwards shewed unto the world, the great affinity and agreement that was between heaven and earth (which study of his the richest and wealthiest citizens where he lived, seemed to scorne and despise) foreseeing by the course of the stars, to wit, by the rising that would be of the Virgiliae or Broodhen (according as I have shewed already, and wil anon declar more at large) that olives would faile that yere, and consequently a dearth insue of oile; bought up all the oile in that tract and country, which as then for the hope of great plenty of Olives, bare no price: whereat the great merchants of the city (who dreamed of nothing lesse than of a scarcity of oile, considering the olives made so faire a shew upon the trees) were astonied and marvelled much, that *Democritus* so learned a Philosopher, and a man who they knew, was wont by his profession to content himself with poverty, to set his mind upon nothing so much as a quiet life, and wholly to busie his braine in attaining of knowledge and learning, was now on a sudden become a merchant.

In the end, they perceived what the cause was, and acknowledged his divine skill in foreseeing and preventing a dearth, and he for his part shewed plainly, That it was not avarice and desire of lucre that moved him to take this course, but to let the world know, that if he were so disposed, hee could by the means of his learning only, be soon a rich man (as indeed he grew hereby to exceeding wealth), for presently of his own accord he restored again to the former owners, who God wot were displeased with themselves for that they had don, and wished with all their hearts, that they had met with the like bargain; he remitted (I say) all this commodity which he had gotten into his own hands, at their own price: resting herein, that he had made good proofe, how soone and easily he could be rich when he would. Long time after him, *Sextius* one of our Roman Philosophers did the like at Athens, and after the same maner: wherby we may see, in what stead learning and literature serveth, if a man will imploy the same to his own benefit.

§ 94

The udder of the Milkeway

(Chap. 29)

T H E R E is besides in the heaven, a certain white circle called the milkway (or Watling street)[1] which is not imaginarie as others, but very conspicuous and easie to be seene. By the influence of this circle, as it were out of some udder, all plants receive their milke, their humidity and nutriment, and namely, by the means of two notable stars observed therein; to wit, the Aegle in the North-side

[1] The Milky Way was called after other famous streets and Pinet's translation has, 'ce cercle blanc que nous appellons le chemin de sainct Jacques'.

thereof, and the Dog Canicula (whereof we made mention in place convenient) scituate toward the South. This circle then passing through the signes of the Zodiacke, Sagittarius and Gemini, and stretching by the centre of the Sun, cutteth the Equinoctial line twice in two severall places: the commissures or joints of which two signes, are possessed of the one side with the Eagle star, and on the other side with the Dog Canicula beforesaid.

No marvel therfore if all countries habitable and fruitfull, be subject to the influence of these two starres and feele their effects; because in those parts only of the Zodiack wherein they are placed, the centre and middle of the earth, together with the centre also of the Sun, agree and meet just in one and the same point of the Equinoctial. Hereupon it is, that if in the several seasons of these two stars abovesaid (to wit, when the Egle and the Dog Canicula, doe either rise or fall, appeare or couch) the aire be pure, cleare, and mild, and thereby the humour genitall distilling from that Milke-way or circle aforesaid downe to the earth, meet with that faire and calme aire, then all plants and fruits of the earth are the better for it, and prosper mightily.

Now in case the moone either at change or full, do send downe and sprinkle upon them a cold congealed dew (in manner above-said) the humor and nouriture likewise descending from the Milk-circle, is infected therwith and becommeth bitter, killing all the fruit upon which it falleth: much like as if a young babe or infant new borne, should sucke bitter and unwholsome milke, and thereupon soon after die. Thus you see, how in every climate whatsoever, the correspondence of the moone and the stars above-said more or lesse, causeth those untoward Blasts, Mildewes, and such like; not in like measure at one time and in every place.

§ 95

Of Corneharvest

(Chap. 30)

As touching the manner of cutting downe or reaping corne, there be divers and sundry devises. In France where the fields be large, they use to set a jade or an asse unto the taile of a mightie great

wheele barrow or cart made in manner of a Van, and the same set
with keen and trenchant teeth sticking out on both sides: now is
this carre driven forward before the said beast upon two wheeles,
into the standing ripe corne (contrary to the manner of other
carts that are drawne after) the said teeth or sharp tines fastened
to the sides of the wheele barrow or car aforesaid, catch hold of the
corn eares, and cut them off: yet so, as they fall presently into the
body of the wheele-barrow.

In some places the fashion is to cut with a hooke or syccle the
straw in the middest: and betweene every two sheaves[1] they sit
down, and then crop off the eares just at the straw. In other
countries they use to plucke up the standing corne by the root:
and in so doing, persuaded they are that this is a very neer and
ready way to save charges, and may serve for one tilth well
enough: but by their leave, they rob the ground by the means of
her kinde and naturall moisture. The reason of this diversitie is
this: in such countries where they use to thatch their houses with
straw, they save it to the full length, and go as neare as possibly
they can: againe, where there is but small store of hay, they make
account of their short chaffe for to litter, yea, and fodder their
beasts. As for Panicke haulme, it never serveth the turne in any
place for thatch. And for Millet straw, they burne it ordinarily.
Barly straw is kept and saved very carefully for an excellent fodder,
that kine and oxen love very wel. To conclude, in France they
have another way to gather their Panicke and Millet especially; to
wit, cutting the same eare by eare upon a combe with a handle to
it (as Barbers use to clip or poll mens heads).

[1] *inter duas mergites spica destringitur*. A good example of those differences
between Holland's and more recent translations that led Bostock and Riley, as
they affirm, to prepare a new version in 1855. *Merges* means a sheaf but can,
in the plural, replace *mergae*, a two-pronged pitchfork. One can read either
that the ear was stripped between two pitchforks or, as Holland prefers, that the
ears were removed as soon as two sheaves were cut; only a comparative study of
hand-reaping in different countries could decide which meaning to choose. As
usual, Holland sounds very confident and he may have seen reapers 'sitting
down' between every two sheaves.

The
NINETEENTH BOOKE
discourseth of Flax, Spart, and
Gardenage

§ 96

Linnen that will not burne in the fire

(Chap. 1)

FURTHERMORE, there is a kind of Line found out which will not consume in the fire: this in Italy they call Quick-line, and I my self have seen table-clothes, towels, and napkins therof, which being taken foule from the bourd at a great feast, have been cast into the fire, and there they burned before our face upon the hearth; by which meanes they became better scoured, and looked fairer and brighter a hundred times, than if they had bin rinsed and washed in water; and yet no part of their substance, but the filth only, was burnt away.

At the roiall obsequies and funeralls of KK.[1] the manner was to wind and lap the corps within a sheet of this cloth, of purpose to separate the cinders comming off the body, from other ashes (of the sweet wood that was burnt therewith.) This manner of Line groweth in the deserts of India, where no rain falls, where the countrey is all parched and burnt with the Sunne, amongst the fell dragons and hideous Serpents; thus it is inured there to live burning; which is the reason, that ever after it wil abide the fire. Geason[2] it is to be found, and as hard to be woven, so short and small it is. Howsoever otherwise it be naturally of colour reddish, yet by the fire it getteth a shining glosse and bright hew. They that can come by it and meet withall, esteeme it as precious as the best orient pearles. In Greeke they call this Line, Asbestinum,

[1] Kings.   [2] Rare, scarce.

according to the nature and propertie that it hath, not to consume with burning.

Over and besides, *Anaxilaus* saith, That if a man would cut downe or fell a tree by stealth and in secret, let him compasse the body thereof with a sheet of this linnen, he may hew as long as he will at it, and all the strokes that he giveth will be so drowned, that they shall not be heard againe. To conclude, in all these respects above said, this Line may well be counted for the principall and best that is in the whole world.

§ 97

Of the Radish

(Chap. 5)

ALL Radishes breed wind wonderfull much, and provoke a man that eateth of them, to belch. A base and homely meat therefore it is, and not for a gentlemans table, especially if it be eaten with other worts, as Beets: mary if a man take them with unripe olives[1] condite,[2] he shall neither belch or rift wind so much, ne yet so soure and stinking will his breath be afterwards. The Egyptians make marvellous great account of radishes, for the plenty of oile that they draw out of the seed: and therefore a great desire they have to sow them if they may: for as they find it more gainful than corn, so they pay lesse tribute and custom in regard of that commoditie, and yet there is nothing yeeldeth more abundance of oile. . . .

Howbeit, in briefe, Radishes are best nourished and maintained in salt grounds: and therfore with such kind of brakish waters they use to be watered, which is the reason, that in Ægypt there are the sweetest and daintiest Radishes in the world, for that they are bedewed and sprinckled with Nitre.[3] And verily it is thought,

---

[1] Here Holland differs again from modern translators and may have been mistaken. The Latin is *druppis*, from δρύππα, meaning over-ripe and wrinkled olives.

[2] Pickled.

[3] Nitre is saltpetre, but the Latin *nitro* refers to the soda in the brackish waters of Egypt.

that they will lose all their bitternes whatsoever if they be corned or seasoned with salt, yea and become as if they were sodden and condite: for be they boiled once, they prove sweet and serve to be eaten instead of Navewes.[1]

And yet Physicians give counsell and prescribe, That they should be eaten raw in a morning with salt, when a man is fasting, for to gather into the stomack the sharp humors and excrements that charge the belly and entrails: and thus taken, they are of opinion, that it is a good preparative to vomit, and to open the passages well for to avoid those superfluities. They give out also, That the juice of Radish roots is singular good and necessarie for the midriffe, and the praecordiall parts about the heart; and namely, that nothing else but it, was able to cure a Phthisicke or ulcer of the lungs, wich had settled deep and taken to the heart: The experiment and proofe whereof was found and seen in Ægypt, by occasion that KK. there, caused dead bodies to be cut up, and anatomies to be made, for to search out the maladies whereof men died.

§ 98

Of Colewort and Colliflories

(Chap. 8)

MOREOVER, like as Coleworts may be cut at all times of the yeare for our use, so may they be sown and set al the yere long: and yet the most appropriat season is after the Æquinox in Autumn. Transplanted they be when they have once gotten five leaves. The tender crops called Cymae after the first cutting, they yeeld the spring next following: now are these Cymae nothing else but the yong delicat tops or daintier tendrils of the maine stem. And as pleasant and sweet as these crops were thought to other men, yet *Apicius* (that notable glutton) tooke a loathing of them; and by his example *Drusus Caesar* also careth not for them, but thought them a base and homely meat; for which nice and dainty tooth of his, he was well checked and shent by his father *Tiberius* the

[1] A kind of turnip.

Emperor: after this first crop or head is gone, there grow out of the same colewort other fine colliflories (if I may so say) or tendrils, in Summer, in the fall of the leafe; and after them, in winter; and then a second spring of the foresaid Cymae or tops against the spring following, as the yeare before; so as there is no hearb in that regard, so fruitfull, untill in the end her owne fertility is her death; for in this manner of bearing she spends her heart, her selfe and all. . . .

If there be want of moisture and skant of muck, the better taste Colewoorts have: if there be plenty and to spare of both, the more fruitfull and ranke they are. The onely muck and that which agreeth best with Coleworts or Cabbages, is Asses dung. I am content to stand the longer upon this Garden-wort, because it is in so great request in the kitchin, and among our riotous gluttons. Would you have speciall and principal Coleworts, both for sweet tast and also for great and faire cabbage? first and foremost, let the seed be sowne in a ground throughly digged more than once or twice, and wel manured; secondly, see you cut off the tender springs and yong stalkes that seem to put out far from the ground; or such as you perceive mounting too ranke and over-high from the earth: thirdly, be sure to raise other mould in manner of a bank up to them, so as there peep no more without the ground, than the very top: these kind of Coleworts be fitly called Tritiana, for the threefold hand and travell about them; but surely the gaine will pay double for all the cost and toile both. . . .

Over and besides, there is a kind of wild Woorts growing in the fields, called Lapsana, much named and renowned by occasion of the sonets and carols chanted in the solemnitie of *Julius Caesar* the Emperors triumph, and especially of the merry rimes and licentious broad jeasts tossed by his soldiers, who at every second verse cast in his teeth, that in Dyrrhachium they lived of nothing els but of those Woorts: noting indeed by way of cavill and reproch, his niggardise in rewarding them so sleightly for their good service: now was this Lapsana a kind of wild Colewort, which they did eat of instead of the fine and dainty tendrils and buds of the garden Coles.

§ 99

The Thistle or Artichoke

(Chap. 8)

A MAN would thinke that I had discoursed already of all such Garden herbes as were of any price and regard: but that there remaineth one thing yet behind, whereof the greatest gaine of all other is raised, and yet me thinks I cannot write thereof, but be abashed to range it amongst the good herbs of the garden; and that forsooth is our Thistle: howbeit this is certaine (to the shame be it spoken of our wanton and wasting gluttons) that the Thistles about Carthage the great, and Corduba especially, cost us ordinarily six thousand . . . Sesterces, to speak within compasse. See how vaine and prodigal we be, to bring into our kitchin and serve up at our table, the monstruosities of other nations, and cannot forbeare so much as these Thistles, which the very asses and other fourfooted beasts, have wit enough to avoid and refuse for pricking their lips and muzzles.

Well, since they be grown into so great request, I must not over-passe the gardinage to them belonging, and namely, how they be ordered two maner of waies; to wit, replanted of yong sets or roots in Autumn, and sowed of seed before the nones of March. As for the plants beforesaid, they ought to be slipped from it,[1] and set before the Ides or mids of November in any hand: or els if the ground be cold, we must stay until February, and then be doing with them about the rising of the Western wind Favonius. Manured ywis it ought to be and dunged, (I would not els) so faire and goodly an herbe it is; and so forsooth (and it please you) they prosper the better and come on trimly.[2] They are condite also and preserved in vineger (or else all were mard) in delicate . . . honey, seasoned also and bespiced (I may say to you) with the costly root of the plant Laser-woort, yea and with Cumin; because wee would not be a day without Thistles, but have them as an ordinary dish all the yeare long.

[1] Slipped from the parent plant.
[2] This is meant of Artichokes (P. H.).

§ 100

Of the simples which are set and sowed in gardens

(Chap. 12)

THUS much may serve concerning garden herbs, such I mean onely as be used in the kitchen about meats. It remaineth now to speake of the chiefe work of Nature contained in them: for all this while we have discoursed of their increase, and the gain that may come thereof: and indeed treated we have summarily of some plants and in generall termes. But forasmuch as the true vertues and properties of each herb cannot throughly and perfectly be known, but by their operations in physick; I must needs conclude, that therein lieth a mighty piece of work, to find out that secret and divine power, lying hidden and inclosed within: and such a piece of worke, as I wot not whether there can be found any greater.

For mine own part, good reason I had, not to set down and anex these medicinable vertues to every herb; which were to mingle Agriculture with Physick, and Physicke with Cookerie, and so to make a mish-mash and confusion of all things. For this I wist ful well, that some men were desirous only to know what effects they had in curing maladies, as a study pertinent to their profession; who no doubt should have lost a great deale of time before they had come to that which they looked for in running thorough the discourses of both the other, in case wee had handled altogether. But now, seeing every thing is digested and ranged in their several ranks, as well pertaining to the fields, as the kitchen, and the Apothecaries shop; an easie matter it will be for them that are willing and so disposed, to sort out each thing, and fit himselfe to his owne purpose, yea, and joine[1] them all at his pleasure.

[1] Combine.

The
TWENTIETH BOOKE
sheweth of garden herbs

§ 101

Of garden Cucumbers or Melons

(Chap. 2)

As for the fruit called Pompions or Melons, being eaten as meat, they cool the body mightily and make it soluble. The fleshy substance of them applied to the eies, assuageth their pain and restraineth their waterish and rheumatick flux. Their root healeth the wens or ulcers gathered in manner of hony-combs: which swellings some call Cerio. Being dried, it staieth vomits, so it be brought into pouder and given to the weight of foure Oboli[1] in honyed water: but the Patient when he hath drunk it, must walke presently upon it half a mile. The same pouder is detersive and scouring, and therefore put into soap and washing balls.

As for the rind or barke thereof, it procureth vomit indeed, but it cleanseth the skin as wel as the other. The same doe the leaves of any domesticall or garden Cucumbers or Melons, if they be made into a liniment. The said leaves also stamped with honey and brought to the form of a cataplasme, cure the bloudy-fals or night-blains, but tempered with wine, they heale the bitings of dogs, as also, of the Millepeed, which the Greeks call Seps, a long worm with hairy feet, doing much harme to cattaile especially; for look where it biteth, the place presently swelleth and putri-fieth. The very Cucumber it selfe is of a comfortable odor, and recovereth the faintings of the heart, and those that swoune. Finally, if you would make a delicate sallad of Cucumbers, boile them first, then pill from them their rind, serve them up with

[1] Two scruples (P. H.), 40 grains or 0·24 gram.

oile, vinegre, and honey: certain it is, they are by this meanes far sweeter and pleasanter than otherwise.[1]

§ 102

Of Onions

(Chap. 5)

ALSO greene Onions applied with vinegre to the place bitten with a mad dog, or els drie, and laid to with Honey and Wine, so that the plaster or cataplasm be not removed, in three daies cureth the hurt without danger. In this maner also they wil heal galled places. Being rosted under the ashes, many use to apply them with Barly floure or meale, as a pultesse or cataplasme to the eies that be watery or rheumatick, as also to the ulcers of the privy parts. The inunction of the eies, with the juice thereof is thought to clense their cicatrises or cloudiness of the eies called the pin and web: as also to cure the pearle there breeding: moreover, the bloudshotting or red streaks, in the white, and the white spots appearing in the blacke circle about the apple.

Moreover, it cureth bitings and stings of serpents, yea, and heales al ulcers, being emplastred with honey. Also the exulcerations and impostumes within the ears, are by it and womens milke cured. And for to amend the ringing and unkind sound and noise therin, and to recover those that be hard of hearing, many have used to droppe the juice of Onions together with Goose grease or els hony. Furthermore, they give it to be drunke with water, to those that suddenly become speechlesse and dumb. A collution also made with Onions, helps the tooth-ach. And being laid upon wounds, made either with prick or bite of any venomous beast, and especially of Scorpions, it is thought to be a soveraign salve. Many are wont (to very good effect) for to bruse Onions, and therewith to rub those parts that be troubled with a skurfe and running

[1] This passage, and § 102, have been included as fairly readable examples of the long pharmacological sections of the *Historia Naturalis* which are of very little general interest. Pliny was proud of his collection of the medical properties of plants and animals, but the modern medical reader can make little of it and must wade through many pages of doubtful information for every nugget he finds.

mange, as also to recover haire where it is shed and gon. Being boiled, they are given for to be eaten, unto those who are diseased with the blodie Flux or pain of the rains and loins. Their outward pillings burnt into ashes and mingled with vinegre, cure the bitings and stings of serpents, if the place be bathed or anointed therwith, yea, and the very Onion it selfe being applied with vinegre, cures the sting of that shrewd worme Milliped.

As for all other vertues and properties of Onions, the Physicians are wonderful contrary one to another in their writings: for our moderne and late writers do hold and so have delivered in their books, That onions are hurtful to the parts about the heart, and other vitall members: as also, that they hinder digestion, breeding wind and ventosities, and causing drought and thirstinesse. *Asclepiades* and his sect or followers, contrariwise affirme, That onions are so wholsome, that they will make them well colored who use to feed upon them: and more than so, they say that if one in health every day eat of them fasting, he shall be sure to continue healthful, strong and lusty: that they be good for the stomack, in this regard, that they cause rifting and breaking of wind upward, which is a good exercise of the stomacke: and withall that they keepe the bodie loose and laxative, yea, and open the Haemorrhoid veines if they be put up in maner of suppositories. Also, that the juice of onions and Fennell together, be marvellous good to be taken in the beginning of a dropsie. *Item*, That their juice being incorporat with Rue and Hony, is soveraigne for the Squinance. As also that they will keep waking those who are fallen into a Lethargie. To conclude, *Varro* saith, that if onions be braied with salt and vinegre, and then dried, no woorms or vermine will come neere that composition.

§ 103

Of the garden Cumin

(Chap. 14)

As touching wild Cumin, it is an herb exceeding small, putting forth foure or five leaves, and not above, and those indented like a saw: but the garden Cumin is of singular use in physicke, but principally for the pain in the stomack. It dispatcheth the grosse vapors arising from flegme; it dissolveth also ventosities, if it be either bruised and eaten with bread, or drunk with water and wine; in which sort it asswageth the wringing torments and other pains of the guts: howbeit it maketh folke look pale, as many as drink of it.

Certes by that devise, namely by ordinary drinking of Cumin (as it is reported) the schollers and followers of *Porcius Latro* (that famous and great Rhetorician) procured themselves pale faces, because they would look like their master, who indeed came to that colour by continuall study and plying his booke. Thus likewise not long since, *Julius Vindex*, being desirous to be affranchised by *Nero*, pretending by his pale visage and poore look, that he had not many daies to live, made faire semblance unto *Nero* by his will and testament, that he should shortly be his heire (which cheat the said *Nero* gaped after,) and so by that means *Vindex* entred so far within him, as hee obtained whatsoever he would at his hands.

The
TWENTY FIRST BOOKE
treateth of flours and garlands

§ 104

The first invention of the Coronet or Guirland

(Chap. 2)

THE maner of which plaiting and broiding of herbes and floures, the antient Greekes took no pleasure in: for at the beginning they used to crowne with branches only of trees, those brave men who had woon the prise in their sacred games and solemne Tournies or exercises of activitie. But afterwards they began to beautifie and enrich their chaplets of triumph with sundry floures entermingled together. And, to say a truth, the Sicyonians passed in this feat of sorting together one with another, floures of sweet savor and pleasant color, in making of posies and garlands. Howbeit the example of *Pausias* the cunning painter, and *Glycera* the artificiall maker of such Chaplets, set them first a worke.

This Painter was wonderfully enamoured upon the said *Glycera*, and courted her by all the meanes hee could devise: among the rest, he would seem to counterfeit and represent lively with his pensil in colours, what floures soever she wrought and set with her fingers into garlands; and shee againe strived avie to change and alter her handiwork every day, for to drive him to a non-plus at the length, or at leastwise to put him to his shifts: insomuch, as it was a very pleasant and worthie sight, to behold on one side the works of Nature in the womans hand, and on the other side the artificiall cunning of the foresaid painter. And verily there are at this day to be seene divers painted tables of his workmanship: and namely one picture above the rest, entituled, Stephane-plocos,[1] wherein hee painted his sweet-heart *Glycera* twisting and braiding Coronets and Chaplets, as her manner was.

[1] A Garland-maker (P. H.).

§ 105

A notable act of Queene Cleopatra

(Chap. 3)

I CANNOT chuse but remember the devise of Queene *Cleopatra*, full of fine wit, and as wicked and mischievous withall: For at what time as *Antonie* prepared the expidition and journey of Actium against *Augustus*, and stood in some doubt of jealousie of the said Queen; for al the fair shew that she made of gratifying him and doing him all pleasure, he was at his taster,[1] and would neither eat nor drink at her table without assay made. *Cleopatra* seeing how timorous he was, and minding yet to make good sport and game at his needlesse feare and foolish curiositie, caused a Chaplet to be made for *M. Antonius*, having before dipped all the tips and edges of the flowres that went to it in a strong and rank poison, and being thus prepared, set it upon the head of the said *Antonie*. Now, when they had sitten at meat a good while, and drunk themselves merrie, the Queen began to make a motion and challenge to *Antonie*, for to diink each of them their chaplets; and withall began unto him in a cup of wine seasoned and spiced (as it were) with those floures which she ware her owne self. Oh the shrewd and unhappy wit of a woman when she is so disposed! who would ever have misdoubted any danger of hidden mischiefe herein?

Well, *M. Antonie* yeelded to pledge her: off goeth his owne Guirland, and with the floures minced small, dresseth his own cup. Now when he was about to set it to his head, *Cleopatra* presently put her hand betweene, and staied him from drinking, and withall uttered these words, My deare heart and best beloved *Antonie*, now see what she is whome so much thou dost dread and stand in feare of, that for thy security there must wait at thy cup and trencher extraordinarie tasters; a straunge and new fashion ywis, and a curiosity more nice than needfull: lo, how I am not to seek of means and opportunities to compasse thy death, if I could find in my heart to live without thee. Which said, she called for a prisoner immediately out of the gaole, whom she caused to drink off the

[1] Made use of his official taster.

wine which *Antonie* had prepared for himselfe. No sooner was the goblet from his lips againe, but the poor wretch died presently in the place.

§ 106

Of Thyme

(Chap. 10)

IN like manner, two kinds there be of Thyme, to wit, the white and the blacke: this hearb doth flourish about the Summer Solstice, at what time as Bees also begin to gather honey from it: and according to the flouring of it more or lesse, a man may guesse ful wel what season there wil be for hony: for honey-masters and such as keep Bees, hope to have a good yere of honey when they see the Thyme to bloume abundantly. Thyme canot well away with rain, and therfore it taketh harme by shoures and sheddeth the floure. Thyme seed lyeth so close, that unneth or hardly it can bee found; wheras the seed of Origan,[1] notwithstanding it be exceeding smal, is evident enough and may soone be seene. But what matter maketh it, that Nature hath so hidden the seed, considering it is wel known, that it lyeth in the very floure, which if it be sown, commeth up as well as any other seed. See the industrie of men, and how there is nothing but they have made trial of and put in practise!

The honey of Athens carieth the name for the best honey in the world, by reason of the Thyme growing thereabout. Men therfore have brought over into other countries, Thyme out of Attica, although hardly and with much ado (being sown thus in the floure as I have said) it commeth up. But there is another reason in Nature, why it should thrive so badly in Italy, or elsewhere, considering that the Atticke Thyme wil not continue and live, but within the aire and breath of the sea. Certes this was an opinion received generally of our auncient fore-fathers, That no Thyme would doe well and prosper, but neere unto the Sea; which should be the cause, that in Arcadia there is none of it to be found.

[1] Wild marjoram.

And in those daies also, men were verily persuaded, that the Olive would not grow but in the compasse of three hundred stadia from the Sea side: howbeit, in this our age verily we are advertised and know for certain, That in Languedoc and the province of Narbon, the very stonie places are all overgrowne and covered with Thyme, upon which there are fed thousands of sheepe and other cattaile: in such sort, as this kind of herbage and pasturage, yeeldeth a great revenue to the inhabitants and paisants of that countrey, by joisting[1] and laying in of the said beasts brought thither out of far remote parts for to feed upon Thyme.

§ 107

Of venomous and poisonfull honey

(Chap. 13)

AT Heraclea in Pontus, in some yeares, all the hony that the Bees do make, is found to be venomous and no better than poison; and yet the same bees in other yeres gather good and wholsome hony. Howbeit, those authors who have delivered thus much in writing, have not set downe what floures they be that yeeld this hurtfull hony: and therefore I thinke it not amisse to write what I have found and knowne as touching this point.

There is an herbe called Ægolethron in Greek, which killeth horses verily, but Goats most of all, feeding therupon; and therfore it took that name: the floures of this herb, if it chance to be a wet and rainy Spring, do conceive and ingender within them a certain deadly venome which doth corrupt and rot them. This may be a probable reason, that the foresaid mischiefe and bane is not alwaies felt alike. This poisonsome honey may be knowne by these signs: first it will never thicken but continue liquid stil; secondly, the colour is more deep and reddish than ordinary; thirdly, it carrieth a strange sent or smell with it, and will cause one to sneese presently; last of all, it is more ponderous and heavy than the good and harmlesse hony. The symptomes or accidents that insue upon the eating of this honey, are these, They that

---

[1] To joist or gist was to put animals out to pasture for a rental.

have tasted thereof, cast themselves upon the ground and there fall a tumbling: they seek by all means they can to be cooled; and no marvell, for they run all to sweat, that one drop overtakes the other.

Howbeit, there be many remedies for this poison, which I will shew in place convenient. Mean while, because a man would not be without some good thing ready at hand, since the world is so ful of villany and set upon such secret mischiefe, I must needs put down one good receit, and that is this: take honied wine that is old, mingle and incorporat it with the best hony you can meet withal, and Rue together: use this confection at your need. *Item*, Eat much of salt-fish, although it come up again, and that your stomack do cast it. Moreover, this hony is so pernicious, that the very dogs if they chance to lick up any excrements that passe from the partie so infected (either by reaching, spitting, vomit, or seege) they are sure to be sped therewith, and to feele the like torments. Howbeit, the honied wine that is made therewith, if it may have age enough and be stale, is knowne for a certainty to do no creature harm. And there is not a better medicine in the world, either to fetch out spots in womens faces, and make their skin faire and cleare (if it be applied with Costus;) or to take out the black and blew marks remaining after stripes in [an] eye or elswhere, so it be tempered with Aloe.

Another kind of honey there is in the same region of Pontus, and namely among the Sanni (a people there inhabiting) which because it driveth folke into a fit of rage and madnesse, they call in Greeke Maenomenon. Some attribute the occasion hereof to the floure of the Oleander, whereof the woods and forrests there be full. This nation selleth no hony at all, because it is so venomous and deadly: notwithstanding they do pay for tribute a huge masse of wax unto the Romans every yeare. Moreover in the kingdom of Persis, and in Getulia, which lieth within Mauritania Caesariensis, a country confining and bordering upon the Massaesuli, there be venomous hony-combs; yea, you shall have in one hive some hony combs full of poisoned hony, whereas others be sound and good: a dangerous thing no doubt, and than which, there could be no greater deceit to poison a number of people; but that they may be known from the rest by their leaden and wan hew that they have.

What should we think was Natures meaning and intent by these secret sleights and hidden mischiefes, That either the same Bees should not every yeare gather venomous hony; or not lay the same up in all their combs [in]differently? Was it not enough that she had bestowed upon us a thing, wherein poyson might be soonest given and least perceived? Was she not content thus to indanger our lives, but she must proceed farther, even to incorporat poison her selfe in hony, as it commeth from the Bee, for to empoison so many living creatures? Certes, I am of this mind and beliefe verily, That shee had no other purpose herein than to make men more warie what they eat, and lesse greedy of sweet meats to content and please the tooth. For the very honey indeed she had not generally infected with this hurtful quality, like as she had armed all Bees with sharp pricks and stings, yea, and the same of a venomous nature; and therfore against these creatures verily she hath not deferred and put off to furnish us with a present remedy: for the juice of Mallowes or of Yvie leaves serveth to annoint the stinged place, and keep it from rankling; yea, and it is an excellent thing for them that be stung, to take the very Bees in drink; for it is an approved cure.

But this I marvell much at, That the Bees themselves, which feed of these venomous herbs, that cary the poison in their mouths, and are the makers of this mischievous honey, do escape and die not thereof? Whereof I can give no reason at all, unlesse dame Nature, that lady and mistresse of the world, hath given unto these poore Bees a certain Antipathy and vertue contrary unto poison: like as among us men to the *Marsi* and *Psylli*, shee hath imprinted (as it were) a repugnancy in their bodies, to resist the venome of all Serpents whatsoever.

§ 108

Of Nettles

(Chap. 15)

MANY kinds there be of these Nettles; namely, the wild Nettle, which some would have to be the female, and this is more milde than the rest. In this wilde kinde is to be reckoned also, that which they cal Canina, and is of the twain more aegre, for the very stalke will sting, and the leaves be purfled as it were and jagged. But that Nettle which carrieth a stinking savor with it, is called Herculanea. All the sort of them are full of seed, and the same blacke.

A strange quality in these Nettles, that the very hairy downe of them (having no evident prickes sticking out) should be so shrewd as it is, that if one touch it never so little, presently there followeth a smarting kind of itch, and anon the skin riseth up in pimples and blisters, as if it had been skalt or burnt: but well knowne is the remedie of this smart, namely, to annoint the place with oyle. Howbeit this biting property that it hath, commeth not to it at the beginning when it is new come up, but it is the heat of the Sun that fortifieth this mordacitie. And verily in the Spring when the Nettle is young and peepeth first out of the ground, they use to eat the crops therof for a pleasant kind of meat, and many be persuaded besides that it is medicinable, and therefore precisely and religiously feed thereupon, as a preservative to put by all diseases for that present yeare. Also the root of the wild Nettle, if it be sodden with any flesh, maketh it to eat more tender.

§ 109

The medicinable vertues of Cypirus

(Chap. 18)

THIS Cyperus, many there be that cannot distinguish from Cypirus, by reason of the great affinity of their two names: but I mean to put a difference betweene them both; for Cypirus is the Petie-glader or Sword-grasse[1] (as I have before shewed) with a bulbous or onion root: the best of which kind, groweth in the Island of Crete: next to it in goodnesse, is that of the Isle Naxos: and in a third degree, is placed that of Phoenice: and indeed that of Crete or Candy, in whitenesse and odor commeth

---

[1] A gladiolus.

neere to Nard.[1] The Naxian Cypirus hath a quicker sent: the Phoenician Cypirus smelleth but a little: as for that in Egypt, it hath no savor at all, for there also groweth Cypirus.

But now to come unto the properties thereof, it hath vertue to discusse and resolve hard swellings in the body. For now my purpose is to speake of their medicinable vertues, forasmuch as there is great use in Physicke, as well of such aromaticall simples, as odoriferous floures. As touching Cypirus therefore, I professe verily that I will follow *Apollodorus*, who forbiddeth expressely to take Cypirus inwardly in any drink: and yet he protesteth, that it is most effectuall for them that be troubled with the stone, and full of gravel; but, by way of fomentation onely. He affirmeth moreover, that without all doubt it causes women to travell before their time, and to slip their untimely fruit.

But one miraculous effect therof he reports, namely, that the Barbarians use to receive the fume of this herb into their mouth, and thereby wast and consume their swelled Spleens: also, they never go forth of dores, before they have drunk a pipe thereof in that maner: for persuaded they are verily (saith he) that by this means they are more youthful, lively, and strong. He saith moreover, that if it be applied as a liniment with oile, it healeth all merry-gals and raw places where the flesh is rubbed off or chafed: it helpeth the rank rammish smel under the arm-holes; and without faile cureth any chilling, numnesse, and through cold. Thus much of Cypirus.

---

[1] Cypirus is identified as the common gladiolus, but the bulb of this has no scent. The best suggestion about this passage is that Pliny *did* get mixed up with the names and is here speaking of a Cyperus or scented rush. It is interesting that Apollodorus records smoking the herb as a cure for enlarged, and presumably malarial, spleens.

In the
TWENTY SECOND BOOK
are contained discourses as touching the
estimation of Hearbes

§ 110

Of Clothes died with certaine Herbs

(Chap. 2)

A N D now of late dayes, we know there hath been taken up a
strange and wonderfull maner of dying and colouring clothes.
For, (to say nothing of the grain[1] brought out of Galatia, Africke
and Portugal, whereof is made the royall Skarlet, reserved for
princes only and great captains to weare in their rich mantles of
estate and coats of armes:) behold, the French inhabiting beyond
the Alps, have invented the means to counterfeit the Purple of
Tyrus, the Skarlet also and Violet in graine, yea, and to set all
other colours that can bee devised, with the juice only of certain
hearbs.

These men are wiser (beleeve mee) than their neighbours of
other nations before them: they hazard not themselves to sound
and search into the bottome of the deepe sea for Burrets, Purples,
and such shell-fishes, These adventure not their lives in strange
coasts and blind baies, where never ship hath rid at anker, offering
their bodies as a prey to feed the monstrous Whales of the sea,
while they seeke to beguile them of their food in fishing for the said
Burrets: and all to feed that, wherby as well unchast dames of
light behaviour might set out themselves and seeme more proper,
to allure and content adulterous ruffians: as also those gallants
again, squaring and ruffling thus in their colours, might court
faire ladies and wedded wives; yea, and with more ease entrap and

[1] Grain was the dried insect from which the red dye, kermes, was made until
the cochineal insect from the New World replaced it.

encompasse them to yeeld to their pleasure: but these men stand safe upon drie land, and gather those hearbs for to die such colors, as an honest minded person hath no cause to blame, nor the world reason to crie out upon. Nay our brave minions and riotous wantons, it might beseeme also to be furnished therewith; if not altogether so glorious to the eye, yet certainly with lesse offence and harm.

But no part it is of my desseigne and intent to discourse upon these matters at this present: neither will I stand on the thrift and good husbandry that may be seen in such a thing as this, least I might seeme to colour any vanitie with a shew of commodity and frugalitie: and to limit excesse and superfluitie within the tearms of profit and cheapnesse, which indeed will not be gaged and brought within any compasse. Besides, I shall have occasion here-after in some other place to make mention both of dying stones, and also of painting walls with herbs. As for the art and mysterie of Diers, if ever it had been counted any of the liberal Sciences, beseeming a gentleman either to professe or practise, I assure you I would not have overpassed it in silence. . . . In which regard, I canot chuse but shew and declare what account we ought to make of these dumbe tinctures in that behalfe; I meane such hearbs and simples, whereof there is but base reckoning or none at all made: for those great princes which were the first founders and establishers of the Roman Empire, did mighty things therewith, and emploied these herbs in the highest matters of state.

For in the affaires of greatest importance, namely, either in publick sacrifice for the averting of some heavy judgement of the gods threatened: or in expiation of any grievous sinne and offence committed (whether they performed divine service to their gods, or dispatched honourable embassages to other States) they used their Sagmina and Verbenae,[1] by which two words verily was meant one and the same thing, even some plain and common grasse plucked up with ceremoniall devotion, turfe and all, from their castle hil or citadel of Rome. And this at all times was observed religiously, that they never sent their heraulds to the enemies of the people of Rome for to clarigat, that is to say, to summone them with a lowd voice for to make restitution of that which they deteined of theirs; without a turfe and tuft of the said grasse: and

[1] See § 118.

evermore there accompanied these heraulds in their train, one
speciall officer who had the charge to carie and tender that hearbe,
who thereupon was called Verbenarius.

§ III

Of the maner of the world in these our daies

(Chap. 6)

BUT what man is there well given and honestly minded, who can
containe and hold his peace, having so just cause to reprove and
rebuke the maner of the world in these our daies? First and formost, our life was never so costly as now it is, in regard of the
dainties, delights, and superfluities, which must be maintained,
if we will live to the fashion of the time: and for to injoy these
pleasures onely, we hold our lives more sweet and precious.

Never were men more desirous of long life, and never lesse
carefull to entertaine the means of long life. The government of our
health we commit to the charge of others, and strangers we credit
with our owne bodies, and yet slacke enough and negligent are
they, to ordain according to our trust and confidence, that which
indeed should do us good.[1] Thus the Physitians are provided well
for; they thrive alone and go away with the gains by this means.
Oh good God, to see the folly and vanity of man! Nature having
put so many good things into our own hands as she hath, and
willing that we should injoy them for our health and pleasure:
yet we (to our great shame and rebuke be it spoken) are so unhappy, as to commit our selves to other mens tuition, and live
under their warrantize and assurance.

Full well I know, that I for my part also, shall have but small
thanks of many a one for all my paines taken in writing this history
of the world and Natures works: nay, I am assured that I make my
selfe a laughing stocke, and am condemned of them for spending
and losing my time in such a frivolous piece of worke as this is.
Howbeit, this is yet my comfort and no small contentment I take
herein, that my labors and travels (excessive and infinit though

---

[1] Pliny returns to this theme at length in § 124, p. 232.

they be) cannot be despised, but the contempt will redound likewise to dame Nature her selfe. And yet she againe, as a kind and tender nurce over mankind, hath not failed (as I wil declare hereafter) for our good, to indue the very weeds which we tread under foot with medicinable vertues, yea, and hath bestowed upon those which otherwise we hate and dare not approch, but with careful heed (for the shrewd pricks and thorns which they carry about them) singular properties to cure diseases.

§ 112

Mushromes or Tad-stoles called Fungi

(Chap. 23)

As touching those excrescenses in manner of Mushromes, which be named Fungi, they are by nature more dull and slow. And albeit there bee many kinds of them, yet they all take their beginning of nothing els but the slimy humor of trees. The safest and least daungerous be those, which have a red callositie or outward skin, and the same not of so weak a red, as that of the Mushromes called Boleti. Next to them in goodnesse are the white, and such as having a white foot also, bear a head much resembling the Flamins[1] turbant or mitre, with a tuffet or crest in the crown. As for the third sort that be called Suilli, as one would say, Swine-Mushromes or Puffs, they are of al others most perilous, and have the best warrant to poison folk. It is not long since that in one place there died thereof, all that were of one household; and in another, as many as met at a feast and did eat thereof at the same bourd. Thus *Anneus Serenus*, captaine of the Emperour *Nero* his guard, came by his death, with divers colonels and centurions, at one dinner.

And I wonder much, what pleasure men should take thus to venture upon so doubtfull and daungerous a meat. Some have put a difference of these mushroms, according to the severall Trees from which they seeme to spring, and have made choise of those that come from the Fig-tree, the Birch, and such as beare gum.

[1] Priest's.

For mine own part, as I have said before, I hold those good that the Beech, Oke, and Cypresse trees doe yeeld. But what assurance can a man have hereof, from their mouths who sit in the market to sell them? for all the sort of those Puffes and Toadstooles look with a leaden hew and wan color, Howbeit, the nearer that a Mushrome or Toadstoole commeth to the color of a fig hanging upon the tree, the lesse presumption there is that it is venomous. . . .

And now for that our fine mouthed and dainty wantons who set such store by their tooth, take so great delight to dresse this only dish with their own hands, that they may feed thereon in conceit and cogitation all the while they bee handling and preparing the same, furnished in this their businesse with their fine knives and rasors of amber, and other vessels of silver plate about them: I for my part also am content to frame and accomodate my selfe to their humerous fansie, and will shew unto them in generall, certaine observations and rules how to order and use them, that they may be eaten with security. Marke then those mushroms, which in the seething prove hard and tough, such be all of them hurtfull. Lesse daungerous they be, if some salt-nitre be put to them whiles they be a boiling over the fire; provided alwaies, that they be fully sodden before they be taken off. Also, a man may be more bold to eat those which be sodden together with flesh meat, or with the tailes or steles of peares. The eating also of peares immediatly after one hath fed upon Mushroms, doth kil or dull all the malice that they may have. Also vinegre is of a contrary nature unto them, and doth extinguish or mortifie their venomous qualitie.[1] To conclude, all these mushromes do come up and are engendred in rain.

[1] None of this advice would have protected mycophagous Romans from poisonous species.

The
THREE AND TWENTIETH BOOKE
showeth the medicinable vertues of wine

§ 113

Of the sophistication of wines

(Chap. 1)

IN summe, every one hath judged of the goodnesse of wine,
according to his owne conceit and fantasie: a most unequall course
of proceeding, without all reason and congruitie, to pronounce
definitively unto al others that for best, that pleased and contented
his owne tast most. And yet set the case and say, they were all
agreed and of one opinion as touching the most excellent wines;
How is it possible, that the whole world should enjoy the benefit
thereof, since that great lords and princes themselves have much
adoe to meet with pure and perfect wines, without one sophistication or other? In good faith, the world is grown to this abuse, that
wines be bought and sold now at an higher or lower price, acord-
ing to the name and bruit that goeth onely of the cellars from
whence they come: whereas in truth, the wines were marred and
corrupted at the first in the very presse or vatt, presently after the
vintage and grape-gathering.

And therefore it is, that now adaies (a wonderfull thing to be
spoken) the smallest and basest wines are of all others least
sophisticate and most harmlesse. Well, how soever it be, and
admit the noblest kinds of wine are most subject to those bruings
and sophistication . . . yet those wines beforenamed, to wit, the
Falern, Albane, and Surrentine, do still import and carrie away
the victory and prise from all the rest, by the generall voice and
constant sentence of al writers.

§ 114

Of drinking wine

(Chap. 1)

FIRST and foremost, wine maintaineth and fortifieth the strength of man, engendreth good bloud, and causeth a fresh and lively colour. And herein verily consisteth the principall difference betweene our temperat climat within the heart (as it were) and middle part of the world, from those intemperat Zones on either hand. And looke how much the distemperature of the two Poles, worketh in the inhabitants of those parts, and hardneth them to endure and support all kind of travell: so much doth this sweet and pleasant liquor of the grape enable us to abide and suffer the like labour. And because we are entred into this theame, note thus much moreover, That the drinking of milke nourisheth the bones: of beere and ale, and such like, made with corne, feedeth the sinewes and nervous parts: but of water, maintaineth the flesh and brawnie muscles onely. Which is the cause, that such nations as drinke either milke, ale, beere, etc. or sheere water, are nothing so ruddie of colour, nor so strong and firme to undergoe painefull travell, as those, whose ordinarie and familiar drink is wine.

And in truth, as the moderat use of wine comforteth the sinews and helpeth the eyesight; so the over-liberal taking thereof offendeth the one, and enfeebleth the other. Wine recreateth and refresheth the stomack: wine stirreth up the appetite to meat: wine allaieth sorrow, care, and heavinesse: wine provoketh urin, and chaseth away all chilling cold out of the body. Finally, wine induceth sleep and quiet repose. . . .

Each wine agreeth best with the stomack, and doth least harme, when it hath no other liquor nor tast, but the owne; and every wine is most pleasant and delightsome when it is taken in due time, that is to say, neither old nor new, but of middle age, which is the very floure. Such persons as would feed, and desire to be corpulent, or to keep their bodies soluble, and have the riddance of their bellie at commaund, shall do well to drinke often at their repast: Contrariwise, they who feed overmuch, and desire to be gant and slender, and withall, to be costive, ought to forbear drinking at meales, so long as they eat, but after meat they may drink moderatly. To drinke wine upon an emptie stomacke fasting, is a new found devise lately come up, and it is most unwholesome for the body, and namely for those who are to goe into the field for to fight a battell: for it hindreth the forecast of the mind, and dulleth the vigor and quicknesse of the spirit:[1] fitter indeed to bring and lull men asleep in the bed of securitie: certes, it was a practise long agoe among such as desired rest and peace, and who loved to sleepe in a whole skin, for to drinke wine fasting: for so we read in *Homer*, how *Helena* that faire ladie, presented a cup of wine before meat.

And hereupon came the proverbe, That wine doth overshadow and darken the light of wisdome and understanding: verily we that are men have this property above all other living creatures, and we may thanke wine for it, That we drinke many times when wee be not dry nor a thirst. And therfore passing good it is to drink fair water otherwhiles between. In like manner such as use ordinarily to be drunk, and are lightly never sober, shall not do amisse to take a good draught of cold water presently upon their liberall pouring in of wine, for it will forthwith dispatch and discusse those fumes which cause drunkennes.

---

[1] The advice on drinking, unlike that on eating fungi, might have been written today; it is still common to advise those who desire to be slender against drinking with meals.

In the
FIVE AND TWENTIETH BOOKE
are contained the natures of hearbes that
come up of themselves[1]

§ 115

The cabinet of Mithridates

(Chap. 2)

FOR *Mithridates* (the most mightie and puissant king in that age, whose fortune notwithstanding was to be vanquished and subdued by *Pompey*) was well knowne unto the world not only by the fame that went of him, but also by good proofe and evident arguments, to have bin of all other before his time, a prince most addicted to the publick benefit of all mankind: for the only man he was who devised to drinke poison every day (having taken his preservatives before) to the end that by the ordinary use and continuall custome thereof, it might be familiar unto his nature, and harmlesse. The first he was also who devised sundry kinds of antidotes or counterpoisons, whereof one retaineth his name to this day: he it was also and none but he, as men think, who first mingled in the said antidotes and preservatives, the bloud of Ducks bred in his own realme of Pontus, for that they fed and lived there, of poisons and venomous hearbs.

Unto him, that famous and renowned professor in Physicke *Asclepiades*, dedicated his books now extant: for this Physitian being solicited to repaire unto him from Rome, sent the rules of Physick digested into order, and set downe in writing, instead of comming himselfe. And *Mithridates* it was (as it is for certaine knowne) who alone of all men that ever were, could speake two and twentie languages perfectly; so as for the space of six and fiftie yeares (for so long he reigned) of all those Nations which were under his dominion, there never came one man to his court, but

---

[1] Book 24 contains recipes for the use of tree products in pharmacy and no passages from it have been selected.

he communed and parled with him in his own tongue without any truchman or interpreter for the matter. This noble Prince (amongst many other singular gifts that he had, testifying his magnanimitie and incomparable wit) addicted himselfe particularly to the earnest studie of Physicke: and because he would be exquisite and singular therein, he had intelligencers from all parts of his dominions (and those took up no small part of the whole world) who upon their knowledge, exhibited unto him the particular natures and properties of every simple: by which means, he had a cabinet full of an infinit number of receits and secrets set down together with their operations and effects, which he kept in his said closet, and left behind him with other rich treasure of his.

But *Pompey* the Great, having under his hands the whole spoile of this mighty Prince, and meeting in that saccage with those notes abovesaid, gave commandement unto his vassall or infranchised servant, the abovenamed *Lenaeus* (an excellent linguist and most learned grammarian) to translate the same into the Latine tongue: for which act of *Pompey*, the whole world was no lesse beholden unto him, than the common-wealth of Rome for the foresaid victorie.

§ 116

Of the sweet Brier or Eglantine and Hydrophobie

(Chap. 3)

LO what the Physick in old time was! and how the same lay wholly couched in the Greek language, and not elswhere to be found. But what might be the reason, that there were no more simples knowne? Surely it proceeds from this, That for the most part they be rusticall peasants, and altogether unlettered, who have the experience and triall of herbs, as those who alone live and converse among them where they grow. Another thing there is, Men are carelesse and negligent, and love not to take any paines in seeking for them. Againe every place swarmeth so with Leeches and Physitians, and men are so ready to run unto them for to receive some compound medicine at their hands, that little or no regard there is made of herbs and good Simples. Furthermore, many of them which have bin found out and knowne, have no name at all: as for example, that herb which I spake of in my Treatise concerning the cure and remedies of corne growing upon the lands: and which we all know, if it be enterred or buried in the foure corners of the field, will skar away the foules of the aire, that they shal not settle upon the corne, nor once come into the ground.[1]

But the most dishonest and shamefull cause why so few simples in comparison be knowne, is the naughtie nature and peevish disposition of those persons who will not teach others their skill, as if themselves should lose for ever that which they imparted unto their neighbor. Over and besides, there is no certain meanes or way to direct us to the invention and knowledge of hearbes and their vertues: for if we looke unto these hearbs which are found already, we are for some of them beholden to meere chance and fortune: and for others (to say a truth) to the immediat revelation from God. For proofe hereof, mark but this one instance which I will relate to you.

For many a yeare untill now of late daies, the biting of a mad dog was counted incureable: and looke who were so bitten, they fell into a certain dread and feare of water: neither could they abide to drink, or to heare talk therof, and then were they thought to be in a desperat case: it fortuned of late, that a souldier, one of the gard about the Pretorium was bitten with a mad dog, and his mother saw a vision in her sleep, giving (as it were) direction unto her for to send the root unto her sonne for to drink, of an Eglantine or wild rose (called Cynorrhodon) which the day before she had espied growing in an hortyard, where she took pleasure to behold it. This occurrent fel out in Lacetania,[2] the nearest part unto us of Spain. Now, as God would, when the souldier before-said upon his hurt received by the dog, was ready to fall into that symptome of Hydrophobie, and began to feare water; there came a letter from his mother, advertising him to obey the wil of God and to do according to that which was revealed unto her by the vision.

Whereupon he dranke the root of the said sweet brier or Eglantine, and not only recovered himselfe beyond all mens

---

[1] See § 88.   [2] Or Lusitania (P. H.).

expectation: but also afterwards as many as in that case tooke the like receit, found the same remedy. Before this time, the writers in Physick knew of no medicinable vertue in the Eglantine, but only of the sponge or little ball, growing amid the pricky branches therof,[1] which being burnt and reduced into ashes, and incorporate with honey into a liniment, maketh haire to come againe where it was shed by any infirmity.

§ 117

What diseases put men to the greatest paine

(Chap. 3)

WHEREAS in this age wherein we now live, I doubt not but there bee some who will mock us for the pains taken in that behalfe, and think us very simple for writing thus as we do of Simples; so base and contemptible in the eies of our fine fooles and delicate persons, are even the best things that serve for the benefit and common utility of mankind: howbeit, for all that, good reason it is and meet that the authors and inventors of them, as many as can be found, should be named and praised with the best; yea, and that the operations and effects of such herbs should be digested and reduced into some method, according as they be appropriat to every kind of disease.

In the meditation whereof, I cannot chuse nor contain my selfe, but deplore and pity the poore estate and miserable case of man: who over and besides the manifold accidents and casualties which may befall unto him, is otherwise subject to many thousands of maladies, which we have much ado to devise names for, every houre of the day happening as they do and whereof no man can account himselfe free, but every one is for his part to feare them. Of these diseases so infinit as they be in number, to determine precisely and distinctly which be most grievous, might seem meere folly, considering that every one who is sicke for the present, imagineth his owne sicknes to be worst and fullest of anguish.

---

[1] The robin's pincushion. No record has been found of more recent trial of wild rose root in hydrophobia.

And yet our forefathers have given their judgement in this case, and by experience have found, That the most extreme pain and torment that a man can indure by any disease, is the Strangury or pissing dropmeale, occasioned by the stone or gravell in the bladder. The next is the griefe and anguish of the stomak: and the third, Head-ach: for setting these three maladies aside, lightly there are no pains that can kill a man or woman so soon.[1]

And here by the way, I cannot for mine owne part but marvell much at the Greeks, who have published in their writings venomous and pestilent herbs as well as those that be good and wholsome. And yet there is an appearance and shew of reason, why some poisons should be knowne: for otherwhiles it falleth out that men live in such extremity, as better it were to die, than so to lie in anguish and torment; insomuch, as death is the best port and harbor of refuge that they have. Certes, *Marcus Varro* reporteth of one *Servius Clodius* a gentleman or knight of Rome who for the extreame pain of the gout, was forced to annoint his legs and feet all over with a narcotick or cold poison, whereby hee so mortified the spirits of the muskles and sinews, that he became paralyticke in that part: and ever after unto his dying day, was rid as well of all sence, as of the paine of the gout.

But say, that in these cases it might be tollerable to set down in their books some poisons: what reason, nay what leave had those Greeks to shew the means how the brains and understanding of men should be intoxicat and troubled? what colour and pretence had they to set downe medicines and receits to cause women to slip the untimely fruit of their womb, and a thousand such like casts and devises that may be practised by herbs of their penning? for mine owne part, I am not for them that would send the conception out of the body unnaturally before the due time: they shall learne no such receits of me, neither will I teach any how to temper and spice an amatorious cup, to draw either man or woman into love, it is no part of my profession.[2]

[1] The meaning is that these three pains most surely drive men or women to suicide.

[2] In the course of his chapters on the medicinal uses of herbs, Pliny does in fact give many such recipes.

§ 118

Of Vervaine

(Chap. 9)

BUT of all other herbs, there is none more honored among the Romans than Hierobotane, called also otherwise in Greek Peristerion: which we in Latine name Verbenaca. This is that hearb, which (as I have declared heretofore[1]) our Embassadors use to cary with them when they go to denounce war, and to give defiance unto our enemies. With this herbe the feastivall table of *Jupiter* is wont to be swept and clensed with great solemnitie; our houses also be rubbed and hallowed, for to drive away ill spirits.

And hereof be two kinds. That which they take to be the female, is stored well with leaves; the male hath them growing but thin: yet both of them put forth many small and slender branches, commonly a cubit long and cornered. The leaves be lesser and narrower than those of the Oke, but deeper they be indented, and the partition wider: the floures be of a gray colour,[2] the root long and small. It groweth every where upon plains subject unto waters. Some writers make no distinction at all of male and female, but hold them all to be of one and the same kind, because they work the same effects. In France the Druidae use them both indifferently, in casting lots, telling fortunes, and foreshewing future events by way of prophesie.

But the wise men or sages called Magi, overpasse themselves mightily in this herb, and shew their foolery and vanity without all sence and reason: They would beare us in hand forsooth, that whosoever be rubbed all over the body therewith, shall obtaine whatsoever their heart desireth, be able to cure and drive away all manner of agues, reconcile them that be fallen out, make friendship between whom they list, and in one word, give remedy to

---

[1] See § 110.

[2] This word, *glaucus*, seems to give trouble to translators, and a grey flower is difficult to imagine. Although the meaning may be grey, it is commonly gleaming, bright or sparkling, and a verbena with bright flowers is more understandable. Grey was the accepted gloss for *glaucus*, but it sometimes meant almost white, as with hair, horses, and cotton cloth.

any disease whatsoever: they give moreover expresse order, that it be gathered about the rising of the great dog-star, but so, as neither Sun nor Moon be at that time above the earth to see it; with this especiall charge besides, that before they take up the herbe, they bestow upon the ground where it groweth, honey with the combes, in token of satisfaction and amends for the wrong and violence done in depriving her of so worthie an hearbe.

They rest not so, but when these ceremonious circumstances be performed, they injoine them also who are to dig it up, for to make a circle round about the place with some instrument of yron, and then to draw and pluck it up with the left hand in any wise: and so to fling it aloft over their heads up into the aire: which done, they appoint precisely that it be dried in the shade, leaves, stalkes, and roots, every one apart by themselves. To conclude, they adde moreover and say, that if the hall or dining chamber be sprinckled with the water wherein Vervaine lay steeped, all that sit at the table shall be very pleasant, and make merrie more jocundly. Well, to leave these toies and fooleries, the truth is this, stamp and beat it, give the juice or pouder therof in wine, it is a good defensative against the poison of serpents.

§ 119

Proper receits for *Alopecia* and *Dandruffe*

(Chap. 11)

SINCE wee are waded so far into the deep secrets of Physick, it will not be amisse to proceed forward and to set downe many good medicines for all the maladies incident either in generall to the whole body, or particularly to every speciall part and member thereof, beginning first at the head.

There is an unseemely accident happening otherwhiles to the head, and disgraceth it much, called Alopecia,[1] when as the haire unnaturally falleth off. The cure of this inconvenience, is to make a liniment with the roots of Nymphaea and Hemlocke stamped

---

[1] Because foxes are much subject unto it, who are called in Greeke *Alopekes* (P. H.).

together, and therwith to annoint the bald and naked places, for it will cause the haire to come up again and grow thick. Polytrichon and Callitrichos[1] . . . differ one from another; for that Polytrichon hath white benty filaments or threds, the leaves be also more in number and greater withall: besides, the very plant it selfe spreadeth and brancheth more than the other: this herb is singular to fasten the haire of the head at the root, and to make it bush and grow thick, being otherwise ready to shed. In like manner, there is an herb called in Latine Lingulaca,[2] which loveth to grow about springs or fountains, and is singular for the same imperfection of shedding haire, if the root together with the leafe burnt and beaten to pouder, be incorporate with the grease of a blacke sow (but in any wise she must be a yong guilt that never farrowed or had pigs) and so brought into a liniment, and the head rubbed and annointed therwith: with this charge besides, That after the annointing, the Patient sit bare headed in the sun; for that helps forward the cure verie much. And in the same case there is the like use of the Cyclamine or Sowbread root.

Touching the scurfe or brannie scales called Dandruffe, the root of Veratrum or Elleborc, sodden either in oile or water, maketh a most excellent medicine to rid it away, and to clense the head thereof.

---

[1] *Capillus veneris*, or Maidenhaire (P. H.).   [2] Adders tongue (P. H.).

In the
TWENTY SIXTH BOOKE
are contained the medicines for the
parts of mans bodie

§ 120

Asclepiades and the new practise in Physicke

(Chap. 3)

WHAT cunning means soever these new Physitians could devise
to overthrow the antient manner of working by simples, yet it
maintained still the remnants of the former credit, built surely
upon the undoubted grounds of long experience; and so it continued till the daies of *Pompey* the Great, at what time *Asclepiades*
a great Oratour and professor of Rhetoricke went in hand to
pervert and reject the same: for seeing that he gained not by the
said Art sufficiently, and was not like to arise by pleading causes
at the bar, to that wealth which he desired (as he was a man otherwise of a prompt wit and quick spirit) he resolved to give over the
law, and suddenly applied himselfe to a new course of Physick.

This man having no skill at all, and as little practice, considering
he neither was well studied in the Theoricke part of this science,
nor furnished with knowledge of remedies which required continuall inspection and use of simples, wrought so with his smooth
and flowing tongue, and by his daily premeditat orations gained
so much, that he withdrew mens mindes from the opinion they
had of former practise, and overthrew all. In which discourses of
his, reducing all Physick to the first and primitive causes, he made
it a meere conjecturall Art; bearing men in hand, that there were
but five principall remedies which served indifferently for all
diseases; to wit, in Diet, Abstinence in meat, Forbearing wine
otherwhiles, Rubbing of the body, Walking, and the Exercise of
gestations.[1] In sum, so far he prevailed with his eloquent speech,

---

[1] *i.* Riding on horsebacke, carrying in coach, litter, barge, etc. (P. H.).

that every man was willing to give eare and applause to his words: for being ready enough to beleeve those things for true, which were most easie; and seeing withall, that whatsoever he commended to them, was in each mans power to perform, he had the general voice of them: so as by this new doctrine of his, he drew al the world into a singular admiration of him, as of a man sent and descended from heaven above, to cure their griefs and maladies.

Moreover, a wonderfull dexterity and artificiall grace he had to follow mens humors, and content their appetites, in promising and allowing the sick to drink wine, in giving them eftsoons cold water when he saw his time, and all to gratifie his patients. Now for that *Herophylus* before him had the honor of being the first Physitian who searched into the causes of maladies: and because *Cleophantus* had the name among the Antients, for bringing wine into request and setting out the vertues thereof: this man for his part also, desirous to grow into credit and reputation by some new invention of his own, brought up first the allowing of cold water beforesaid, to sick persons; and (as *M. Varro* doth report) took pleasure to be called the Cold-water Physitian. He had besides other pretty devises to flatter and please his patients, one while causing them to have hanging litters or beds like cradles, by the moving and rocking whereof too and fro, he might either bring them asleep, or ease the pains of their sicknes; otherwhiles ordaining the use of bains, a thing that he knew folk were most desirous of: besides many other fine conceits very plausible in hearing, and agreeable to mans nature. And to the end that no man might think this so great alteration and change in the practise of Physick, to have bin a blind course and a matter of smal consequence, one thing above the rest that woon himselfe a great fame, and gave no lesse credit and authority to his profession, was this, that meeting upon a time by chance with one he knew not, carried forth as a dead corse in a biere for to be burned, he caused the body to be carried home from the funerall fire, and restored the man to health again.

Certes, this one thing, wee that are Romanes may be well ashamed of and take in great indignation, That such an old fellow as he, comming out of Greece (the vainest nation under the sun) and beginning as he did of nothing, should only (for to inrich himselfe) lead the whole world in a string, and on a sudden set

down rules and orders for the health of mankind, notwithstanding
many that came after him, repealed as it were, and annulled those
lawes of his. And verily, many helps had *Asclepiades*, which much
favored his opinion and new Physick; namely the manner of curing
diseases in those daies, which was exceeding rude, troublesome,
and painfull; such adoe there was in lapping and covering the
sicke with a deale of cloaths, and causing them to sweat by all
meanes possible: such a worke they made sometime in chafing
and frying their bodies against a good fire. . . . In lieu whereof,
not onely there, but throughout all Italy (which now commanded
the whole World, and might have what it list) hee followed mens
humours in approoving the artificiall baines and vaulted stouves
and hot houses, which then were newly come up and used exces-
sively in every place by his approbation.

Moreover, he found means to alter the painefull curing of some
maladies, and namely of the Squinancie; in the healing whereof
other Physitians before him went to worke with a certain instrument which they thrust down into the throat. He condemned also
(and worthily) that dog-physick which was in those daies so
ordinary, that if one ailed never so little, by and by he must cast
and vomit. He blamed also the use of purgative potions, as contrary and offensive to the stomack; wherein he had great reason
and truth on his side: for to speake truely, such drinks are by
most Physitians forbidden, considering our chiefe care and drift
is in all the course of our physick, to use those means which be
comfortable and wholsom for the stomack.

§ 121

Of the infirmities of the Belly

(Chap. 8)

TOUCHING the panch or belly, much ado there is with it: and
although most men care for nothing els in this life, but to content
and please the belly, yet of all other parts it putteth them to most
trouble: for one while it is so costive, as that it will give no passage
to the meat; another while so slippery, as it will keep none of it:

one time you shal have it so peevish, as that it can receive no food; and another time so weake and feeble, that it is able to make no good concoction of it. And verily now adaies the world is growne to that passe, that the mouth and panch together are the chiefe meanes to worke our death.

The wombe[1] (I say) the wickedest vessell belonging to our bodies, is evermore urgent, like an importunat creditour, demanding debt, and oftentimes in a day calleth unto us for victuals: for the bellies sake especially we are so covetous to gather good; for the belly we lay up so many dainties and superfluities; to content the belly we stick not to saile as far as the river Phasis; and to please the belly, we seek and sound the bottome of the deep seas: and when all is done, no man ever thinketh how base and abject this part of the body is, considering that filthy ordure and excrement which passeth from it in the end. No marvell then if Physitians be much troubled about it.

[1] Stomach, cf. wame.

In
THE TWENTY EIGHTH BOOKE
are comprehended the medicinable vertues
from living creatures[1]

§ 122

Of Spels and Charmes

(Chap. 2)

As for *Caesar* the Dictatour, it is commonly said of him, that having beene once endangered with the fall or overthrow of his coach wherein he rode, [he] would never afterwards ride in coach againe, unless so soone as ever hee had taken his place, and before that he set forward upon his way, he had pronounced a certaine charm that he had in store: and persuaded he was, that if he said it over three times together, he should come by no mischance in his journey, but travel in security. A thing that I know many now adaies to practise ordinarily as well as he.

But for farther proofe and confirmation of this opinion, I report me to every mans conscience and knowledge; to that (I say) which there is not one but knoweth: What is the cause I pray you, that the first day of every yeare we salute one another for luck sake, with wishing a good new yere? What is the reason, tel me, that in all our publick processions and generall solemnities every fifth yeare for the health and good estate of the city, they made choice of such persons for to lead the beasts appointed to sacrifice, whose names were good and fortunat? or how commeth it about, that for to prevent or divert witchcraft and sorcery, we observe a peculiar adoration, and invocat upon the Greekish (goddesse of vengeance) *Nemesis*; in which regard onely, we have her statue or image set up in the Capitoll, notwithstanding we know not yet what name in Latine to give her? How is it, that in making

[1] Book 27 consists of recipes for herbal medicines.

mention of those that be dead, we speake with reverence and protest that we have no meaning to disquiet their ghosts thereby, or to say ought prejudiciall to their good name and memoriall?

If there be nothing in words, how hapneth it, I would fain know, that we have such an opinion of odd numbers, beleeving that they be more effectuall in all things than the even? a matter I may tell you of great consequence, if we do but observe the criticall daies in fevers. Also in the gathering of our first fruits, be they Pears, Apples, Figs, &c. wherfore use we to say, These be old, God send us new? What mooveth us to wish health and say, God helpe, or blesse, when one sneezeth? for even *Tiberius Caesar*, who otherwise was known for a grim sir, and the most unsociable and melancholick man in the world, required in that manner to be salved and wished well unto, whensoever he sneezed, though he were mounted in his chariot. And some there be who in this case do ceremoniously salute the party by name, and thinke there is a great point of religion lies in that. Moreover, is not this an opinion generally received, That when our ears do glow and tingle, some there be that in our absence doe talke of us!

§ 123

Of the properties of a mans spittle

(Chap. 4)

As touching the fasting spittle specially of man or woman, I have shewed already how it is a soveraigne preservative against the poison of serpents. But that is not all: for in many other cases it is found by daily experience to be of great operation, and to worke effectually. For first and formost, if we see any surprised with the falling sicknesse, we spit upon them, and by that means we are persuaded, that we our selves avoid the contagion of the said disease. *Item,* an ordinary thing it is with us to put by the danger of witch-craft, by spitting in the eies of a witch: so do we also, when we meet with one that limpeth, and is lame of the right leg. Likewise when we crave pardon of the gods for some audacious and presumptuous praiers that wee make, we use to spit even into

our bosoms. Semblably, for to fortifie the operation of any medicines, the manner is to pronounce withal a charm or exorcisme
three times over, and to spit upon the ground as often; and so we
doubt not but it will do the cure and not faile. Also when we
perceive a fellon[1] or such like uncom sore a breeding, the first
thing that we doe, is to marke it three times with our fasting
spittle.[2]

I will tell you of a strange effect, and whereof it is no hard
matter ywis to make the triall. If one man hath hurt another,
either by reaching him a blow neare at hand, or by letting flie
somwhat at him farther off, and repent him when he hath so done;
let him presently spit just in the midst of the palm of that hand
which gave the stroke, the party immediately that was smitten,
shall be eased from pain and take no harm thereby. And verily we
find this to be so, by experiments oftentimes made upon the
bodies of fourfooted beasts: for let them be swaied in the back, or
hipped by some stripe given them with stone or cudgel, do no
more then but spit into that hand which did the deed, and streight-
waies they will goe upright again upon all foure. Contrariwise
some there be, who before they either strike or discharge any
thing from them against another, after the same manner first
spit into the bal of their hands, and so they make account to do
a greater displeasure, and to hurt more dangerously.

But this we may assure our selves, that there is not a better
thing in the world for to kil tettars,[3] ringworms, and the foule
leprie, than to rub and wet them continually with our owne
fasting spittle: likewise to annoint therewith every morning our
eies, keepeth them from being bleared: also cankerous sores are
cured with the root of Sowbread, which we call the earth-apple,
if the same be wrought into a salve with our fasting spittle.
Moreover, if a man have a cricke and ach in the nape of his neck,
let him take the spittle of a man that is fasting, some in his right
hand, and there with anoint the ham of his right leg; and the rest
with his left, and do the like to the left leg: and thereupon hee shall
find ease. If an earwig or such like vermin be gotten into the eare,

---

[1] Whitlow.
[2] This is still recommended for cure of warts. A Cumberland prescription
insists that the spittle be used on waking before the first swallow.
[3] Scabs.

make no more ado but spit into the same, and it will come forth anon. Among countercharms, and preservatives against sorcerie, these be reckoned, namely, that a man spit upon his own urine as soon as he hath delivered it out of his body; likewise to spit into the shooe that serveth his right foot, before he put it on in a morning; also whensoever he goeth over or passe by a place where sometime he was in danger, to remember that he spit upon it. . . . Now, if we beleeve these things to be true, we may as well give credit to all that which followeth. . . .[1]

[1] Much more of the same kind follows. Pliny makes it clear that he believed little or none of it and only reported the tales of others.

THE TWENTY NINTH BOOKE

treateth of the first authors and inventors
of Physicke, also of medicines taken from
other creatures

§ 124

How many times the order of Physick hath bin changed

(Chap. 1)

THE admirable nature of a number of medicines, as wel those
which I have already shewed as those which remain as yet to be
handled, forceth me to write yet more of Physicke, and to sound
the very depth and bottome: albeit I know full well, that there is
not a Latine writer who hath travelled hitherto in this argument;
and am not ignorant how ticklish and dangerous a point it is at
first to set abroch any new matters, especially such, whereby a
man is sure to reape but small thanks, and in deliverie whereof, is
to make account of a world of difficulties. But forasmuch as it is
very like that those who are well acquainted with this study, will
muse how it is come about, that the remedies drawn from simples,
so easie to be found and so accomodat to maladies, are cast behind
and grown out of use in the practise of Physick; it cannot be, but
withall they must marvell much, and think it a great indignity,
that no science and profession in the world hath lesse solidity
in it and bin more unconstant, yea, and how it daily changeth still,
notwithstanding there is not any other more profitable and gain-
full than it.

But to enter into the discourse thereof, First and formost, the
invention of this Art hath been fathered upon the gods, such I
mean as are canonized gods in heaven: yea, and even at this day
we have recourse stil unto divine Oracles for many medicines.
Moreover, the fabulous tales devised by Poets have given a greater

name and reputation thereto, in regard of the offence committed by *Aesculapius* in raising prince *Hippolytus* again to life: for which bold part of his, *Jupiter* being highly displeased, smote him dead with lightning. And yet for al this, Antiquity hath not staid there, but made relation of others, who were revived by the means of the said *Aesculapius* or his art: which during the Trojan[1] war, whereof the fame and bruit is more certain, grew into much request and estimation: and yet in those daies there was no other part of Physicke professed and practised, but Chirurgery; and that in the cure of wounds only. But in the age insuing, and for many a yeare after, wonderful it is, in what obscurity this noble science lay dead, and as it were buried in darknesse and oblivion, even untill the famous Peloponesiacke war: for then arose *Hippocrates*, who revived and set on foot againe the antient practise of *Aesculapius*, so long forelet: and being borne in Coos, a renowned and wealthie Island, altogether devote and consecrated to *Aesculapius*, he made an extract of al the receits, which were found written in the temple of the said god (for the maner was in that Island, that whosoever were cured and delivered of any disease, registred there upon record, the experiments of medicines whereby they had remedie; to the end, that afterward they might have help again by the same in like cases) and therupon (as our countreyman *Varro* is persuaded) after that the said temple was burned, hee professed that course of Physick which is called Clinice.[2] Wherby Physitians found such sweetnes, that afterwards there was no measure nor end of fees: insomuch as *Prodicus*,[3] a disciple of *Hippocrates*, and borne in Silymbria, erecting that kind of practise in Physicke, which is called Iatraliptice,[4] opened by that meanes the way to inrich even those, who under Physitians were employed in rubbing and annointing mens bodies, yea, and brought gaine to other base and servile ministers atending upon their cures.

After them came *Chrysippus* in place: who through his much

[1] At what time and where, his 2 sons, Podalyrius and Machaon practised Chirurgerie (P. H.).

[2] Chamber-Physicke. So called, because hee visited his patients lying sicke in bed (P. H.).

[3] Perhaps Herodicus, the tutor of Hippocrates.

[4] The manner of maintaining of health and curing diseases by frictions and outward application of oiles and ointments (P. H.).

babble and pratling, wherewith he was well furnished, altered the Theoricke and speculative Physicke of *Hippocrates* and *Prodicus,* with all their principles: whom succeeded *Erasistratus, Aristotles* sisters son, and he chaunged also many of *Chrysippus* his rules and receits, notwithstanding he was a scholler of his and brought up under him. This *Erasistratus* for curing king *Antiochus,*[1] received of his sonne *Ptolomaeus* (king after him) one hundred talents: which to beginne withall, I note by the way, that you may see how (even in those daies) Physitians were well rewarded for their pains and skill. But in processe of time one *Acron,* a citizen of Agrigentum in Sicilie, much commended by the authority of *Empedocles* the famous naturall Philosopher, began in that Island to institute another faction and sect of Physitians, who grounding altogether their worke and operation upon experience, called themselves Empiriques.

Thus there beeing divers schooles of Physick, the professors in every one of them entred into contention and variance, some siding this way and others taking the contrary; untill at length *Herophilus* entred the stage, who reproved and condemned as well the one as the other: and reduced the pulses or beating of the arteries unto the times and measures in Musicke, according to the degrees of every age. Long after it was not, but this Philosophicall subtilty of his sect was given over and abandoned, because the profession thereof required of necessitie so much learning and literature: and albeit that *Asclepiades* when he began to professe Physick, brought with him an alteration of all that was before, yet (as I have already related) his Physick continued no longer than others: for *Themison* (a scholler and auditor of his) so soon as ever his master was departed this life, altered quite all that hee wrote and noted at first from his mouth, and betooke himselfe to a new practise, according to his owne head and fantasie. But what became of it? Surely within a while after, *Antonius Musa,* Physitian to *Augustus* the Emperour, put downe that which *Themison* had set up: and that by the authority and warrant of the said Emperor his patient, whom he delivered from a dangerous disease, using

---

[1] Antiochus was cured of his hopeless passion for his stepmother Stratonice. Erasistratus persuaded his old father, Seleucus I Nicator, king of Syria, to give her up to his son. The son of Antiochus was Antiochus II Theos, and it is not clear who Ptolomaeus was.

directly a contrary cure to that which had bin practised before-time.

Many other Physitians there were of great name, whom I over-passe: but the principall and most renowned of them all, were the *Casii, Calpitani, Arruntii,* and *Rubrii,* who in their time might dispend in fees allowed them out of the Princes and Emperours Exchequer, under whom they lived, 250000 Sesterces apeece, by the yeare. And as for *Q. Stertinius* the Physitian, he complained of the Emperors whom hee served, and challenged them for that hee had no greater revenues than 500000 Sesterces by the yeare from them: whereas he was able to make account, that by his practise in the city he gained yearely 600000 Sesterces, being retained Physitian to certain houses, which he could readily name at his fingers ends. A brother of his received no lesse in fees from *Claudius Caesar* the emperor. And albeit these brethren spent a great part of their wealth and substance in building sumptuously at Naples, whereby they adorned and beautified that city, yet they left behind them in goods unto their heires after them, to the worth of thirty millions; which was such an estate, that unlesse it were *Arruntius* only, there was never any known before those daies to have died so wealthy.

After these men, there arose one *Vettius Valens,* who over and besides his profession of Physicke and Rhetorick, which he earnestly followed, grew into a greater name, by reason of the familiar acquaintance hee had with *Messalina* the Empresse, wife to *Claudius Caesar.* This minion of hers taking his time, and seeing how mighty he was, followed his fortunes and erected a new sect and practise of Physicke. But within the compasse of that age, and namely in the daies of the Emperour *Nero,* in commeth *Thessalus,* who woon the name from all the Physitians of former times, and overthrew the precepts and doctrine of his predecessors; raging and faring as if he were mad, in open invectives against all the professors of Physicke that ever were: and with what spirit, policie, wit, and dexterity he performed this, it may be gathered sufficiently by this one argument (if there were no more) that upon his sepulchre or tomb, which remaineth at this day to be seen in the high way or causey Appia, he triumphed over them all, and intituled himself by the name of *Iatronices.*[1] And in very truth, never

[1] *i.* The master and conqueror of all Physitians (P. H.).

marched there player to the stage, or coachdriver to the publick cirque for to run a race, better attended and with a greater traine of followers, than hee when he passed along the streets: and yet *Crinas* of Marsiles put him down and outwent him far in credit and authoritie: and that by the means of a twofold skill and knowledge wherein he was seen: For besides his ordinary profession of Physicke, he shewed himselfe more warie and ceremonious in all his practise than all before him, by reason of the deepe insight that he had in the Mathematicks; observing the course of the starrs, chusing good daies and houres, and going ever by his Almanakes and Ephemerides, whensoever he ministred unto his patients, insomuch, as in their very diet he was so precise, that he would not allow them to eat or drink but with great regard of times and seasons. Whereby he grew to such wealth, that of late he bequeathed by his last will and testament ten millions of Sesterces unto his native city Marsils toward the fortifications therof, besides the walls that he caused to be built and emmanteled about other towns, which cost him little under the foresaid summe.

Whiles this *Crinas*, with such other as himself, seemed with their astrologie to command the course of the destinies, and to have mens lives at their own disposition, all on a suddain one *M. Charmis*, a Marsilian likewise, put himself forward and entred the citie of Rome, who not onely condemned the former proceedings of the ancient Physitians, but also put downe the baines and hot houses: hee brought in the bathing in cold water, and persuaded folke to use the same even in the middest of Winter: nay, he feared not to give direction unto his sicke patients for to sit in tubs of cold water. And I assure you, my selfe have seen ancient Senatours, such as had been Consuls of Rome, all chilling and quaking, yea and starke againe for cold, in these kind of baths: and yet they would seeme to endure the same, to shew how hardy they were. And verily, there is a treatise extant of *Annaeus Seneca*, wherein he approves highly of this course.

Neither is it to be doubted, but such Physicians as these, who having won credit and estimation once by such novelties and strange devises, shoot at no other marke but to make merchandise and enrich themselves even with the hazard of our lives. And hereupon come these lamentable and wofull consultations of theirs about their patients, wherein you shall see them ordinarily to argue and disagree in opinion, whiles one cannot abide that another mans judgment should take place, and seem to carry away the credit of the cure. From hence also arose that Epitaph of his (whosoever he was) that caused these words to be engraven upon his unhappy tombe, *Turba medicorum perii, i.* The variance of a sort of Physitians about me, were the cause of my death.[1]

Thus you see how often this art from time to time hath been altered, and daily still it is turned like a garment new dressed and translated: insomuch, as wee are carried away with the vain humor of the Greeks, and make sail as it were with the puffes of their proud spirit: For ever as any of these new commers can venditat and vaunt his owne cunning with brave words, strait-waies we put our selves into his hands, and give him power to dispose of our life and death at his pleasure; and without further regard, are as obedient to him as a souldiour to his captaine and Generall of the field. A strang matter that we should so do, considering how many thousands of nations there be that live in health wel ynough without these Physicians, and yet I canot say altogether without Physicke. Like as the people of Rome also (notwithstanding the Romanes were ever knowne to be forward ynough to entertaine all good arts and disciplines) continued for the space of six hundred yeares and above, after the foundation of their citie, and knew not what a Physician meant, but afterwards they did cast a great fancie to Physick also: howbeit upon some little experience thereof, they were as ready to loath and condemne it, as they were desirous before to have a tast and triall of it.

§ 125

Imperfections and defaults in this art of Physicke

(Chap. 1)

BUT surely, wel enough are we served, and we may thank none but our selves, if we come by a shrewd turn, so long as there is not

---

[1] The brawling of the doctors killed me.

one of us hath any care or desire to know that which is good for his life and health. We love to walk (forsooth) with other mens feet. We read, we looke by the eies of others: we trust the remembrance of another, when we salute any man: and to conclude, in the very main point of all we commit our bodies and lives to the care and industry of others: No reckoning is there now made of the riches and treasure of Nature: but the most precious things indeed which serve for the maintenance and preservation of health and life, are utterly rejected and cast away: no account make we of anything and think our owne, but to live in pleasures and dainty delights.

I will not leave my hold of *M. Cato*, whom I have opposed as a shield and buckler against the envie and spight of this ambitious and vain-glorious Art: neither will I give over the protection of that honorable Senat which hath judged no lesse: and that without catching advantage of the sinfull pranks and lewd parts which are committed and practised under the pretence of this art, as some man haply would look that I should set them abroad: for to say a truth, is there any trade or occupation goeth beyond it for poisoning? what is the cause of more gaping and laying wait after wils and testaments, than this? What adulteries have beene committed under the colour hereof, even in Princes and Emperors palaces? as for example, *Eudemus* with *Livilla* the Princesse, and wife to *Drusus Caesar*: *Valens* likewise with the Queen or Empresse above named, *Messalina*. But say that these crimes and odious offences are not to be imputed unto the Art it selfe, but rather to be charged upon the persons, I meane the corrupt and lewd professors thereof: yet surely I am of this beleefe, that in regard of these enormities, *Cato* was as much afraid of the entrance of Physicke, as of some Queene into the citie of Rome.[1]

For mine own part, I mean not to say ought of their extreme avarice; of the merchandise, spoile, and havocke that they make when they see their patients in danger of death, and drawing to their end; nor how high they hold (as it were in open market) the easement and release of the sicke mans pains, whiles he is under their hands; ne yet what pawnes and pledges they take as earnest of the bargaine, to dispatch the poore Patient out of the way at once; and lastly of their hidden secrets and paradoxes,

---

[1] Cato was a staunch republican.

which forsooth they will not divulge abroad, but for some round summe of money; as for example, that a cataract or pearle in the eie is to be couched[1] rather and driven down by the needle, than quite to be plucked forth. Wherby it is come to passe, that it is a very good turne and the best for us (as the case standeth) that we have so great a number of such murderers and theeves in the commonwealth: for I assure you it is not long of any shame and honesty (whereof there is none in them) but their malicious aemulation, being so many as they are, that the market is well fallen, and the prices come down of their workmanship. Notorious it is that *Charmis* the abovenamed Physitian that came from Marsiles, bargained with one patient that he had, to have 200000 Sesterces for his cure, and yet hee was but a stranger and a provinciall inhabitant. Also as well knowne it is, that *Claudius Caesar* upon a condemnation and judgement, tooke at one time by way of confiscation one hundred thousand sesterces from one *Alcon*, who was no better than a Chirurgion or Wound-healer: who beeing confined into France, and afterwards restored, gathered up his crums again and got as much within few yeares.

I am content also, that these faults should be laid not upon the art, but upon the men that profess it: Neither verily do I mean to shew and reprove the base, abject, and ignorant sort of that crew: nor how little order and regiment they observe in the cure of diseases, or in the use of bains and hot waters: how imperiously they prescribe otherwhiles to their patients most strait diet: and again, when they are ready many times to faint and die under their hands for want of sustenance, how they be forced to cram them as it were, and give them meat upon meat, oftentimes in one day, before they have digested the former viands. Moreover, how they do and undo, altering the manner and course of their proceedings a thousand waies, misliking and bethinking themselves after they have done a thing: making a mish mash and mingle mangle in the kitchin of those victuals which they ordain for their poore patients: besides a deal of mixtures and sophisticat compositions of drugs and ointments. For there is no superfluity tending unto vain pleasures and wanton delights that hath overpassed their hands.

---

[1] To couch a cataract was to depress the cornea; the patient could be expected to return for further treatment.

THE
THIRTIETH BOOKE
speaketh of Magicke

§ 126

The originall and beginning of Art Magicke

(Chap. 1)

THE folly and vanitie of Art Magicke I have oftentimes already taxed and confuted sufficiently in my former books, when and wheresoever just occasion and fit opportunitie was offered; and still my purpose and intention is to discover and lay open the abuse thereof in some few points behind. And yet I must needs say the argument is such as deserveth a large and ample discourse, if there were but this only to enduce me, That notwithstanding it be of all arts fullest of fraud, deceit, and cousenage, yet never was there any throughout the whole world either with like credit professed, or so long time upheld and maintained. Now if a man consider the thing well, no marvell it is that it hath continued thus in so great request and authoritie: for it is the onely Science which seemeth to comprise in it selfe three professions besides, which have the command and rule of mans minde above any other whatsoever.

For to begin withall, no man doubteth but that Magicke tooke root first and proceeded from physicke, under the pretence of maintaining health, curing and preventing diseases: things plausible to the world crept and insinuated farther into the heart of man, with a deepe conceit of some high and divine matter therein more than ordinarie, and in comparison thereof all other physicke was but basely accounted. And having thus made way and entrance, the better to fortifie it selfe, and to give a goodly colour and lustre to those faire and flattering promises of things, which our nature is most given to hearken after, on goeth the habit also and cloke of religion: a point I may tel you that even in these days holdeth captivate the spirit of man, and draweth away with it a greater part of the world, and nothing so much. But not content with this success and good proceeding, to gather more strength and win a greater name, she intermingled with medicinable receits and Religious ceremonies, the skill of Astrologie and arts Mathematical; presuming upon this, That all men by nature are very curious and desirous to know their future fortunes, and what shal betide them hereafter, persuading themselves, that all such foreknowledge depends on the course and influence of the stars, which give the truest and most certain light of things to come. Being thus wholly possessed of men, and having their sences and understanding by this meanes fast enough bound with three sure chaines, no marvell if this art grew in processe of time to such an head, that it was and is at this day reputed by most nations of the earth, for the paragon and chief of al sciences: insomuch as the mighty kings and monarchs of the Levant are altogether ruled thereby.

And verily there is no question at all, but that in those East parts, and namely in the realme of Persia, it found first footing, and was invented and practised there by *Zoroaster*, as all writers in one accord agree. But whether there was but that one *Zoroaster*, or more afterward of that name, it is not yet so certainly resolved upon by all Authors: for *Eudoxus* (who held art Magicke to be of all professions philosophicall and learned disciplines, the most excellent and profitable science) hath recorded, that this *Zoroaster*, to whom is ascribed the invention therof, lived and flourished 6000 yeares[1] before the death of *Plato*. And of his minde is *Aristotle* also. Howbeit *Hermippus*, who wrot of that art most exquisitely, and commented upon the Poëme of *Zoroaster*, containing a hundred thousand verses twenty times told, of his making; and made besides a Repertorie or Index to every booke of the said Poësie: this *Hermippus* (I say) reports, That one *Agonaces* taught *Zoroaster* Art Magick; which master of his lived 5000 yeres before the war of Troy.

Certes I cannot chuse but marvell much, first, That this Science and the memoriall thereof should so long continue, and

---

[1] Or els that hee means *Lunares annos* (P. H.).

R

the Commentaries treating of it not miscary and be lost all the while, during such a world of years: considering besides, that neither it was ordinarily practised and continued by tradition from age to age; nor the successors in that facultie were professors of the greatest name, and renowned by any writings. For what one is there thinke you among so many thousands, that hath any knowledge, so much as by bare heare-say of those who are named for the only Magitians in their time, to wit, *Apuscorus* and *Zaratus* Medians, *Marmaridius* of Babylon, *Hippocus* the Arabian, and *Zarmocenidas*[1] of Assyria. For bookes have we none extant of their writing, nor any monuments which beare record and give testimonie of such clerks. But the greatest wonder of all is this, that *Homer* the Poet in his Ilias (a poem composed purposedly of the Trojan war) hath not so much as one word of Magick; and yet in his Odyssaea, where he discourseth of the adventures, travels, and fortunes of prince *Ulysses*, such a do and stirre there is with it, as if the whole work consisted of nothing else but magicke. For what is meant by the variable transformations of *Proteus*, or by the songs of the Meremaids, whereof he writeth so much; but that the one was a great sorcerer, the other famous witches or Inchantresses. As for that which he relateth of lady *Circe*, how shee wrought her feats by conjuration only, and raising up infernal spirits; surely it savoreth of art Magick and nothing else. . . .

No question there is verily, but that this Art of Magicke was professed in France, and continued untill our daies: for no longer is it agoe than since the time of *Tiberius Caesar*, that their Druidae (the Priests and Wisemen of France) were by his authority put down, together with all the pack of such Physitians, prophets, and wizards. But what should I discourse any longer in this wise, of that Art which hath passed over the wide ocean also, and gone as far as any land is to be seene, even to the utmost bounds of the earth; and beyond which, there is nothing to be discovered but a vast prospect of Aire and Water. And verily in Brittaine at this day it is highly honored, where the people are so wholly devoted unto it, with all reverence and religious observation of ceremonies that a man would think, the Persians first learned all their Magick from them. See how this Art and the practise thereof is spread over the

[1] These names are probably corrupt.

face of the whole earth! and how those nations[1] were conformable enough to the rest of the world in giving entertainment thereto, who in all other respects are far different and divided from them, yea and in manner altogether unknowne to them. In which regard, the benefit is inestimable that the world hath received by the great providence of our Romanes, who have abolished these monstrous and abhominable Arts, which under the shew of religion, murdred men for sacrifices to please the gods; and under colour of Physicke, prescribed the flesh to bee eaten as most wholesome meat.

[1] No doubt he meaneth England, Scotland, and Ireland, which seemed to be separat from the rest of the world; where, in old time Magicke bare a great sway, and witches still swarm too much (P. H.).

THIRTY FIRST BOOKE
sheweth wonderfull things as touching the Waters

§ 127

The fountaines of Cicero

(Chap. 2)

NOW there is a memorable manour or faire house of plaisance, situat upon the sea side in the very high way which leadeth from the lake Avernus to the cittie Puteoli; much renowmed for the grove or wood about it, as also for the stately galleries, porches, allies, and walking places adjoyning therunto, which set out and beautifie the said place very much: this goodly house, *M. Cicero* called Academia, in regard of some resemblance it had unto a colledge of that name in Athens, from whence he tooke the modell and patterne: where he compiled those books of his which carrie the name of the place, and be called *Academicae quaestiones*: and there he caused his monument or sepulchre to be made, for the perpetuitie of his memoriall, as who would say, he had not sufficiently immortalized his name throughout the world, by those noble works which he wrote and commended unto posteritie.

Well, soone after the decease of *Cicero*, this house and forrest both fell into the hands and tenure of *Antistius Vetus*; at what time, in the very forefront as it were and entrie thereof, there were discovered certaine hot fountaines breaking and springing out of the ground, and those passing medicinable and wholesome for the eies. Of these waters, *Laurea Tullius* (an enfranchised vassall of *Cicero*) made certaine verses, and those carying with them such a grace of majestie, that at first sight a man may easily perceive how affectionat and devout he was to the service of his lord and master: and for that the said Epigram is worthy to be read not onely there, but also in every place, I will set it downe here as it standeth over those baines to be seene, in this Decasticon.

O prince of Romane Eloquence, loe here thy Grove in place
How greene it is, where planted first it was to grow apace:
And *Vetus* now, who holds thy house, Faire Academie hight,
Spares for no cost, but it maintains and keeps in better plight.
Of late also, fresh fountains here brake forth out of the ground,
Most wholesome for to bath sore eies, which earst were never found.
These helpfull springs, the Soile no doubt, presenting to our view,
To *Cicero* her ancient lord, hath done this honour due;
That since his books throughout the world are read by many a wight
More waters still may cleare their eyes, and cure decaying sight.

§ 128

Of the fishes of Limyra

(Chap. 2)

N o w if any man suppose some of these strange reports to be incredible, let him learne and know, that in no part of the world Nature hath shewed more admirable works than in this element of Water. And albeit in the beginning of this mine historie I have written in ample manner of many a wonder observed in the waters, yet somewhat remaineth still to be related. . . .

The fountaine Limyra is wont ordinarily to change his seat, and to passe into places adjoyning, but never for nought, presaging alwaies thereby some strange accident to ensue. And wonderfull it is, that the fishes therein should follow and do the like. Now when this water is thus removed, the inhabitants of the country, desirous to know the issue of things to come, repaire thither as to an Oracle, and seek to be resolved by the foresaid fishes, and therwith offer to them some meat: if they come unto it and swim away with all, it is a good token, and this they take for an affirmative answer, as if they said, Yea, to their demands: but in case they refuse the meat and flirt it away with their tailes, they collect the contrary, and this is their flat nay.

§ 129

Of fresh water from the Sea

(Chap. 6)

MOREOVER, for as much as sea-faring men and saylers be many times at a fault for fresh water, and thereby much distressed, I think it good to shew the means how to be provided for the supply of this defect. First and foremost therefore, if they spread and display abroad certaine fleeces of wooll round about a ship, the same will receive and drinke in the vapours of the Sea, and become moist and wet withall; presse or wring them well, you shall have water fresh enough. *Item*, let downe into the sea within small nets, certain pellets of wax that be hollow, or any other void and empty vessels wel closed and luted, they will gather within them water that is fresh and potable: for we may see the experience hereof upon the land: take sea-water and let it run through cley, it will become sweet and fresh.

§ 130

Of the nature of Spunges

(Chap. 11)

MANY sorts there be of Spunges, according as I have shewed already more amply in my treatise of water beasts, and those especially of the Sea, and their severall natures: howbeit some writers distinguish them after another manner; into male and female: for some of them they have thought to be of the male sex, to wit, those which have smaller pipes or concavities, and those growing thicker and more compact, whereby they sucke up more moisture; and these our delicat and dainty people, die in colours, and otherwhile give them a purple tincture. Others they count of the femal sex, namely such as have bigger pipes, and the same running throughout one continuity without interruption. Of the male kind, some be harder than others, which they call Tragos;

the pipes whereof are the finest, and stand thickest together. There is an artificiall device to make spunges look white; to wit, if the softest and tendrest of them be taken whiles they be fresh in summer time, and so bathed and soked wel in fome of salt: after which they ought to be laid abroad in the moon-shine, to receive the thick dew or hoary frosts (if any fall) with their bellies upward into the aire, I meane that part whereby they cleave fast to rocke or sand where they grew, that therby they may take their whitening.

That spunges have life, yea and a sensible life, I have proved heretofore; for there is found of their bloud settled within them. Some writers report, that they have the sense of hearing, which directs them to draw in their bodies at any sound or noise made, and therwith to squize out plenty of water which they contained within; neither can they easily be pulled from their rocks, and therefore must be cut away; wherby they are seen to shed a deale of bloud, or that which resembleth bloud very neer. . . . As touching the softest and finest spunges, called Penicilli,[1] if they be applied unto the eies after they have been soked in honyed wine, they do allay and bring down any swelling in them.

[1] The origin of a name, now on everyone's lips, is of interest. *Penicillus*, diminutive of *penis*, means a little tail. Painters' brushes, or pencils, were later called by this name, perhaps because they resembled or were made from tails of animals.

THIRTY SECOND BOOKE
sheweth other properties of fishes

§ 131

The stay-ship fish

(Chap. 1)

THE currant of the Sea is great, the tide much, the winds vehement and forcible; and more than that, ores and sails withall to helpe forward the rest, are mighty and powerfull: and yet there is one little sillie fish, named Echeneis, that checketh, scorneth and arresteth them all: let the winds blow as much as they will, rage the stormes and tempests what they can, yet this little fish commandeth their fury, restraineth their puissance, and maugre all their force as great as it is, compelleth ships to stand still: A thing, which no cables, be they never so big and strong, no ankers, how massie and weightie soever they be, sticke they also as fast and unmovable as they will, can performe. Shee bridleth the violence, and tameth the greatest rage of this universall world, and that without any paine that she putteth her selfe unto, without any holding and putting backe, or by any other meanes, save only by cleaving and sticking fast to a vessell: in such sort, as this one small and poore fish, is sufficient to resist and withstand so great power both of sea and navie, yea and to stop the passage of a ship, doe they all what they can possible to the contrary.[1]

What should our fleets and armadoes at sea, make such turrets in their decks and forecastles? what should they fortifie their ships in warlike maner, to fight from them upon the sea, as it were from mure and rampier on firme land? See the vanity of man! alas, how foolish are we to make all this adoe? when one little fish, not above halfe a foot long, is able to arrest and stay perforce, yea and hold

---

[1] One of Holland's best passages. This remarkable fish, as mentioned in the last sentence, is the Remora or sucker-fish. Mark Antony and Caligula must have been deceived about the cause of their sluggish sailing, but no doubt large numbers of Echeneis attached to a ship's bottom could slow her down.

as prisoners our goodly tall and proud ships, so well armed in the beake-head with yron pikes and brasen tines; so offensive and dangerous to bouge and pierce any enemie ship which they do encounter. Certes, it is reported, that in the navall battell before Actium, wherein *Antonius* and *Cleopatra* the queene were defeated by *Augustus*, one of these fishes staied the admirall ship wherein *M. Antonius* was at what time as he made all the hast and means he could devise with help of ores, to encourage his people from ship to ship, and could not prevaile, till he was forced to abandon the said admirall and go into another galley. Meane-while the armada of *Augustus Caesar* seeing this disorder, charged with great violence, and soone invested the fleet of *Antony*.

Of late daies also, and within our remembrance, the like happened to the roial ship of the Emperour *Caius Caligula*, at what time as he rowed back and made saile from Astura to Antium; when and where, this little fish detained his ship, and (as it fell out afterward) presaged an unfortunat event thereby: for this was the last time that ever this Emperor made his returne to Rome: and no sooner was he arrived, but his owne souldiers in a mutinie fell upon him, and stabbed him to death. And yet it was not long ere the cause of this wonderful stay of his ship was knowne: for so soone as ever the vessell (and a galliace it was, furnished with five banks of ores to a side) was perceived alone in the fleet to stand still, presently a number of tall fellows leapt out of their ships into the sea, to search about the said galley, what the reason might be that it stirred not? and found one of these fishes sticken fast to the very helme: which being reported unto *Caius Caligula*, he fumed and fared as an Emperour, taking great indignation that so small a thing as it, should hold him back perforce, and checke the strength of all his mariners, notwithstanding there were no fewer than foure hundred lusty men in his galley that laboured at the ore all that ever they could to the contrary. But this prince (as it is for certaine known) was most astonied at this, namely, That the fish sticking onely to the ship, should hold it fast; and the same being brought into the ship and there laid, not worke the like effect. They who at that time and afterward saw the fish, say it resembled for all the world a snail of the greatest making: . . . Some of our Latine writers do call the said fish that thus staieth a ship, by the name of Remora.

THIRTY THIRD BOOKE
declareth the natures of Mettals

§ 132

Of Mettals and Minerals

(Proem)

N O W is it time to enter into the discourse of the Mettals and
Minerals, the very riches and precious treasure of the World,
which men so curiously and carefully seeke after, as that they
sticke not to search into the very bowels of the earth by all the
meanes they can devise: for some you shall have (to enrich themselves) for to dig into the ground for mines of gold and silver . . .
Electrum, Copper and Brasse: others againe upon a desire of
daintie delights and braverie, to lay for gems and precious stones,
for such Minerals (I say) which may serve partly to adorne their
fingers, and partly to set out the walls of sumptuous buildings
with costly colours, rich marble, and porphyries. Lastly there bee
many, who maintaine rash quarrels and audacious attempts, and
spare for no labour to get yron and steele, esteeming it better than
gold, for cruell warres and bloudie murthers. In summe there is
not a vaine in the whole earth but we prie and search into it: we
follow it also so farre as it goeth. Thus having undermined the
poore ground, wee live and goe aloft upon it, as over hollow vaults
and arches under our feet: and yet we would seeme to wonder,
that otherwhiles she cleaveth asunder into wide and gaping
chinkes, or else trembleth and quaketh againe: and wee will not
see how these be apparant signes of the wrath of this our blessed
mother, which we bring and force from her, to expresse the
indignation that she taketh for this wrong and misusage. We
descend into her entrailes: we goe downe as far as to the seat and
habitation of the infernall spirits, and all to meet with rich treasure:

as if the earth were not fruitfull ynough and beneficiall unto us in the upper part thereof, where she permitteth us to walke and tread upon her.

Howbeit, in all this paines that wee take to ransacke the mines therof, the least matter of all other is to seeke for anything that concerneth Physick and the regiment of our health: For among so many masters as there be of mines, where is there one that would be at such expence of digging, in regard of any medicines? And yet I must needs say, that as the earth otherwise is no niggard, but bounteous and liberall, readie also and easily entreated to bring forth all things good and profitable for us: so in this behalfe she hath furnished us sufficiently with wholesome drougs and medicinable simples growing above and fit for our hand, without need of digging deepe for the matter.

But the things that shee hath hidden and plunged (as it were) into the bottome, those be they that presse us downe, those drive and send us to the divell in hell: even those dead creatures (I say) which have no life nor doe grow at all. In such sort, as to consider the thing aright, and not to captivat our spirits to such base matters, How farre thinke wee, will covetous minded men pierce and enter into earth? or when will they make an end of these mines, hollowing the ground as they doe in all ages from time to time, and making it void and emptie? Oh how innocent a life, how happy and blessed, nay, how pleasant a life might we lead, if we coveted nothing else but that which is above the ground: and in one word, if we stood contented with that which is ready at hand and even about us. But now, not sufficed with the gold which we fetch out of the mines, we must seeke for the greene earth Borras[1] also, which lieth hard by, yea, and give it a name respective unto gold, whereby it might be thought more deare and pretious. For why? we thought not the invention and finding out of gold alone to be enough for to infect and corrupt our hearts, unlesse we made great account also of that vile and base minerall, which is the very ordure of gold and no better. Men upon a covetous mind would needs seeke for silver, and not satisfied therwith, thought good withall to find out Minerall vermilion, devising meanes how to use that kind of red earth.

Oh the monstrous inventions of mans wit! What a number of

[1] *Chrysocolla, i.* Gold-soder (P. H.).

waies have we found to enhaunce the price and value of every
thing! for painters of the one side with their artificiall painting
and enameling: the gravers on the other side with their curious
cutting and chasing, have made both gold and silver the dearer
by their workemanship: such is the audacitie of man, that hee
hath learned to counterfeit Nature, yea, and is so bold as to challenge her in her workes. And wherein is the art and cunning of
these artificers so much seene, as in the workemanship of such
pourtraitures upon their gold and silver plate, which might incite
and provoke men to all kinds of vices: for in processe of time we
tooke pleasure to have our drinking boles and goblets engraven
all over with those workes which represent lust and wantonnesse:
and our delight was to drinke out of such beastly cups which might
put us in mind of sinfull and filthie lecherie: but afterwards these
cups also were cast aside and laid away, men began to make but
base account of them; gold and silver was so plentifull and common,
that we had too much thereof.

What did we then: Forsooth we digged into the same earth for
Cassidonie and Crystall, and we loved to have our cups and other
vessels of such brittle minerals; and the more precious we held
them, as they were more subject to breaking: so as now adaies hee
is thought to have his house most richly furnished, who hath his
cupbourds best stored with this ticklish ware: and the most
glorious shew that we can make of excesse and superfluitie, is this,
To have that which the least knocke may breake, and being once
broken, the pieces thereof might be worth nothing. Neither is this
all, for stay we cannot here, we are not yet at cost enough, unlesse
we may drinke out of a deale of precious stones. Our cups otherwise chased, engraved, and embossed in gold, must be set out
with hemeraulds besides: to maintaine drunkennesse, to make
a quarrell, to carouse and quaffe, we must hold in our hand and
set to our mouth the riches of India. So as, to conclude, our
golden plate comes behind pretious stones and pearles, and
we count it but an accessarie and dependant, which may be
spared.

§ 133

Of Rings

(Chap. 1)

THE manner was in old time to weare rings but upon one finger onely, and namely that which is the fourth or next to the little finger, as we may see in the statues of *Numa* and *Servius Tullius*, Kings of Rome: but afterward they began to honour the forefinger which is next unto the thumbe, with a ring, according to the manner which we see in the images of the gods: and in processe of time they took pleasure to weare them upon the least finger of all: and it is said, that in France and Brittaine they used them upon the middle finger. But this finger now adayes is excepted onely and spared, whereas all the rest be sped and charged with them; yea and every joint by themselves must have some lesser rings and gemmals to fit them. Some will have the little finger loden with 3 rings; others content themselves with one and no more upon it, wherewith they use to seale up the signet that is to signe ordinarily; for this signe manual (I may tell you) the manner was to lay up safe among other rare and pretious things: this might not come abroad everie day, as beeing a jewell that deserved not to be misused by handling commonly, but to be taken forth out of the cabinet or secret closet never but when need required: so that whosoever weareth one ring and no more upon the least finger, hee giveth the world to understand, that he hath a secret cabinet at home stored with some speciall things more costly and pretious than ordinarie.

Now, as some there bee that take a pride and pleasure to have heavy rings upon their fingers, and to make a shew how massive and weighty they are; so others againe are so fine and delicat, as they thinke it a paine to weare more than one. Some hold it good, for saving of the stone or collet (if the Ring should chance to fall) to have the round hoope or compasse thereof wrought hollow or enchased within, yea and the same filled up with some lighter matter than is gold, that it may fall the softer. You shall have many that use to carry poyson hidden within the collet under the stone, like as *Demosthenes* did, that renowned Prince of Greeke Orators;

so as their rings serve no other use or purpose but to carry their owne death about them. Finally the greatest mischiefes that are practised by our mighty men in these dayes, are for the most part performed by the meanes of rings and signets.

O the innocence of the old world! what a heavenly life led men in those dayes, when as there was no use at all of seale and signet? But now we are faine to seale up our ambries[1] and hogsheads with our signets, for feare we be robbed and beguiled of our meat and drinke. This is the good that commeth of our legions and troupes of slaves, which we must have waiting and following at our heeles: this commoditie we have by our traine and retinue of strangers that wee keepe in our houses: insomuch as wee are driven to have our Controllers and Remembrancers to tell us the names of our Servants and people about us, they are so many. It was otherwise ywis by our ancestors and fore-fathers daies, who had no more but one yeoman or groome apiece, and those of the linage and name of their Lords and Masters: as may appeare by the ordinary names of *Marci-pores* and *Luci-pores*:[2] and these had all their victuals and diet ordinarily at their masters bourd. And therefore there was no great need to keep safely any thing under lock and key from such household servitors: whereas now adayes the cater goeth to the market to provide cates and viands for to be stollen and carried away as soon as they come home, and no remedy there is against it: for no seale will serve to make sure either such lurchers themselves from filching, or keep the very locks and keies safe and whole that lead to the provision. And why? an easie matter it is to plucke the rings from their lord and maisters fingers that are oppressed with dead sleep, or when they lie a dying.

And verily we hold in these daies a seale to be the best assurance in contracts that may be: but I wot not how long it is since that custom first came up. . . . Howbeit, the ordinarie use of these signets (as I suppose by all reason and likelihood) began together with usurie: for proofe whereof, marke how still at this day, upon any stipulation and bargaine paroll made, off goes the ring presently to confirme and seale the same. The which custome no doubt came from old time, when there was no earnest nor godspennie more ready at hand than a signet. So as we may conclude

---

[1] Pantry or cupboard.
[2] *i.* the pages or groomes of *Marcus* or *Lucius* (P. H.).

assuredly and affirme, That amongst us here at Rome, when the use of money and coyne was taken up, soone after came the wearing of rings in place. But as touching the devise and invention of mony, I will write anone more at large.

§ 134

Other uses besides of gold

(Chap. 3)

ALL the gold imploied in sacrifices to the honor of the gods, was in guilding the horns of such beasts as were to be killed, and those onely of the greater sort. But in warfare among souldiers, the use of gold grew so excessive, that the field and campe shone againe withall, insomuch as at the voiage of Macedony, where the Marshals of the field and colonels bare Armour set out with rich buckles and clasps of gold, *M. Brutus* was offended and stormed mightily at it, as appeareth by his letters found in the plaines about Philippi.

Well done of thee, O *M. Brutus*, to find fault with such wastfull superfluitie: but why saidst thou nothing of the gold that the Roman dames in thy time wore in their shoos? And verily this enormity and abuse, I must needs impute unto him (whosoever he was) that first devised rings, and by that means caused gold to be esteemed a mettal of much worth: which evill precedent brought in another mischiefe as bad as it, which hath continued a long time; namely, that men also should weare about their arms, bracelets of gold next to their bare skin: which devise and ornament of the arm is called Dardanium, because the invention came from the Dardanians. . . . Oh the monstrous disorders that are crept into the world! But say that women may be allowed to weare as much gold as they will, in bracelets, in rings on every finger and joynt, in carkanets about their necks, in earings pendant at their ears, in staies, wreaths, and chinbands; let them have their chains of gold as large as they list under their arms or crosse over their sides, scarf-wise; [let] gentlewomen and mistresses be at their collars of gold, beset thicke and garnished with massie pearls pendant from their necke, beneath their wast; that in their beds also when they should sleepe they may remember what a weight of gold they carried about them: must they therfore weare gold upon their feet, as it were to establish a third estate of women answerable to the order of knights, betweene the matrons or dames of honour in their side robes, and the wives of meane commoners?

Yet me thinkes, we men have more reason and regard of decencie, thus to adorne with brooches and tablets of gold, our youths and yong boies, and a fairer sight it is to see great men attended upon to the baines by beautifull pages thus richly decked and set out, that all mens eies may turne to behold them. But what meane I thus bitterly to inveigh against poore women; are not men also growne to such outragious excesse in this kind, that they begin to weare upon their fingers either Harpocrates, or other images of the Aegyptian gods engraven upon some fine stone? But in the daies of the Emperor *Claudius* there was another difference and respect had, That none might carrie the pourtraiture of that prince engraven in his signet of gold, without expresse licence given them by those gratious enfranchised slaves who were in place to admit unto their lord the Emperor, whom it pleased them:[1] which was the occasion and means of bringing many a man into danger, by criminall imputations. But all these enormities were happily cut off as soon as the Emperour *Vespasian* (to the comfort and joy of us all) came once to the crowne: for by an expresse edict, he ordained, That it might be lawfull for any person what-soever to have the image of the Emperour in ring, brooch, or otherwise without respect. Thus much may suffice concerning rings of gold, and their usage.

§ 135

Of Silver and Gold, in money[2]

(Chap. 3)

To come now to the next mischiefe that is crept into the world; I hold that it proceedeth from him who first caused a denier of

---

[1] The text here is variable; the meaning may be that only those with right of access to Claudius could wear his likeness in a ring.

[2] This piece, although mainly of interest to numismatists and historians of coinage, has been included for the description among the Romans of that modern expedient, debasement of the currency.

gold to be stamped: although, to say a truth, I know not certainly
who he was that devised this coine. As for the people of Rome,
sure I am that before king *Pyrrhus* of Epirus was by them vanquished, they had not so much as silver mony stamped and currant.
Well I wot also, that in old time the manner was to weigh our
brasse by the Asse, which was a pound weight, and thereupon
called As Libralis; and yet at this day, Libella: like as the weight
in brasse of two pound, they named Dipondium. And hereupon
came the custome of adjudging any fine or penaltie under the
tearme of Aeris gravis that is to say, of brasse Bullion or in Masse.
From hence it is also, that still in reckonings and accounts whatsoever hath bin laid out or delivered, goeth under the name of
Expensa (*id est*, Expences) as a man would say, weighed forth,
because in times past all paiments passed by weight. The Latines
likewise use the nowne Impendia, for cost bestowed or the
charges of interest in usurie above the principall; even as the
verbe Dependere, betokeneth to pay because paiments ordinarily
were performed by poise. Moreover the under treasurers of war,
or paimasters in the camp, were in ancient time named Libri-
pendes, for weighing out unto the souldiers their wages; and their
very pay thereupon was called Stipendium, from whence commeth
Stipend, a word commonly received. According to which manner
and custome, all buyings and sellings at this day which passe with
warrantise, are usually performed by interposition of the ballance,
which serveth to testifie the realitie of the contract and bargaine
on both parts.

Touching brasse mony, *Servius Tullius* a king of Rome, caused it
first to be coined with a stampe, for before his daies, they used it
at Rome rude in the masse or lumpe, as *Timaeus* mine author doth
testifie. And what was the marke imprinted thereupon? even a
sheepe, which in Latine they call Pecus: and from thence proceedeth
the word Pecunia, that signifieth mony. And note here by the way,
that during the reigne of that king, the best man in all Rome was
valewed to be worth in goods not above 110000 Asses in brasse:
and at this rate were assessed the principall houses of the city in
the kings bookes: and this was counted the first Class.

Afterwards, in the 485 yere from the foundation of the city,
when *Q. Ogulnius* and *C. Fabius* were Consuls, five yeares before the
first Punicke warre, they began to stampe silver mony at Rome,

and three severall pieces were coined. At what time ordained it was, That the Denarius or Denier should goe for tenne Asses or pounds of brasse mony; the halfe Denier, Quinarius, should be currant for five; and the Sesterce reckoned worth two and a halfe.

Now, for as much as during the first Punick war against the Carthaginians, the city was growne much behind hand and farre indebted, so as they were not able to goe through the charges which they were to defray, agreed it was and ordained to raise the worth of the brasen mony by diminishing the poise: wheras therfore the Asse weighed a pound of twelve ounces, they made the Asse of two ounces: By which devise, the Commonwealth gained five parts in six: and the Fisque or city chamber by that means was soone acquit of all debts. But if you would know what was the marke of this new brasen Asse: of the one side it was stamped with a two faced *Janus,* on the other side with the beake-head of a ship, armed with brasen pikes. Other smaller pieces there were, according to that proportion, to wit, Trientes, the third part of an Asse; and Quadrantes the fourth; which had the print of punts or small boats upon them. As for the piece Quadrans, it was before time called Triuncis, because it weighed three ounces. Howbeit in processe of time, when *Anniball* pressed hard upon the city, and put them to an exigent for mony to maintaine the wars against him, driven they were to their shifts and forced (when *Q. Fabius* was Dictator) to bring downe the foresaid Asse of two ounces unto one. Yea, and enacted it was, That the silver denier, which went beforetime for ten Asses, should be worth sixteene; the halfe Denier or Quinare, eight; and the Sesterce foure: and by this means the State gained the one halfe full. And yet I must except the mony paied to the souldiers for their wages: for a Denier unto them was never reckoned above ten Asses. As for the silver Deniers, stamped they were with the pourtraiture of coches drawne with two horses or foure horses, whereupon they were called Bigati and Quadrigati. Within a while after there passed an act promulged by *Papyrius,* by vertue whereof the Asses weighed not above halfe an ounce. Then came *Livius Drusus* in place, who being one of the Provosts or Tribunes of the commons, brought in base money, and delaied the silver with one eight part of brasse. . . .

Concerning gold coined into mony, it came up threescore and two yeres after the stamping of silver pieces: and a scriptule of gold was taxed and valued at twenty sesterces, which ariseth in every pound according to the worth of sesterces as they were rated in those daies, to nine hundred Sesterces. But afterwards it was thought good to cast and stampe pieces of gold, after the proportion of fiftie to a pound: And those, the Emperors by little and little diminished stil in poise, till at length *Nero* brought them downe to the lowest, and caused them to be coined after the rate of five and fiftie pieces to the pound.

In summe, the very source and originall of all avarice proceedeth from this mony and coine, devised first by lone and usurie, and continued still by such idle persons that put forth their mony to worke for them, whiles they sit still, and find the sweetnes of the gaine comming in so easily. But this greedy desire of having more still, is growne after an outragious manner to be excessive, and no more to be named covetousnesse, but rather insatiable hunger after gold: ... the whole name of the Romanes hath beene infamous among forraine nations for avarice and corruption in this kind: as may appeare by the conceit that king *Mithridates* had of them, who caused *Aquilius* (a Generall of theirs, whose hap was to fall into his hands) for to drinke molten gold. See what covetousnesse brings home with it in the end.

§ 136

The manner of finding gold

(Chap. 4)

T H E third manner[1] of searching for this mettal is so painfull and toilesome, that it surpasseth the wonderfull works of the Geants[2] in old time. For necessary it is in this enterprise and business, to undermine a great way by candlelight, and to make hollow vaults under the mountains. In which labor the pioners work by turns

---

[1] The other two methods were panning in rivers and surface mining.
[2] Who were said to reare one mountain upon the head of another (P. H.).

successively, after the maner of the reliefe in a set watch, keeping every man his houres in just measure: and in many a moneths space they never see the Sun or day light. This kind of work and mines thus made they call Arrugiae, wherin it falleth out many times that the earth above head chinketh, and all at once without giving any warning setleth and falleth, so as the poore pioners are overwhelmed and buried quick: insomuch as considering these perils, it seemes that those who dive under the water into the bottom of the Levant seas for to get pearls, hasard themselves nothing so much as these pioners: a strange thing, that by our rashnesse and folly wee should make the earth so much more hurtfull to us than the water.

Wel then, to prevent as much as possibly may be these mis-chiefes and dangerous accidents, they underprop the hils, and leave pillars and arches as they go, set thick one by another to support the same. And yet, say they worke safe enough, and be not in jeopardy of their lives by the fall of the earth, yet there be other difficulties that impeach their work: for otherwhiles they meet with rocks of flint and rags, as wel in undermining forward, as in sinking pits downeright; which they are driven to pierce and cleave through with fire and vineger. But, for that the vapor and smoke that ariseth from thence, by the means, may stifle and choke them within those narrow pits and mines, they are forced to give over such fire work, and betake themselves to great mattocks and pickaxes, yea and to other engines of iron, weighing 150 pounds apiece, wherewith they hew such rocks in pieces, and so sinke deeper, or make way before them. The earth and stones which with so much ado they have thus loosed, they are fain to cary from under their feet in scuttles and baskets upon their shoulders, which passe from hand to hand evermore to the next fellow.

Thus they moile in the dark both day and night in these infernal dungeons, and none of them see the light of the day, but those that are last and next unto the pits mouth or entry of the cave. If the flint or rock that they work into seem to run in a long grain, it will cleave in length, and come away by the sides in broad flakes, and therefore the pioners with ease make way, trenching and cutting round about it. Howbeit, be the rock as ragged as it will, they count not that their hardest work: for there is a certaine earth resembling a kinde of tough clay which they call white Lome, and the same intermingled with gritty sand so hard baked together, that there is no dealing with it; it so scorneth and checketh al their ordinary tooles and labour about it, that it seemeth impenetrable. What doe the poore labourers then? They set upon it lustily with iron wedges, they lay on lode uncessantly with mighty beetles;[1] and verily they thinke that there is nothing in the world harder than this labour, unlesse it bee this unsatiable hunger after gold, which surpasseth all the hardnesse and difficulty that is.

Wel, when the work is brought to an end within the ground, and that they have undermined and hollowed the ground as far as they think good, down they go with their arch-work abovesaid, which they builded as they went: they begin first at those props which are farthest off, cutting the heads of the stancheons still as they return backward to the entrance of the work. Which don, the sentinel only, which of purpose keeps good watch without upon the top of the same mountain that is thus undermined, perceives the earth when it begins to chink and cleave, menacing by that token a ruin thereof anon. Whereupon presently he gives a signe either by a loud cry, or some great knock, that the pioners under neath may have warning thereby to get them speedily out of the mines, and runneth himselfe apace down from the hil as fast as his legs will give him leave. Then all at once on a sudden the mountain cleaveth in sunder, and making a long chink, fals downe with such a noise and crack, as is beyond the conceit of mans understanding, with so mighty a puf and blast of wind besides, as it is incredible. Wherat these miners and pioners arc nothing troubled, but as if they had done some doughty deed, and atchieved a noble victorie, they stand with joy to behold the ruin of Natures workes which they have thus forced. And when they have all don yet are they not sure of gold, neither knew they all the whiles that they labored and undermined, that there was any at all within the hill: the hope only that they conceived of the thing which they so greatly desired, was a sufficient motive to induce them to enterprise and endure so great dangers, yea and to go through withall and see an end.

And yet I cannot wel say that here is all; for there is another labor behind, as painfull every way as the other, and withall of

[1] Mallets.

greater cost and charges than the rest, namely, to wash the breach of this mountaine (that is thus cloven, rent, and laid open) with a currant: for which purpose they are driven many times to seek for water a hundred miles off, from the crests of some other hils, and to bring the same in a continued channel and stream all the way along unto it. These Rivers or furrows thus devised and conveyed, the Latines expresse by the name of Corrivi, a word as I take it derived *a Conrivatio,* i. of drawing many springs and rils together into one head and chanel. And herein consisteth a new piece of worke as laborious as any that belongs to mines. For the level of the ground must be so taken aforehand, that the water may have the due descent and currant when it is to run: and therefore it ought to be drawn from the sources springing out of the highest mountaines; in which conveiance regard would be had as well of the vallies as the rising of the ground between, which requireth otherwhiles, that the waters be commanded by canels and pipes to ascend, that the carriage thereof be not interrupted, but one piece of the work answer to another. Otherwhiles it falleth out, that they meet with hard rockes and crags by the way, which do impeach the course of the water; and those are hewed through, and forced by strength of mans hand to make room for the hollow troughs of wood to lie in, that carrie the foresaid water. But a strange sight it is to see the fellow that hath the cutting of these rockes, how he hangeth by cables and ropes between heaven and earth; a man that beheld him afar off would say it were some flying spirit or winged divell of the aire. These that thus hang for the most part take the level forward, and set out by lines the way by which they would have the water to passe; for no treading out is there of the ground, nor so much as a place for a mans foot to rest upon. Thus you see what ado there is. And these good fellowes whiles they bee aloft, search with the hands and pluck forth the earth before them, to see whether it be firme and fast, able to beare the trunks or troughs for the water; or otherwise loose and brittle, which defect of the earth they call Urium: for the avoiding whereof the fountainers feare neither rocks nor stones to make passage for their pipes or trunks aforesaid.

Now when they have thus brought the water to the edge and brow of the hils where these mines of gold should be, and from whence as from an head there is to be a fall thereof to serve their purpose, they dig certaine square pooles to receive the water, 200 foot every way, and the same ten foot deep: in which they leave five several sluces or passages for the deliverie of water into the mines, and those commonly three foot square. When the said pools stand full, as high as their banks, they draw up the floudgates: and no sooner are the stopples driven and shaken out, but the water gusheth forth amaine with such a force, and carrieth so violent a streame therewith, that it rolleth downe with it any stones, be they never so big, lying in the way. And yet are we not come to an end of the toile, for there remaineth a new piece of work to do in the plaine beneath. Certain hollow ditches are to bee digged for to receive the fall of the water both from the pooles that are above, and the mines also. These trenches the Greekes tearme Agogae, as a man would say Conduits, and those are to be paved by degrees one under another.

Besides, there is a kinde of shrub or bush, named Ulex,[1] like to Rosemarie, but that it is more rough and prickely, and the same is there planted because it is apt to catch and hold whatsoever pieces of gold do passe beside; ... after it is once dried, they burn it, and the ashes that come thereof, they wash over turfs of greene grasse, that the substance of gold may rest and settle therupon. ... Lo what a worke it is to search out and meet with gold!

§ 137

Of Electrum

(Chap. 4)

THERE is a base kind of pale and whitish gold, which hath in it a fifth part of silver: and whersoever this is found, they call it Electrum. Such mettall lieth commonly in trenches and pits minerall, and namely with that gold which I called before Canaliense.[2] Moreover, there is an artificiall Electrum made, namely,

---

[1] Gorse.

[2] This is gold found in thin veins on the surface of marble and worked from pits and tunnels. Pliny's description of grinding, washing, and heating the ore is short and to the point, but it shows that the uncertain, wasteful method of the Arrugiae, just described at length, was not the only way of mining gold.

by intermingling gold with silver according to the naturall mixture; but if it exceed that proportion of one part to five, it wil not abide the hammer and the anvill. This white gold also hath bin of great account, time out of mind, as may appeare by the testimony of the Poet *Homer*, who writeth, that the pallace of prince *Menelaus* glittered with gold, electrum, silver, and yvorie. At Lindos (a city within the Island of the Rhodians) there is the temple of *Minerva*, wherein Lady *Helena* did dedicate unto that goddesse a cup made of Electrum: and as the story saith moreover, it was framed and wrought just to the proportion and bignesse of one of her own paps.

This property hath Electrum naturally, To shine by candlelight more cleare and bright than silver. This singularitie and proper vertue it hath besides (if it bee naturall) to discover and shew any poison: for be there poison in a cup of this mettall, a man shal see therein certain semicircles resembling rainbows, and perceive besides the liquor to keep a hissing and sparkling noise as the fire doth; which 2 signs do certainly give warning of poison.

§ 138

Of Silver Mines

(Chap. 6)

IT followeth by good order to write in the next place, of silver mines, from whence proceedeth the second rage that hath set men a madding: where first and formost this is to be noted, that there is but one means to find silver, and that is in pits sunke of purpose for it: neither is there any shew at all of silver to give light thereof, and to put us in hope of finding: no sparkes shining, like as there be in gold mines which direct us to it. The earth that engendreth the veine of silver, is in one place reddish, in another of a dead ash color.

But this is a generall rule, that it is not possible to melt and trie our silver ore, but either with lead, or the veine and ore of lead. This minerall or metall they call Galena, found for the most part neer to the veins and mines of silver. Now by the means of fire, when these are melted together, part of the silver ore setleth downeward and turneth to be lead, the pure silver floteth aloft, like as oile upon water. In al our provinces, yea and parts of the world to speake of, there be mines of silver to be found: howbeit the fairest be in Spaine, and yeeld the finest and most beautiful silver: and the same also, like as gold, is engendred in a barraine soile otherwise and fruitlesse, and even within mountains: look also where one vein is discovered, there is another alwaies found not farre off: which is a rule observed not in mines of silver only, but also in all others of what mettals soever; and hereupon it seemeth that the Greekes doe call them Metalla.[1]

And verily, strange it is and wonderfull, that the mines of silver in Spaine which were so long agoe begun by *Anniball*, should continue still as they do, and retaine the names of those Carthaginians who first found, discovered and brought them to light: of which, one named then Bebelo, and so called at this day, yeelded unto *Anniball* daily 300 pound weight; which mine even at that time had gone under the ground and hollowed the mountain a good mile and a halfe. . . . In old time those that digged for silver, if they met once with allum, were wont to give over their worke and seeke no farther: but of late daies it happened, that under alume there was found a veine of white brasse or laton, which fed mens hopes still, and cause them now to sink lower, and never rest so far as they can dig. And yet there is a damp or vapor breathing out of silver mines, hurtfull to all living creatures, and to dogs especially. Moreover, this point is well to be marked, that gold and silver both, the softer that they be and tender, the better they are esteemed: and silver being white as it is, most men marvell how it commeth to passe, that if one rule paper or any thing therewith, it will draw black lines and sully as it doth.

§ 139

Of Quicksilver

(Chap. 6)

F U R T H E R M O R E, within these veines and mines abovesaid, there is a certaine stone found which yeelds from it an humor continually,

[1] *quasi* μετ᾽ ἄλλα, one after another (P. H.).

and the same continues alwaies liquid: men call it Quick-silver[1] (howbeit being the bane and poison of all things whatsoever, it might be called Death-silver well enough) so penetrant is this liquor, that there is no vessel in the world but it wil eat and breake through it, piercing and passing on stil, consuming and wasting as it goes: it supports any thing that is cast into it, and wil not suffer it to settle downward, but swim aloft, unlesse it be gold only, that is the only thing which it loveth to draw unto it and embrace: very proper it is therefore to affine gold; for if gold and it be put together into earthen pots, and after often shaking be poured out of one into another, it mightily purifies the gold and casts forth al the filthy excrements thereof; and when it hath rid away all the impurities and grosse refuse, it selfe ought then to be separated from the gold: for which purpose poured forth the one and the other ought to be, upon certaine skinnes of leather well tewed and dressed untill they be soft, through which the quick-silver may passe: and then shall you see it stand in drops upon the other side like sweat sent out by the pores of our skin, leaving the gold pure and fine behind it: and verily the affinitie betwixt gold and quick-silver is so great, that if any vessels or pieces of brasse are to be gilded, rub the same over first with quick-silver before the gold foile be laid on, it will hold the same most surely: mary, this one discommodity there is in it, that if the leaves of gold be either single or very thin, the whitenesse of the quicke-silver will appeare through, and make the gilding more pâle and wan: where-fore our cunning goldsmiths who would make their Chapmen to pay for their plate as double gilt, when it is indeed but thin laid and single, and so picke their purses, set a rich and deep colour upon their work for the time, by laying under the gold instead of quick-silver natural, the white of an egg, and then upon it artificial quick-silver. . . .[2]

[1] Or Life-silver (P. H.).

[2] '. . . named Hydrargyrum, whereof I purpose to write in place convenient. And to say a truth, the right quick-silver which is of the own kind, is not commonly found in great plenty.' Hydrargyrum was the mercury obtained by heating vermilion (mercury sulphide); it must have been cheaper than the rare natural product.

§ 140

Of Vermilion

(Chap. 7)

THERE is found also in silver mines a mineral called Minium,
i. Vermilion, which is a colour at this day of great price and estimation, like as it was in old time: for the antient Romans made
exceeding great acount of it, not only for pictures, but also for
divers sacred and holy uses. And verily *Verrius* alledgeth and rehearseth many authors, whose credit ought not to be disproved,
who affirm, That the maner was in times past to paint the very
face of *Jupiters* image on high and festival daies with Vermilion:
as also, that the valiant captains who rode in triumphant maner
into Rome, had in former times their bodies[1] coloured all over
therewith: after which manner (they say) noble *Camillus* entred the
city in triumph. . . . The cause and motive that should induce our
ancestors to this ceremony I marvel much at, and canot imagin
what it should be. True it is and well known, that in these daies
the Aethiopians in generall set much store by this colour, and
have it in great request, insomuch as not onely the Princes and
great Lords of those countries have their bodies stained throughout therewith, but also the images of their gods are painted with
no other colour: in which regard I am moved to discourse more
curiously and at large of all particulars that may concerne it.

Theophrastus saith, that 90 years before *Praxibulus* was established
chiefe ruler of the Athenians (which falls out just upon the 249[2]
yere after the foundation of our city of Rome) *Callias* the Athenian
was the first that devised the use of Vermilion, and brought the
lively colour thereof into name: for, finding a kinde of red earth
or sandy grit in the mines of silver, and hoping that by circulation
there might be gold extracted out of it, he tried what he could do
by fire, and so by that means brought it unto that fresh and

[1] To shew the bloudy battles they had fought, and what carnage of their
Enemies they had made: for without much effusion and drawing of their bloud
they might not triumph (P. H.).

[2] In fact the 439th year.

pleasant hue that it hath: which was the first original of Vermilion. . . .

But the best simply (saith he) was gotten in the territorie of the Cilbians, somewhat higher in the country than Ephesus: in sum, That the said Minium or Vermilion is a certaine sandy earth of a deepe scarlet colour, which was prepared in this order: first they pun and beat it into pouder, and then washed it being thus pulverised. Afterwards, that which setled in the bottom they washed a second time. In which artificiall handling of Minium this difference there is, that some make perfect Vermilion of it with the first washing: others thinke the Vermilion of that making to be too pale and weake in colour, and therefore hold that of the second washing to be best. And verily I wonder not that this colour was so highly esteemed: for even beforetime during the state of Troy, the red earth called Rubrica was in great request, as appeareth by the testimony of *Homer*; who being otherwise spary enough in speaking of pictures and colours, yet commends the ships painted therwith. The Greeks call our Minium by the name of Miltos, and yet some terme it Cinnabari: and hereof arose the error occasioned by the Indian name Cinnabari. For so the Indians call the bloudy substance of a dragon, crushed and squeesed with the weight of the Elephants lying upon them ready to die, to wit, when the said dragons are full with sucking out the Elephants bloud before: and now their owne and it are mingled together, according as I have shewed before in the story of those beasts.[1] And verily there is not a color besides, which expresseth the lively colour of bloud in pictures so properly as Minium. . . .

Furthermore this hath beene observed, That the shining beams either of Sun or Moone, do much hurt to the lustre of Vermillion, or any thing painted therewith. But what meanes to prevent this inconvenience? Even to vernish the wall after the colour is dried upon it in this manner: Take white Punicke wax,[2] melt it with oyle, and while it is hot, wash the said painting all over with pensils or fine brushes of bristles, wet in the said vernish. But when

[1] See § 32.
[2] The best beeswax. The varnish dulls the colours somewhat but is practically everlasting, and many attempts have been made to revive the art of applying it. There are two more references to painting and varnishing with wax (encaustic) in Book 35.

this vernish is laid on, it must be well chafed and heat again with red hot coales made of Gall-nuts held close to it, that the wall may sweat and frie again: which done, it ought afterwards to be rubbed over well with cerecloths, and last of all with cleane linen cloths, that it may shine again and be slicke as statues of marble be.

Moreover, the workemen that are emploied in their shops about the making of Vermillion, doe bind unto their faces in manner of Maskes, large bladders, that they may take and deliver their wind at libertie, and yet not be in danger of drawing in with their breath that pernicious and deadly pouder, which is no better than poyson: yet so, as they may see out of the said masks neverthelesse.

To conclude, Vermillion is used much in limming the titles and inscriptions of roles and books, it setteth forth the letters also, and maketh them more faire and beautifull which are written in tables over sepulchres, be they enriched otherwise either with gold or marble stone.

§ 141

Of superfluitie and frugalitie
touching plate and silver vessels

(Chap. 11)

THE world is given to so much inconstancy as touching silver plate, that a wonder it is to see the nature of men how variable they be in the fashion and making of such vessel: for no workmanship wil please them long. One while we must have our plate out of *Furnius* his shop; another while we will be furnished from *Clodius*: and againe in a new fit, none wil content us but of *Gratius* his making (for our cupboords of plate and tables, forsooth, must beare the name of such and such Goldsmiths shops). Moreover, when the toy takes us in the head, al our delight is in chased and embossed plate; or els so carved, engraven, and deep cut in, as it is rough againe in the hand, wrought in imagery or floure-work, as if the painter had drawne them. And now adaies we are growne to this passe, that our dishes are set upon the table borne up with feet and supporters to sustaine the viands and meat therein, but in any wise their sides must be pared very neere; for herein I may tell you lieth a great matter, and the more that the sides and edges hath lost by the file, the richer is the plate esteemed to be.

As touching the vessell serving in the kitchen: did *Calvus* the noble Oratour complaine in his time that it was of silver? Why, wee in these dayes doe more than so, for we have devised that our coaches should bee all silver, and these curiously wrought and engraven. And within the remembrance of man, even in this age, *Poppaea* the Empresse, wife to *Nero* the Emperour, was known to cause her Ferrers ordinarily to shooe her coach-horses and other palfreis for her saddle (such especially as shee set store by, and counted more daintie than the rest) with cleane gold. To what excesse and prodigalitie is the world now grown to? *Scipio Africanus* the second of that name when hee dyed, left no more unto his Heire in Silver Plate and Coine than two and thirtie pound weight: and yet this worthie Knight, when hee rode in triumph for the conquest of the Carthaginians shewed in that solemne pompe, and brought into the chamber of Rome, as much treasure as amounted to foure thousand foure hundred and seventy pounds weight of silver. . . .[1] This was all the treasure in silver that the whole state of Carthage was able to make in those daies; Carthage (I say) that great and proud city which pretended a title to the Empire of the world, and maintained the same against Rome: and yet see! in this age there is as much laid out in our cupboords of plate, and furniture of our tables.

The same *Africanus* afterwards, upon the winning and finall ruine of Numantia, gave among his souldiers in a triumph, 17000 pound weight of silver:[2] O brave souldiers and worthy so noble a captain, who stood contented with such a reward. A brother of this *Scipio*, syrnamed *Allobrogicus*, was the first knowne to have in plate, one thousand pound weight: but *Livius Drusus*, whiles he was but Tribune or Provost of the comminalty, had in silver vessell as much as weighed eleven thousand pounds. Now if I should tell you that the Romane Censors upon a time disgraced, yea and degraded an antient captain and one who in his time had rode in triumph, only for that he had in plate five pound weight, it would

---

[1] '. . . a thousand times told', but the usual reading is 4,470 pounds.
[2] Or 7 denarii a head (alternative reading).

be taken in these daies for a meere tale and vaine fable: as also that *Catus Aelius* in his Consulship, was found sitting at dinner served with earthen vessell of potters worke, when the Embassadors of the Aetolians came unto him: that he refused also silver plate presented to him for the furniture of his boord, and to his dying day had never in silver more than two drinking cups, which *Lusius Paulus* his wives father bestowed upon him after the defeiture of K. *Perseus*, in regard to his valiant service; we hold it now for no lesse than an untruth and incredible.

The
THIRTY FOURTH BOOKE
treateth of other mettals

§ 142

The most renowned Colosses

(Chap. 7)

As touching the bold and venturous pieces of worke that have been performed and finished by this art, we have an infinite number of such examples: for we see what huge and gyant-like images they have devised to make in brasse, resembling high towers more like than personages, and such they called Colossi.

Of this kind is the image of *Apollo* within the Capitoll, transported by *M. Lucullus* out of Apollonia, a city within the kingdome of Pontus, which in height was thirtie cubits, and cost a hundred and fifty talents the making. Such another is that of *Jupiter* within *Mars* field, dedicated by *Claudius Caesar* the Emperour, which because it standeth so neere unto *Pompeys* theatre, men commonly call *Jupiter Pompeianus*, and full as big he is as *Apollo* above-named.

Like unto these, is the colosse or stately image (of *Hercules*) at Tarentum, the handiwork of the said *Lysippus*, but he is forty cubits high: and miraculous is the devise of this colosse, if it be true which is commonly reported thereof, namely, that a man may moove and stirre it easily with his hand, so truly ballanced it stands and equally counterpoised by Geometry; and yet no wind, no storme or tempest, is able to shake it. Certes, it is said, that the workeman himselfe *Lysippus*, provided well for this danger, in that a pretty way off he reared a columne or pillar of stone full opposit to the winds mouth, for to breake the force and rage thereof, from that side where it was like to blow and beat most upon the colosse: and verily so huge it was to weld, and so hard to bee removed, that *Fabius* surnamed *Verrucosus*, durst not meddle withall, but was forced to let it alone and leave it behind him; notwithstanding he brought with him from thence another *Hercules*, which now standeth within the Capitoll.

But the Colosse of the Sun which stood at Rhodes, and was wrought by *Chares* of Lyndus, apprentice to the abovenamed *Lysippus*, was above all others most admirable; for it carried seventy cubits in height:[1] well, as mighty an image as it was, it stood not on end above threescore yeares and six; for in an earthquake that then happened, it was overthrowne: but lying as it doth along, a wonderfull and prodigious thing it is to view and behold: for first and foremost, the thumbs of the hand and great toes of the foot are so big, as few men are able to fadome one of them about: the fingers and toes are bigger than the most part of other whole statues and images: and looke where any of the members or lims were broken with the fall, a man that saw them would say they were broad holes and huge caves in the ground: for within these fractures and breaches, you shall see monstrous big stones, which the workemen at the first rearing and setting of it had couched artificially within, for to strengthen the colosse, that standing firme and upright so ballaised, it might checke the violence of wind and weather. Twelve yeares (they say) *Chares* was in making of it before he could fully finish it, and the bare workemanship cost three hundred talents.

§ 143

Of Praxiteles

(Chap. 8)

As for *Praxiteles*, his workmanship was more seene in cutting of marble, and making Images thereof, wherein he had a singular grace and rare felicitie, and in which regard his name was the greater. Yet he shewed good proofe of his skil in foundery also, for there be most beautiful cast images of brasse which he made, to wit, the ravishing of *Proserpina* by *Pluto*, a Spinster spinning,

---

[1] *Festus* saith 105 foot: wherby it appeareth that a cubit was one foot and a halfe ... (P. H.).

which he called *Catagusa*: the image of Drunkennesse, god *Bacchus*
attended with one of the Satyrs; a noble piece of worke, and which
for the great voice and bruit that went of it, the Greekes sirnamed
Periboetos. The brasen images likewise, which stood sometimes in
the forefront of the temple at Rome dedicated unto *Felicity*, were
of his making: as also the goddesse *Venus*, which when the chappel
wherein she stood erected was burnt, during the raign of *Claudius
Caesar* the emperor, was melted; an exquisit piece of work, and
comparable to that *Venus* of his cutting in marble, which all the
world speakes so much of.

He portraied also in brasse a woman making coronets and
Chaplets of floures, which goes under the name of *Stephusa*: a foule
old trot and a nasty, bearing the title of *Spilumene*:[1] a carier also of
flaggons or wine-pots, knowne by the addition of *Oenophorus*. He
expressed moreover in brasse, and that most lively, *Harmodius* and
Aristogiton, massacring the tyrant *Pisistratus*:[2] which images being
with other pillage taken and caried away by *Xerxes* K. of Persia,
and recovered by King *Alexander* the Great when he had conquered the kingdom of Persis, the said prince and conquerer sent
them home to the Athenians again. Furthermore, he cast in brasse
a youth[3] lying in wait with an arrow to kill a Lizard, which was
readie to creepe close unto him and to sting; which piece of work
hee termed Sauroctonus.

Two images there are besides of his making, which people take
much pleasure to behold, and those in countenance shew divers
affections; to wit, a sober Matron weeping, and a light Courtesan
smirking: It is thought that this Courtesan was his owne Sweet-
heart *Phryne*; for men doe note both (in the curious workemanship of the Artificer) the love of him which fancied her, and also
(in the pleasant countenance of the harlot) the contentment that
she took by receiving her hire.

There is an image also of his making, which doth expresse his
own benignity and bountifull mind; for to a coach of *Calamis*
his doing, drawn with foure horses, he set a coachman of his owne

---

[1] From σπίλος, impurity or vice. Another reading is Pseliumene, said to mean
a woman putting a bracelet on her arm, from ψέλιον, an armlet.
[2] Harmodius and Aristogeiton did not kill Peisistratus. They attempted to
attack his sons, Hippias and Hipparchus, but only succeeded in killing Hipparchus.   [3] Some thinke he meaneth this of Apollo (P. H.).

handiworke: and why? because the posteritie another day should not thinke, That *Calamis* having done so well in pourtraying the horses, failed of the like cunning in expressing the man: and to say a truth, *Calamis* was not altogether so perfect and ready in personages of men and women as in the pourtraiture of horses. This *Calamis* was he who made many other coaches and chariots, as well with two steeds as foure; and verily, for absolute workmanship about horses, wherein he never missed, he had not his fellow againe in the world: and yet because hee would not be thought unlike himselfe, but be taken for as good an imageur in expressing men and women, as in representing horses, one statue hee made in resemblance of Ladie *Alcmena*, which is so exquisitly wrought as no man could ever set a better piece of worke by it.

The
THIRTY FIFTH BOOKE

§ 144

With what colours they painted in old time

(Chap. 7)

AND when I consider so many colours, and those so variable, as be now adaies in use, I must needs admire those artificers of old time; and namely of *Apelles, Echion, Melanthius,* and *Nicomachus,* most excellent painters, and whose tables were sold for as much apiece, as a good town was worth; and yet none of these used above foure colours in all those rich and durable workes.

And what might those be? Of all whites they had the white Tripoli of Melos; for yellow ochres they took that of Athens: for reds, they sought no farther than to the red ochre or Sinopic ruddle in Pontus: and their black was no other than ordinarie vitriol or shoomakers black. And now adaies, when we have such plenty of purple, that the very walls of our houses be painted all over therwith, when there commeth from India store enough not only of Indico, which the mud of their rivers do yeeld, but also of Cinnambre, which is the mixed bloud of their fel dragons and mighty elephants, yet among all our modern pictures we cannot shew one faire piece of worke: insomuch as wee may conclude, All things were done better then, notwithstanding the scarcitie that was of stuffe and matter. But to say a truth, the reason is, Given wee are now (as I have oftentimes said) to esteem of things that be rich and costly, never regarding the art that is imployed about them. And here I thinke it not amisse to set down the outragious excesse of this age, as touching pictures.

Nero the emperor commanded, that the portraict of himselfe should be painted in linnen cloth, after the maner of a gyant-like colosse 120 foot high; a thing that never had been heard or seen before. But see what became of it! When this monstrous picture

(which was drawne and made in the garden of Maius) was don
and finished, the lightning and fire from heaven caught it, and not
only consumed it, but also burnt withall the best part of the building about the garden. A slave of his infranchising (as it is wel
known) when he was to exhibit at Antium certain solemnities,
and namely a spectacle of sword-fencers fighting at sharp, caused
all the scaffolds, publique galleries, and walking places of that
city to be hung and tapissed with painted cloths, wherein were
represented the lively pictures of the sword-players themselves,
with all the wifflers and servitors to them belonging. But to
conclude, the best and most magnanimous men, that for many a
hundred yeares our country hath bred, have taken delight (I must
needs say) in this art, and set their minds upon good pictures.

§ 145

Of Zeuxis

(Chaps. 9, 10)

WHEN this man [Apollodorus] had opened the dore once, and
shewed the way to this art, *Zeuxis* of Heraclea entred in, and that
was in the fourth yere of the 95 Olympias: and now that the pensill
was taken in hand . . . he seeing that it made good worke, followed
on therewith, and by continuall practise brought the same to great
perfection, whereby he wan much credit to the art, and reputation
to himselfe. Some writers there bee who range him wrong in the
89 Olympias; at which time it must needs be, that *Demophilus* the
Himeraean and *Neseus* the Thracian lived; for to one of them
apprentice he was: but whether of the two was his master, there
is some doubt made; and verily so excellent he proved in his art,
that the abovenamed *Apollodorus* made verses of him; in which he
signifieth, that *Zeuxis* had stollen the cunning from them al, and
he alone went away with the art.

He grew in processe of time to such wealth by the means only
of his excellent hand, that for to make shew how rich he was,
when he went to the solemnity of the games at Olympia, he
caused his owne name to be imbrodered in golden letters, within

the lozenge worke of his clokes, whereof he had change,[1] and which he brought thither to be seen. In the end, he resolved with himselfe to work no longer for mony, but to give away al his pictures, saying, That he valued them above any price.

Thus he bestowed upon the Agrigentines, one picture of queen *Alcmena*, and to king *Archelaus* he gave another of the rustical god *Pan*: there was also the pourtraict of lady *Penelope*, which he drew in colours; wherein he seemeth not only to have depainted the outward personage and feature of the body, but also to have expressed most lively the inward affections and qualities of her mind: and much speech there is of a wrestler or champion of his painting; in which picture he pleased himselfe so well, that hee subscribed this verse under it, *Invisurus aliquis facilius quam imitaturus, i*, Sooner will a man envy me, than set such another by me. Which thereupon grew to be a by-word in every mans mouth. One stately picture there is of his workmanship, *Jupiter* sitting upon a throne in his Majestie, with all the other gods standing by and making court unto him. Hee pourtraied *Hercules* also as a babe lying in a cradle, and strangling two fell serpents with his hand, together with his mother *Alcmena*, and her husband K. *Amphytrion* in place, affrighted both at the sight thereof.

Howbeit, this *Zeuxis* as excellent a painter as he was, is noted for one fault and imperfection; namely, that the head and joints of his pourtraicts, were in some proportion to the rest somwhat with the biggest; for otherwise so curious and exquisite hee was, that when he should make a table with a picture for the Agrigentines, to be set up in the temple of *Juno Lacinia*, at the charges of the city, according to a vow that they had made, he would needs see all the maydens of the city naked; and from all that company he chose 5 of the fairest to take out, as from several patterns, whatsoever he liked best in any of them; and of all the lovely parts of those five, to make one body of incomparable beauty. . . .

There lived in his time *Timanthes*, *Androcydes*, *Eupompus*, and *Parrhasius*, who were his concurrents, and thought as well of themselves as he did. Of those foure . . ., *Parrhasius* by report was so bold as to challenge *Zeuxis* openly and to enter the lists with him for the victory; in which contention and triall, *Zeuxis* for

---

[1] Whereof he had many changes.

proofe of his cunning, brought upon the scaffold a table, wherein were clusters of grapes so lively painted, that the very birds of the aire flew flocking thither for to bee pecking at the grapes. *Parrhasius* againe for his part to shew his workmanship, came with another picture, wherin he had painted a linnen sheet, so like to a sheet indeed, that *Zeuxis* in a glorious bravery and pride of his heart, because the birds had approoved of his handy-worke, came to *Parrhasius* with these words by way of a scorn and frumpe, Come on sir, away with your sheet once, that we may see your goodly picture. But taking himselfe with the manner, and perceiving his own error, he was mightily abashed, and like an honest minded man yeelded the victory to his adversary, saying withall, *Zeuxis* hath beguiled poore birds, but *Parrhasius* hath deceived *Zeuxis*, a professed artisane.

This *Zeuxis*, as it is reported, painted afterwards another table, wherein he had made a boy carrying certaine bunches of grapes in a flasket, and seeing again that the birds flew to the grapes, he shook the head, and comming to his picture, with the like ingenious mind as before, brake out into these words, and said, Ah, I see well enough where I have failed, I have painted the grapes better than the boy, for if I had don him as naturally, the birds would have bin afraid and never approched the grapes.

§ 146

The great Apelles

(Chap. 10)

BUT what should I speake of these painters, whenas *Apelles* surmounted all that either were before, or came after. This *Apelles* flourished about the 112 Olympias, by which time hee became so consummate and accomplished in the art, that hee alone did illustrate and inrich it as much, if not more, than all his predecessors besides: who compiled also divers bookes, wherein the rules and principles, yea and the very secrets of the art are comprised. The speciall gift that he had was this, that he was able to give his pictures a certain lovely grace inimitable: and yet there were in his time most famous and worthy painters, whom he admired, whose works when hee beheld hee would praise them all, howbeit not without a but: for his ordinarie phrase was this, Here is an excellent picture, but that it wants one thing, and that is the *Venus*[1] it should have; which *Venus* the Greeks call *Charis*, as one would say, the grace: and in truth he would confesse, that other mens pictures had all things els that they should have, this onely excepted; wherein hee was persuaded that he had not his peere or second.

Moreover, he attributed unto himselfe another propertie, wherein hee gloried not a little, and that was that hee could see to make an end when a thing was well done. For beholding wistly upon a time a piece of worke of *Protogenes* his doing, wherein he saw there was infinite pains taken, admiring also the exceeding curiositie of the man in each point beyond all measure, he confessed and said, That *Protogenes* in everie thing else had done as well as himselfe could have done, yea and better too. But in one thing he surpassed *Protogenes*, for that he could not skill of laying worke out of his hand when it was finished well enough. A memorable admonition, teaching us all, That double diligence and overmuch curiositie doth hurt otherwhiles. This painter was not more renowned for his skill and excellencie in art, than he was commended for his simplicitie and singlenesse of heart: for as he gave place to *Melanthius* in disposition, so hee yeelded to *Asclepiodorus* in measures and proportion, that is to say, in the just knowledge how far distant one thing ought to be from another.

And to this purpose impertinent it is not, to report a pretty occurrent that fell between *Protogenes* and him: for being very desirous to be acquainted with *Protogenes*, a man whom hee had never seen, and of his works, whereof there went so great a name, he imbarqued and sailed to Rhodes, where *Protogenes* dwelt: and no sooner was hee landed, but he enquired where his shop was, and forthwith went directly thither. *Protogenes* himselfe was not at home, only there was an old woman in the house who had the keeping of a mighty large table set in a frame, and fitted ready for a picture: and when he enquired for *Protogenes*, she made answer, that he was not within; and seeing him thereupon ready to depart,

---

[1] *venerem*, charm, attraction, rather than grace as now understood.

demanded what his name was, and who she should tell her master asked for him. *Apelles* then, seeing the foresaid table standing before him, tooke a pensil in hand and drew in colour a passing fine and smal line[1] through the said table, saying to the woman, Tell thy master, that he who made this line enquired for him; and so he went his wayes. Now when *Protogenes* was returned home, the old woman made relation unto him of this that hapned in his absence; and as it is reported, the artificer had no sooner seene and beheld the draught of this small line, but he knew who had been there, and said withall, Surely *Apelles* is come to town; for unpossible it is, that any but hee should make in colour so fine workemanship.

With that hee takes me the pensill, and with another colour drew within the same line a smaller than it: willing the woman when hee went forth of dores, that if the party came againe, she should shew him what he had done, and say withall, that there was the man whom he inquired after. And so it fell out indeed, for *Apelles* made an errand againe to the shop, and seeing the second line, was dismaied at first and blushed withal to see himselfe thus overcome; but taking his pensil, cut the foresaid colours throughout the length, with a third colour distinct from the rest, and left no room at all for a fourth to be drawn within it. Which when *Protogenes* saw, hee confessed that he had met with his match and his master both; and made all the hast he could to the haven to seek for *Apelles* to bid him welcome and give him friendly entertainment. In memorial whereof it was thought good both by the one and the other, to leave unto posterity this table thus naked without any more work in it, to the wonder of all men that ever saw it, but of cunning artisans and painters especially: for this table was kept a long time, and as it is well known, consumed to ashes in that first fire that caught *Caesars* house within the Palatine hil: and verily we took great pleasure before that, to see it many times, containing in that large and extraordinarie capacitie that it had, nothing els but certaine lines, which were so fine and small, that unneth or hardly they could be discerned by the eie. And in truth, when it stood among the excellent painted tables of many other workemen, it seemed a very blanke having nothing in it: howbeit as void and naked as it was, it drew many to it even in

---

[1] Perhaps an outline of some object.

that respect, being more looked upon and esteemed better than any other rich and curious work whatsoever.

But to come again unto *Apelles*, this was his manner and custom besides, which he perpetually observed, that no day went over his head, but what businesse soever he had otherwise to call him away, he would make one draught or other (and never misse) for to exercise his hand and keep it in use, insomuch as from him grew the proverbe, *Nulla dies sine Linea*, i. Be alwaies doing somewhat, though you doe but draw a line. His order was when he had finished a piece of work or painted table, and layd it out of his hand, to set it forth in some open gallerie or thorow-fare, to be seen of folke that passed by, and himselfe would lie close behind it to hearken what faults were found therewith; preferring the judgement of the common people before his owne, and imagining they would spy more narrowly, and censure his doings sooner then himselfe: and as the tale is told, it fell out upon a time, that a shoomaker as he went by seemed to controlle his workemanship about the shoo or pantofle that he had made to a picture, and namely, that there was one latchet fewer than there should be: *Apelles* acknowledging that the man said true indeed, mended that fault by the next morning, and set forth his table as his manner was. The same shoomaker comming again the morrow after, and finding the want supplied which he noted the day before, took some pride unto himselfe, that his former admonition had sped so well, and was so bold as to cavil at somewhat about the leg. *Apelles* could not endure that, but putting forth his head from behind the painted table, and scorning thus to be checked and reproved, Sirrha (quoth hee) remember you are but a shoomaker, and therefore meddle no higher I advise you, than with shoos. Which words also of his came afterwards to be a common proverbe, *Ne sutor ultra crepidam.*[1]

Over and besides, very courteous he was and faire spoken, in which regard King *Alexander* the Great accepted the better of him, and much frequented his shop in his owne person: for, as I have said before, he gave streight commandement, That no painter should bee so hardie as to make his picture but only *Apelles*. Now when the King being in his shop, would seeme to talke much and reason about his art, and many times let fal some words to little

[1] Let the shoemaker stick to his last.

purpose, bewraying his ignorance; *Apelles* after his mild manner, would desire his grace to hold his peace, and said, sir, no more words, for feare the prentise boies there that are grinding of colours, do laugh you to scorn: So reverently thought the king of him, that being otherwise a cholericke prince, yet hee would take any word at his hands in that familiar sort spoken in the best part, and be never offended.

And verily, what good reckoning *Alexander* made of him, he shewed by one notable argument; for having among his courtesans one named *Campaspe*, whom he fancied especially above the rest, in regard as wel of that affection of his as her incomparable beauty, he gave commandement to *Apelles* for to draw her picture all naked: but perceiving *Apelles* at the same time to be wounded with the like dart of love as wel as himself, he bestowed her on him most frankly. By which example, hee shewed moreover, that how great a Commander, and high minded a prince he was otherwise, yet in this mastering and commanding of his affections, his magnanimity was more seen: and in this act of his he wan as much honor and glory, as by any victory over his enemies; for now he had conquered himselfe, and not onely made *Apelles* partner with him of his love, but also gave his affection clean away from her unto him, nothing mooved with the respect of her whom before he so dearly loved, that being the concubin of a king, she should now become the bedfellow of a painter. Some are of opinion, That by the patterne of this *Campaspe*, *Apelles* made the picture of *Venus Anadyomene*.[1]

Moreover, *Apelles* was of a kind bountiful disposition even to other painters of his time, who commonly as concurrents, do envie one another. And the first he was that brought *Protogenes* into credit and estimation at Rhodes; for at the first, his owne countrymen made no account at all of him (a thing ordinarily seen, that in our own country we are least regarded) but *Apelles*, for to countenance and credit the man, demanded of him what price he would set of al the pictures that he had ready made; *Protogenes*

---

[1] *i. Ortam mari, i.* rising out of the sea (P. H.). Venus was born from the foam of the sea and Apelles' famous picture, painted for the islanders of Cos, made this name for her popular. So celebrated was this picture that when Augustus took it away from Cos to Rome (see p. 285) he reduced the Coans' taxes in payment.

asked some small matter and trifle to speake of: howbeit, *Apelles* esteemed them at fifty talents, and promised to give so much for them: raising a bruit by this means abroad in the world, that he bought them for to sel againe as his owne. The Rhodians hereat were moved and stirred up to take better knowledge of *Protogenes*, what an excellent workeman they had of him: neither would *Protogenes* part with any of his pictures unto them, unlesse they would come off roundly and rise to a better price than before time.

As for *Apelles*, he had such a dexterity in drawing pourtraits so lively, and so neer resembling those for whom they were made, that hardly one could be known from the other; insomuch, as *Appio* the Grammarian hath left in writing (a thing incredible to be spoken) that a certain Physiognomist or teller of Fortune, by looking onely upon the face of men and women, such as the Greekes call Metoposcopos, judged truly by the portraits that *Apelles* had drawne, how many yeres they either had lived or were to live, for whom those pictures were made. But as gracious as he was otherwise with *Alexander* and his train, yet he could never win the love and favor of prince *Ptolomaeus*, who at that time followed the court of K. *Alexander*, and was afterwards king of Egypt. It fortuned, that after the decease of *Alexander*, and during the reigne of K. *Ptolomae* aforesaid, this *Apelles* was by a tempest at sea cast upon the coast of Aegypt, and forced to land at Alexandria; where, other painters that were no well willers of his, practised with a jugler or jeaster of the kings, and suborned him in the kings name to train[1] *Apelles* to take his supper with the king. To the court came *Apelles* accordingly, and shewed himself in the presence. *Ptolomae* having espied him, with a stern and angry countenance demanded of him what he made there, and who had sent for him? and with that shewed unto him all his servitors who ordinarily had the inviting of ghests to the kings table, commanding him to say which of all them had bidden him: whereat *Apelles*, not knowing the name of the party who had brought him thither, and beeing thus put to his shifts, caught up a dead cole of fire from the hearth thereby, and began therewith to delineat and draw upon the wall the proportion of that cousiner beforesaid. He had no sooner pourfiled a little about the visage, but the king presently

[1] Persuade.

tooke knowledge thereby of the party that had played this pranke by him and wrought him this displeasure.

This *Apelles* drew the face of K. *Antiochus* also, who had but one eie to see withall: for to hide which deformity and imperfection, he devised to paint him, turning his visage a little away, and so he shewed but the one side of his face, to the end, that whatsoever was wanting in the picture, might be imputed rather to the painter, than to the person whom he portraied. And in truth, from him came this invention first to conceale the defects and blemishes of the visage, and to make one halfe face onely, when it might be represented full and whole, if it pleased the painter.

Among other principall pieces of worke, some pictures there be of his making, resembling men and women lying at the point of death, and even ready to gasp and yeeld up the ghost. But of all the pictures and portraitures that he made, to say precisely which be the most excellent, it were a very hard matter: as for the painted table of *Venus*, arising out of the sea (which is commonly knowne by the name of *Anadyomene*) *Augustus Caesar*, late Emperour of famous memory, dedicated it in the temple of *Julius Caesar*, his father; which hee inriched with an Epigram of certaine Greeke verses, in commendation as well of the picture, as the painter. And albeit the artificall contriving of the said verses went beyond the worke, which they seemed to praise, yet they beautified and set out the table not a little. The nether part of this picture had caught some hurt by a mischance: but there never could be found that painter yet, who would take in hand to repaire the same and make it up again as it was at first: so as, this wrong and harm done unto the work, and continuing still upon the same, turned to the glory of the workeman. This table remained a long time to be seen, untill in the end for age it was worm-eaten and rotten: in such sort, as *Nero* being Emperor was fain to set another in the place, wrought by the hand of *Dorotheus*. . . .

One secret he had himselfe, which no man was ever able to attaine and reach unto, and that was a certain blacke vernish[1] which hee used to lay upon his painted tables when he had finished them; which was so finely tempered, and withall driven upon the worke so thin, that by the repercussion thereof it gave an excellent glosse and pleasant lustre to the colors; the same also

[1] The Latin is *atramento*, or ink. It is usually translated as a dark varnish.

preserved the picture from dust and filthinesse: and yet a man could not perceive any such thing at all, unlesse he held the table close at hand, and looked very neere. And great reason hee had besides to use this vernish, namely, lest the brightnesse of the colours without it, might offend and dazzle the eyes, which now beheld them as it were afarre off through a glasse stone; and withall, the same gave a secret deeping and sadnesse to those colours which were too gay and gallant. And thus much may suffice for *Apelles*.

§ 147

The Pictures of Protogenes

(Chap. 10)

ABOUT the same time, there flourished (as I have said before) *Protogenes*; born he was at Caunos a city in Cilicia, and subject to the Rhodians: he was so exceeding poore at the beginning, and withall, so studious, intentive, and curious in his worke without all end, that fewer pictures by that means came out of his hands, and himselfe never rise to any great wealth. . . . But of all the painted tables that ever he wrought, that of *Ialysus*[1] is accounted the principall, which is now dedicated at Rome within the temple of *Peace*: whiles he was in painting this *Ialysus*, it is said, that he lived only upon steeped Lupines, which might serve him in stead of meat and drinke both, to satisfie his hunger and quench his thirst: and this hee did, for feare least too much sweetnesse of other viands should cause him to feed over liberally, and so dul his spirit and senses. And to the end that this picture should be lesse subject to other injuries, and last the longer, he charged it with foure grounds of colours, which he laid one upon another: that ever as the upper coat went, that underneath might succeed in the place and shew fresh againe.

In this table, the pourtraiture of a dog is admirable and miraculous; for not only art, but fortune also met together in the painting thereof; for when he had done the dog in all parts to the contentment of his owne minde (and that ywis was a very hard and rare

[1] A worthy knight, sonne of *Ochimus* (P. H.).

matter with him) and could not satisfie and please himselfe in
expressing the froth which fell from his mouth as he panted and
blowed almost windlesse with running; displeased he was with the
very art it selfe: and albeit he thought that he had bin long enough
already about the said froth, and spent therein but too much art
and curiositie, yet somewhat (he wist not what) was to be
diminished or altered therein: the more workmanship and skill
that went thereto, the farther off it was from the truth indeed and
the nature of froth (the onely marke that he shot at): for when he
had done all that he could, it seemed still but painted froth, and
not that which came out of the dogs mouth; whereas it should have
been the very same and no other, which had been there before.
Hereat he was troubled and vexed in his mind, as one who would
not have any thing seene in a picture of his, that might be said
like, but the very same indeed. Many a time he had changed his
pensill and colours; as often, he had wiped out that which was done,
and al to see if he could hit upon it, but it would not be, for yet it
was not to his fansie.

At the last, falling clean out with his own workmanship, because the art might be perceived in it, in a pelting chase he flings
me the spunge-ful of colours that he had wiped out, full against
that unhappy place of the table which had put him to all this
trouble: but see what came of it! the spunge left the colours behind,
in better order than hee could have laied them, and in truth,
as well as his heart could wish. Thus was the froth made to his full
mind, and naturally indeed by meere chance, which all the wit and
cunning in his head could not reach unto. (After whose example,
Nealces another painter did the like, and sped as wel, in making the
froth falling naturally from a horses mouth; namely, by throwing
his spunge against the table before him, at what time as he painted
a horse-rider cheering and cherking up his horse, yet reining him
hard as he champed upon his bit.) Thus (I say) Fortune taught
Protogenes to finish his dog.

This picture of *Ialysus* and his dog, was of such name and so
highly esteemed, that K. *Demetrius* when hee might have forced
the city of Rhodes, on that side onely where *Protogenes* dwelt,
forbare to set it on fire, because he would not burne it among
other painted tables: and thus for to spare a picture, he lost the
opportunitie of winning a towne. During this strait siege and hot

assault of Rhodes, it chanced that *Protogenes* himselfe was at
worke in a little garden that he had by the townes side, even as
a man would say within the compasse of *Demetrius* his camp. And
for all the fury of warre and the daily skirmishes within his sight
and hearing, yet he went on still with his workes that he had in
hand, and never discontinued one hour. But being sent for by the
king, and demanded, How he durst so confidently abide without
the walls of the city in that dangerous time? he answered, That
he knew full well that *Demetrius* warred against the Rhodians, and
had no quarrell to good Arts and Sciences. The king then (glad
in his heart that it lay now in his hand to save those things, which
he had spared before, and whereof he had so good respect)
bestowed a very strong guard about *Protogenes* for his better
safety and security: and as great an enemy as he was to the
Rhodians, yet he used otherwhiles to visit *Protogenes* of his owne
accord in proper person, because he would not eftsoones call him
out of his shop from worke: and setting aside the maine point and
occasion of lying before Rhodes, which was the winning thereof,
the thing that he so much desired; even amid the assaults, skirmishes, and battels, hee would finde time to come to *Protogenes*,
and took great pleasure to see his worke.

By occasion of this siege and hostilitie, arose this tale moreover
of one table of his making, That all the whiles he painted it, the
dagger (forsooth) was set to his heart, and a sword ready to cut his
throat: and it was the picture of a Satyre playing upon a paire of
bag-pipes, which he called *Anapauomenos*:[1] by which name, as well
as by the thing it selfe, hee would seem to signifie, that he tooke
but little thought and care during those dangerous troubles.

§ 148

Of other painters

(Chap. 10)

MEET it is to annex unto the rest, such as have bin famous with
the pencill in smaller works and lesse pictures; among whom I may

[1] One at rest, or reposing himselfe (P. H.).

reckon *Pyraeicus,* who for art and skill had not many that went
before him; and verily of this man, I wot not well, whether he
debased himselfe and bare a low sale, of purpose, or no? for surely
his mind was wholly set upon painting of simple and base things:
howbeit, in that humble and lowly carriage of himselfe, hee attained to a name of glory in the highest degree; his delight was to
paint shops, of barbers, shoomakers, coblers, taylers, and semsters:
hee had a good hand in pourtraying of poore asses, with the victuals that they bring to market, and such homely stuffe: whereby he
got himselfe a by-name, and was called *Rhyparographus.*[1]

Howbeit, such rude and simple toies as these were so artificially
wrought, that they pleased and contented the beholders, no thing
so much. Many chapmen he had for these trifling pieces, and a
greater price they yeelded unto him, than the fairest and largest
tables of many others. Whereas contrariwise, *Serapio* used to make
such great and goodly pictures, that (as *M. Varro* writeth) they
were able to take up and fill all the stals, bulks, and shops, jutting
forth into the street under the old market place Rostra; this
Serapio had an excellent grace in pourtraying tents, booths, stages,
and theaters; but to paint a man or woman, he knew not which
way to begin.

§ 149

The wall paintings of Ludius

(Chap. 10)

FOR this *Ludius*[2] was he who first devised to beautifie the wals of
an house with the pleasantest painting that is in all varietie, to wit,
with the resemblance of manors, farms, and houses of pleasure in
the country, havens, vinets, floure-work in knots, groves, woods,
forrests, hils, fish-pooles, conduits, and drains, rivers, riverets,
with their banks, and whatsoever a man would wish for to see:
wherin also he would represent sundry other shews of people,

---

[1] Rhyparographus meant a painter of sordid subjects.
[2] Other readings are Studius or S. Tadius.

some walking and going to and fro on foot; others sailing and rowing up and down the stream upon the river, or els riding by land to their farms, either mounted upon their mules and asses, or els in wagons and coaches: there a man should see folk in this place fishing and angling, in that place hauking and fouling: some hunting here, the hare, the fox, or deere both red and fallow; others busie there in harvest or vintage.

In this maner of painting a man should behold of his workman-ship faire houses standing upon marishes, unto which all the ways that lead be ticklish and full of bogs; where you should see the paths so slipperie, that women as they goe are afraid to set one foot afore another; some at every step ready to slide, others bend-ing forwards with their heads as though they caried some burdens upon their neck and shoulders, and all for feare lest, their feet failing under them, they should catch a fal; and a thousand more devises and pretty conceits as these full of pleasure and delight. The same *Ludius* devised walls without dores, and abroad in the open aire to paint Cities standing by the sea side. All which kinde of painting pleaseth the eie very well, and is besides of little or no cost. Howbeit, neither hee nor any other in this kinde (howso-ever otherwise respected) grew ever to be famous and of great name; that felicitie they only attained unto, who used to paint in tables: and therefore in this regard, venerable antiquitie we have in greater admiration; for painters in old time loved not to garnish wals for to pleasure the master only of the house, ne yet to bedeck houses in that maner which canot stir out of the place, nor shift and save themselves when fire commeth, as painted tables may, that are to be removed with ease.

Protogenes, as excellent a painter as he was, contented himselfe to live within a little garden in a small cottage, and I warrant you no part therof was painted. *Apelles* himselfe might well have the walls of his house rough cast or finely plaistered, but never a patch thereof had any painting: they took no pleasure, nay they had no lust at all to paint upon the whole wals, and to work upon them from one end to another; al their skil and cunning attended upon the publique service of states and cities: and a painter was not for this or that place only, but imploied for the benefit indifferently of all countries and nations.

§ 150

Of the last peeces of Painters

(Chap. 11)

BUT one thing more there is, of rare admiration and worthie to be remembered, That the last peeces of excellent Painters, and namely such tables as bee left unperfect, are commonly better esteemed than those that bee fully finished: as wee may see by the Raine-bow or Iris which *Aristides* was entered into, the two brethren *Castor* and *Pollux*, begunne by *Nicomachus*; the Picture of *Medea*, killing the children that shee had by *Jason*, which *Timomachus* was in hand with; and the *Venus*, that as I sayd before, *Apelles* lived not to make an end of: for in these and such like imperfect tables, a man may (as it were) see what traicts and lineaments remayne to bee done, as also the very desseignes and cogitations of the Artificers: and as these beginnings are attractive allurements to moove us for to commend those hands that began such Draughts: so the conceit that they be now dead and missing, is no small griefe unto us, when wee behold them so raw and fore-lct.

§ 151

Of drugs that drinke and take colour

(Chap. 11)

MOREOVER, in Aegypt they have a devise to staine cloths after a strange and wonderful maner: They take white clothes, as sailes or curtaines when they have bin worne, which they besmeare not with colours but with drugs that are apt to drinke and take colour: when they have so don, there is no apparence in them at all of any dye or tincture. These clothes they cast into a lead or cauldron of some colour that is seething and scalding hot: where, after they have remained a pretty while, they take them forth againe, all stained and painted in sundry colours.

An admirable thing, that there being in the said cauldron but only one kind of tincture, yet out of it the cloth should be stained with this and that colour, and the foresaid boiling liquor change so as it doth, according to the quality and nature of the drugs which were laied upon the white at first.[1] And verily, these stains or colours are set so sure, as they can never be washed off afterwards: thus the scalding liquor, which no doubt if it had divers tinctures and colours in it, would have confounded them all into one; now out of one doth dispense and digest them accordingly, and in boiling the drugs of the clothes, setteth the colour and staineth surely. And verily, this good moreover have the clothes by this scalding, that they be alwaies more firme and durable, than if they had not come into the boiling cauldron.

[1] The description of mordanting with different drugs and dyeing with a single dye is remarkably clear and correct.

THE
THIRTY SIXTH BOOKE
treateth of marble and stone for building

§ 152

The excessive expence in columnes and buildings of Marble

(Chaps. 1–3)

IT remaines now to write of the nature of stones, that is to say, the principal point of all enormious abuses, and the very height of wastful superfluities, yea though we should keep silence, and say nothing either of precious stones and Amber, or of Chrystall and Cassidonie. For all things els which we have handled heretofore even to this Booke, may seem in some sort to have been made for man; but as for mountaines, Nature has framed them for her owne selfe; partly to strengthen (as it were) certain joints within the veines and bowels of the earth; partly to tame the violence of great rivers, and to break the force of surging waves and inundations of the sea; and in one word, by that substance and matter whereof they stand, which of all others is most hard, to restraine and keep within bounds that unruly element of the water.

And yet notwithstanding, for our wanton pleasures and nothing els, we cut and hew, we load and carry away those huge hils and inaccessible rockes, which otherwise to passe only over, was thought a wonder. Our Ancestors in times past reputed it a miracle, and in manner prodigious, that first *Annibal*, and afterwards the Cimbrians, surmounted the Alps: but now, even the same mountaines wee pierce through with picke-axe and mattocke, for to get out thereof a thousand sorts of marble; wee cleave the capes and promontories: we lay them open for the sea, to let it in; downe we goe with their heads, as if wee would lay the whole world even, and make all levell. The mightie mountains set as limits to bound the frontiers of divers countries, and to separate one Nation from another, those wee transport and carrie from their native seat: ships wee build of purpose for to fraught with marble: the cliffes and tops of high hills they carrie too and fro, amid the waves and billowes of the sea, and never feare the danger of that most fell and cruell element: wherein verily wee surpasse the madnesse and vanitie of those, who search as high as the clouds for a cup to drink our water cold; and hollow the rocks that in manner touch the heaven, and all to drink out of yce.[1]

Now let every man thinke with himselfe what excessive prices of these stones hee shall heare anone, and what monstrous pieces and masses he seeth drawne and carried both by land and sea; let him consider withall, how much more faire and happy a life many a man should have without all this, and how many cannot chuse but die for it, whensoever they go about to doe, or if I should speake more truely, to suffer this enterprise: also, for what use else, or pleasure rather, but onely that they might lie in beds and chambers of stones that forsooth are spotted, as if they never regarded how the darknesse of the night bereaveth the one halfe of each mans life of these delights and joies. When I ponder and weigh these things in my mind, I must needs think great shame, and impute a great fault to our forefathers that lived long since, and blush in their behalfe. Lawes were enacted, and prohibitions published by the Censors, and those remaining upon record, forbidding expressely, That neither the kernelly part of a Bores neck, nor dormice, and other smaller matters than these to be spoken of, should be served up to the boord at great feasts: but as touching the restraint of bringing in marble, or of sailing into forraine parts for the same, there was no act or statute ordained.

But some man haply might reply againe upon me, and say: what need was there of any such ordinance, considering there was no marble in those daies brought in from strange countries? Unto whom I answer, That it is a meere untruth, for even our progenitors, of whom I speak, saw well enough how in that yere when *M. Scaurus* was Aedile, there were not fewer than 360 pillars of marble transported to Rome, for the front and stage of a Theater,[2]

---

[1] *Ut bibatur glacie*, for they held Crystall to be a kinde of yce (P. H.).
[2] See § 158, p. 311, for a description of this theatre.

which was to continue a small while, and scarcely to be used one moneth to an end: and yet no law there was to checke and controule him for it. But it may be inferred againe, the Magistrats winked hereat, because he did all this for a publicke pleasure to the whole citie, during the plaies exhibited by him in his Aedileship: . . . What reason I pray you had they so to doe? By what means more doe abuses and inormities creepe into a citie or state, than by a publicke president given? for I assure you it was nothing else but such examples at the first that brought those other things, I meane, yvorie, gold, jewels, and precious stones, to be used by privat persons, so commonly as they be, in their houses, plate, and ornaments.

And what have we left and reserved at all for the very gods to have, since that we lay so much upon our selves? But say that in those daies they did tolerat this excesse in *Scaurus*, because of the pastimes he did exhibite to the whole city; What, were they silent also and made no words, when the said *Scaurus* caused the biggest of all these columnes (yea those that were fortie foot high within twain, and the same of Lucullan black marble) to be erected and placed in the court before his owne house in mount Palatine? And least any man should say, that this is done in secret and hucker mucker, know he, That when these pillars were to be carried up into the mount Palatine where his house stood, the Bailife that had the charge of the publick sinkes vaulted under the ground, dealt with *Scaurus* for good securitie, yea, and demanded cautions and sureties for satisfying of all harmes and dammages that might be occasioned by their carriage, so huge and heavie they were. Considering then this bad example, so prejudiciall to all good manners, and so hurtfull to posterity, had it not bin better for the city to have cut off these superfluities by wholsome laws and edicts, than thus to permit such huge and proud pillars to be carried unto a privat house up into the Palatine mount, even under the nose of the gods, whose images were but of earth, and hard by their temples that had for their covers and louvers no better than such as were made of potters cley?

Neither can it be alledged for excuse of this tolleration in *Scaurus*, that hee tooke the vantage and spied his time when the city of Rome was not ware of any such matter toward, as having not been acquainted beforetime with the like, and therefore he stale upon them with these superfluous pompes, as doubting[1] nothing lesse than such new devises, and therefore having no time to prevent and stay them: for long before this, *L. Crassus* that great Orator, who was the first that inriched his house (within the same Palatium) with pillars of outlandish marble, although they were but of the Quarry in Hymettus hill, and neither more in number than six, nor carying in length above 12 foot apiece, was reproved and reproched for this pride and vanity by *M. Brutus,* who among other hot words and biting terms that passed interchangeably between them, taunted him by the name of *Venus Palatina.* Certes, considering how all good orders and customs otherwise were trodden under foot, we are to presume thus of our predecessors, That when they saw other injunctions and prohibitions as touching divers abuses crept in, take no effect, but daily broken, they thought it better policy to make no lawes at all for restraint of such columns, than to have them infringed, or at leastwise, not observed when they were made: yet are we in these daies in better order than so, and I doubt not but the age and generation following will justifie and approve of us in comparison of them: for where is there one in Rome at this day, who hath in the portaile or entrie of his house any columns, that for bignesse and pride come near to those of *Scaurus?*

§ 153

The Venus of Praxiteles

(Chap. 5)

To come now to *Praxiteles*: what time hee lived I have declared already in my catalogue of Founders and Imageurs in brasse: who albeit he was singular in that kind, yet in marble he went beyond himselfe: his workes are to be seen at Athens, in that conspicuous street called Ceraunicum: but of all the images that ever were made (I say not by *Praxiteles* only, but by all the workmen that

---

[1] Fearing.

were in the world) his *Venus* passeth, that hee made for them of Gnidos:[1] and in truth so exquisit and singular it was, that many a man hath embarked, taken sea and sailed to Gnidos for no other busines, but onely to see and behold it.

Hee made two of them, and sould them both together; the one with a vaile and arraied decently in apparell, which in that regard the men of Cos bought: for being put to their choice, they like honest men preferred it before the other which was naked (notwithstanding *Praxiteles* tendred them both at one and the same price) in the good mind that they carried, and having respect and regard unto their gravity and modest carriage of themselves: that which they refused and rejected, the Gnidians bargained for: and indeed, to speak of workmanship, it was infinitely better, and there was no comparison betweene them, by the generall fame and opinion of all men: and verily King *Nicomedes* would afterwards gladly have bought it againe of the Gnidians, and offered them enough; for he promised in consideration thereof to discharge al debts that their city was ingaged in, which were very great summes; but they would not give eare or hearken unto him: content they were rather to live in debt and danger still, yea and to abide and endure any forfeitures, exigents, executions, and extents whatsoever, than to part with their *Venus*.

And to say a truth, good reason they had so to do, for, that one image of Praxiteles his making was their chiefe credit, innobled their city, and drew resort from all parts thither. This *Venus* was shrined in a little chappell by her selfe within a tabernacle; but of purpose so devised, that it might be set open on all sides, for to be seen and viewed all and whole on every part: wherewith the goddesse her selfe (as men were verily persuaded) was well enough pleased, and shewed her contentment therein to al commers; for looke upon her as one would, amiable shee was, and admirable every way.

[1] This statue, modelled from Phryne the Athenian courtesan, was moved from Rhodes to Constantinople, where it was destroyed in the fire of A.D. 532 in the reign of Justinian.

§ 154

Of the images of Scopas

(Chap. 5)

B U T of all that ever he [Scopas] wrought, there is most account made of those images which are in the chappell of *Cneus Domitius,* within the cirque of *Flaminius,* to wit, *Neptune* himselfe, and dame *Thetis,* and her sonne *Achilles;* the Sea-nymphs or Meere-maides also called *Nereides,* mounted upon Dolphins, Whales, and mightie Sea-horses called Hippocampi, and sitting upon them: moreover, the sea trumpeters *Tritones,* with all the quire and traine attending upon sir *Phorcus* a Sea-god, and the mighty fishes called Pistrices, besides many other monsters of the sea: all wrought by one and the same hand so curiously, that if he had sitten about the making of them al his life time and done nothing at all els, a man would have thought it worke enough, and a great deed.

But moreover and besides these above rehearsed, and many more which wee are not come to the knowledge of, we have here with us at Rome the image of *Mars* made gyant like after the manner of a colosse, yet sitting within the temple of *Brutus Callaecus,* which stands close unto the said cirque, in the way as men goe from thence to the gate Labicana. In the same place there is moreover another *Venus* naked, and wrought by the hands of *Scopas,* which seemeth to goe beyond that other *Venus* of Gnidos that *Praxiteles* made;[1] which image alone were able (no doubt) to give name to any other citie where it should stand, and to innoble the place: But at Rome verily there bee so many pieces besides, and those so stately and sumptuous withall, that they obscure and darken it (as it were) in some sort. Moreover, the exceeding great affaires and the busie negotiations (whereof there is such a multitude and a world as it were in that Citie) withdraw all men from the contemplation and beholding of such things, bee they never so singular: for to say a truth, it belongeth rather to idle persons to look and gaze upon these matters and fitter for a place where there is little or no stirring, but all quiet and silent.

[1] This has also been translated as another Venus of earlier date than that of Praxiteles.

§ 155

Of the Egyptian Pyramides, and of Sphinx

(Chap. 12)

HAVING thus discoursed of the Obelisks, it were good to say somwhat of the Pyramids also in Egypt; a thing I assure you that bewraieth the foolish vain-glory of the Kings in that countrey, who abounding with wealth, knew not what to doe with their money, but spent it in such idle and needlesse vanities. And verily most writers doe report, That the principall motive which induced them to build these Pyramides, was partly to keepe the Common people from idlenes, partly also because they would not have much treasure lying by them, lest either their heirs apparant, or other ambitious persons who aspired to be highest, should take occasion thereby to play false and practise treasons.

Certes a man may observe the great follies of those princes herein, That they began many of these Pyramides, and left them unfinished, as may appeare by the tokens remaining thereof. One of them there is within the territory under the jurisdiction of *Arsinoë*; two within the province that lieth to the government of Memphis, not far from the Labyrinth, whereof also I purpose to speake: there are other twaine likewise in the place where sometimes was the lake Moeris, which was nothing else but a mighty huge fort intrenched by mans hand in manner of a mote or poole: but the Aegyptians (among many other memorable and wonderfull works wrought by their princes) speake much of these two Pyramides,[1] the mighty spires and steeples whereof (by their saying) do arise out of the very water. As for the other three which are so famous throughout the world (as indeed they are notable marks to be kenned a far off by sailers, and directions for their course) these are scituat in the marches of Affrick[2] upon a craggy and barren mountaine, betweene the city Memphis and a certain Island or division of Nilus which (as I have said before) was called Delta, within foure miles of Nilus and six from Memphis, where

---

[1] *Herodotus* saith, they were 250 foot high above the water, and as many deepe under (P. H.).
[2] The African or western bank of the Nile.

there standeth a village hard unto it named Busiris, wherein there be certaine fellows that ordinarily use to clime up to the top of them.

Over against the sayd Pyramides there is a monstrous rocke called Sphinx, much more admirable than the Pyramides, and forsooth the peisants that inhabit the countrey esteemed it no lesse than some divine power and god of the fields and forrests: within it, the opinion goeth, that the body of K. *Harmais* was intombed; and they would bear us in hand, that the rock was brought thither, all and whole as it is: but surely it is a meere crag growing naturally out of the ground; howbeit wrought also with mans hand, polished and very smooth and slippery. The compasse of this rocks head (resembling thus a monster) taken about the front, or as it were the forehead, containeth one hundred and two foot, the length . . . 143 foot; the heigth from the belly to the top of the crowne in the head, ariseth to 62 foot.

But of all these Pyramides, the biggest doth consist of the stone hewed out of the Arabicke quarries: it is said, that in the building of it there were 366000 men kept at worke twentie yeares together: and all three were in making threescore and eighteene yeares and foure moneths. . . . But (as many as have written hereof) yet a man cannot know certainly and say, This Pyramis was built by this king: a most just punishment, that the name and authors of so monstrous vanity, should be buried in perpetuall oblivion: but some of these Historiographers have reported, that there were a thousand and eight hundred talents laid out only for raddish, garlicke, and onions, during the building of these Pyramides. The largest of them taketh up eight acres of ground at the foot, foure square it is made, and every face or side thereof equall, containing from angle to angle eight hundred fourescore and three foot, and at the top five and twenty: the second made likewise foure cornered, is on every side even, and comprehendeth from corner to corner seven hundred thirty and seven foot: the third is lesse than the former two, but far more beautifull to behold, built of Aethiopian stones;[1] it carrieth at the foot in each face

---

[1] The lower sixteen courses of the sheathing are of red Assouan granite, the rest being of Tura limestone. The length of each face of this pyramid (of Mycerinus) was 356 feet, much as Pliny states it. His figures for the great and second pyramids have reached us greater than they should be; the great pyramid

betweene foure angles, three hundred threescore and three foot.

And yet of all these huge monuments, there remaine no tokens of any houses built, no apparence of frames and engins requisit for such monstrous buildings; a man shall find all about them far and neare, faire sand and small red gravell, much like unto Lentill seed, such as is to be found in the most part of Affricke. A man seeing all so cleane and even, would wonder at them how they came thither; but the greatest difficultie mooving question and marvell, is this, What meanes were used to carry so high as well such mightie masses of hewen squared stone, as the filling, rubbish, and mortar that went thereto? For some are of opinion, that there were devised mounts of salt and nitre heaped up together higher and higher as the worke arose and was brought up; which being finished, were demolished, and so washed away by the inundation of the river Nilus: others thinke, that there were bridges reared with bricks made of clay, which after the worke was brought to an end, were distrubuted abroad and imploied in building of privat houses; for they hold, that Nilus could never reach thither, lying as it doth so low under them when it is at the highest, for to wash away the heaps and mounts above-said. Within the greatest Pyramis there is a pit 86 cubits deep, and thither (some thinke) the river was let in. As touching the heigth of these Pyramides and such like, how the measure should be taken, *Thales Milesius* devised the meanes; by taking just length of a shadow when it is meet and even with the bodie that casteth it.

These were the wonderfull Pyramides of Egypt, whereof the world speaketh so much. But to conclude this argument, That no man should need to marvell any more of these huge workes that kings have built, let him know this much, that one of them, the least (I must needs say) but the fairest and most commended for workmanship, was built at the cost and charges of one *Rhodope*,[1]

measured 756 feet (cf. 883) on each side at the base, and the second pyramid measured 707 feet (cf. 737). The area of the great pyramid was 13.1 acres.

[1] Herodotus says that some Greeks wrongly believed that Mycerinus' pyramid was built by Rhodope. He describes her history in Egypt and gives detailed reasons why she could never have had enough money to build a pyramid. The daughter of Cheops is said to have built the middle one of the three small pyramids in front of the great pyramid with her immoral earnings, and the two stories may have become mixed.

a very strumpet: this Rhodope was a bondslave together with Aesope a Philosopher in his kind, and writer of morall fables, with whom she served under one master in the same house: the greater wonder it is therefore and more miraculous than all I have said before, that ever she should bee able to get such wealth by playing the harlot.

§ 156

Of the Labyrinths

(Chap. 13)

SINCE wee have finished our Obelisks and Pyramides, let us enter also into the Labyrinths; which we may truly say, are the most monstrous workes that ever were devised by the head of man: neither are they incredible and fabulous, as peradventure it may be supposed; for one of them remaineth to be seen at this day within the jurisdiction of Heracleopolis, the first that ever was made, to wit, three thousand and six hundred yeares ago, by a king named *Petesuchis*, or as some thinke, *Tithoes*: and yet *Herodotus* saith, it was the whole worke of many KK. one after another, and that *Psammetichus* was the last that put his hand to it and made an end thereof: the reason that moved these princes to make this Labyrinth, is not resolved by writers, but diverse causes are by them alledged: *Demoteles* saith, that this Labyrinth was the roiall pallace and seat of king *Moteris*: *Lycias* affirmeth it to be the sepulchre of K. *Moeris*: the greater part are of opinion, that it was an aedifice dedicated expressely and consecrated unto the Sun, which in my conceit commeth nearest to the truth.

Certes, there is no doubt made that *Daedalus* tooke from hence the pattern and platforme of his Labyrinth which he made in Crete; but surely he expressed not above the hundreth part thereof, chusing onely that corner of the Labyrinth which containeth a number of waies and passages, meeting and incountring one another, winding and turning in and out every way, after so intricat manner and so inexplicable, that when a man is once in, he cannot possibly get out againe: neither must wee thinke that these turnings and returnings were after the manner of mazes which are drawne upon the pavement and plain floore of a field, such as we commonly see serve to make sport and pastime among boies, that is to say, which within a little compasse and round border comprehend many miles; but here were many dores contrived, which might trouble and confound the memorie, for seeing such variety of entries, allies, and waies, some crossed and encountred, others flanked on either hand, a man wandred still and knew not whether he went forward or backward, nor in truth where he was. And this Labyrinth in Crete is counted the second to that of Aegypt: the third is in the Isle Lemnos: the fourth in Italy: made they were all of polished stone, and besides vaulted over head with arches.

As for the Labyrinth in Aegypt, the entrie thereof (whereat I much marvell) was made with columns of stone, and all the rest stuffed so substantially and after such a wonderfull maner couched and laid by art of Masonrie, that impossible it was they should in many hundred yeres be disjointed and dissolved, notwithstanding that the inhabitants of Heracleopolis did what they could to the contrary; who for a spight that they bare unto the whole worke, annoied and impeached it wonderfully. To describe the site and plot thereof, to unfold the architecture of the whole, and to rehearse every particular thereof, it is not possible; for divided the building is into sixteene regions or quarters, according to the sixteene severall governments in Aegypt (which they call Nomes) and within the same are contained certain vast and stately pallaces which bear the names of the said jurisdictions, and be answerable to them: within the same precinct are the temples of all the Aegiptian gods: over and above, fifteen little chappels or shrines, everie one enclosing a *Nemesis*, to which goddesse they be all dedicated: to say nothing of many Pyramides forty ells in height apiece, and every of them having six walls at the foot, in such sort, that before a man can come to the Labyrinth indeed which is so intricat and inexplicable, and wherein (as I said before) he shall be sure to lose himselfe, he may make account to be weary and tyred out: for yet he is to passe over certain lofts, galleries, and garrets, all of them so high that he must clime staires of ninety steps apiece ere he can land at them; within the which a number of columns and statues there be, all of porphyrit or red marble, a world of images and statues representing as well gods as men, besides an infinit sort of other pieces pourtraied in monstrous and ougly shapes, and there erected.

What should I speake of other roums and lodgings which are framed and situat in such manner, that no sooner are the dores and gates opened which lead unto them, but a man shall heare fearfull cracks of terrible thunder: furthermore, the passages from place to place are for the most part so conveighed, that they be as dark as pitch, so as there is no going through them without fire light: and still be we short of the Labyrinth, for without the main wall therof there be two other mighty upright wals or wings. . . ; and when you are passed them, you meet with more shrouds under the ground, in manner of caves and countermines vaulted over head, and as dark as dungeons. Moreover, it is said, that about 600 yeares before the time of K. *Alexander* the Great, one *Circamnos* (an eunuch or groome of K. *Necthebis* chamber) made some small reparations here about this Labyrinth, and never any but hee would go about such a piece of work. It is reported also, that while the main arches and vaults were in rearing (and those were made all of foure square ashler stone) the place shone all about and gave light with the beams and plancher made of the Aegyptian Acacia sodden in oile. And thus much may serve sufficiently for the Labyrinths of Aegipt and Candy.

§ 157

The temple of Diana in Ephesus

(Chap. 14)

BUT to speake of a stately and magnificent work indeed, the temple of *Diana* in Ephesus is admirable, which at the common charges of all the princes in Asia was two hundred and twenty yeres a building. First and foremost, they chose a marish ground to set it upon, because it might not be subject to the danger of earthquakes, or feare the chinkes and opening of the ground: againe, to the end that so mighty and huge building of stone-worke should stand upon a sure and firme foundation (notwithstanding the nature of the soile given to be slipperie and unsteadfast) they laid the first couch and course of the ground-worke with charcole well rammed in manner of a pavement, and upon it a bed of wool-packs:[1] this temple carried in length throughout, four hundred twenty and five foot, in breadth two hundred and twenty: in it were a hundred and seven and twenty pillars, made by so many KK. and every one of them threescore foot high; of which, six and thirtie were curiously wrought and engraven, whereof one was the handiworke of *Scopas*: *Chersiphron* the famous architect was the chiefe deviser or master of the workes, and who undertooke the rearing thereof.

The greatest wonder belonging thereto was this, How those huge chapters of pillars, together with their frizes and architraves, being brought up and raised so high, should be fitted to the sockets of their shafts: but as it is said, he compassed this enterprise and brought it to effect, by the meanes of certaine bags or sacks filled with sand; for of these he made a soft bed as it were raised above the heads of the pillers, upon which bed rested the chapters, and ever as he emptied the nethermost, the foresaid chapters settled downeward by little and little, and so at his pleasure he might place them where they should stand: but the greatest difficultie in this kind of worke, was about the very frontispiece and maine lintle-tree which lay over the jambes or cheekes of the great dore of the said temple; for so huge and mighty it was, that hee could not weld it to lay and bestow the same as it ought, for when he had done what he could, it was not to his mind, nor couched and settled in the right place: whereupon the workman *Chersiphron* was much perplexed in his mind, and so wearie of his life, that he purposed to make himself away: but as he lay in bed in the night season, and fell asleep all wearie upon these dumpish and desperat cogitations, the goddesse *Diana* (in whose honor this temple was framed, and now at the point to be reared) appeared sensibly unto him in person, willing him to be of good cheare and resolve to live still, assuring him that she her self had laid the said stone of the frontispiece, and couched it accordingly: which appeared true indeed the morrow morning, for it seemed

---

[1] As under the piers of old London Bridge which lasted for 613 years and was replaced because of its inconvenience and not its instability in 1824.

Excavators in 1874 came upon the charcoal layer beneath the foundations of the temple.

that the very weight thereof had caused it to settle just into the place, and made a joint as *Chersiphron* would have wished it.

As touching all the other singularities belonging to this temple, and namely the gorgeous ornament that set it out, they would require many volumes to discipher and particularize upon them; and when all is done, little or nothing pertinent they are to the illustration of Natures worke, which is the principall marke I aime at.

§ 158

The sumptuous and admirable aedifices in Rome

(Chap. 15)

AND now since the coherence of matters hath brought me to Rome, me thinks I should not doe amisse to proceed unto the miraculous buildings of this our city, to shew the docilitie of our people, and what proofe there is of their progresse in all things, during the space of nine hundred yeres; that it may appeare how not only in magnanimitie and prowesse they have conquered the world, but in magnificence also of stately and sumptuous buildings surmounted all nations of the earth.

And as a man shall find this singularity and excellencie of theirs in the particular survey of every one of their stately and wonderfull aedifices as they have bin reared from time to time, so if he put them all together and take a generall view of them at once, he shall conceive no otherwise of their greatnesse, than of another world assembled (as it were) to make shew in one place: for if I should reckon among great workes (as needs I must) the grand cirque or shew-place built by *Caesar* Dictator, which took up of ground three stadia or furlongs in length, and one in breadth, containing also in aedifices and roums foure acres or jugera, wherin were bestowed to sit at ease and behold the sight with pleasure, two hundred and threescore thousand persons: what tearme shall I give, but of Stately and magnificent buildings, either unto the royall pallace of *Paulus Aemilius*, enriched with goodly pillars of Sinadian marble out of Phrygia, most admirable to behold; or to the sumptuous Forum of *Augustus Caesar* late Emperour, or yet the temple of *Peace* built by the Emperour *Vespasianus Augustus*, now living, the goodliest and fairest buildings that ever were? What should I speake of the temple *Pantheon*,[1] made by *Agrippa* to the honor of *Jupiter Revenger*? as also how before this time, *Valerius* of Ostia the architector enginer, made a roufe over the great Theatre at Rome against the time that *Libo* exhibited his solemnitie of games and plaies to the people? Wonder we at the dispences that KK. were at about their Pyramides? and wonder we not rather that *Julius Caesar* Dictatour disbursed for the purchase of that plot of ground only and no more wherin he built his Forum, a hundred millions of sesterces? And if there be any here that take pleasure to hoord up mony, and be loth to part with a penny, and love not to be at charges and lay forth ought, wil they not make a wonder when they heare that *P. Clodius* (whom *Milo* slew) paid for the house wherein he dwelt, fourteene millions and eight hundred thousand sesterces? surely if they do not, I do; and take it to be as foolish an expence and as wonderfull, as that of the KK. in Aegypt above named: likewise when I consider the debts that *Milo* himselfe owed, and which amounted to seventy millions of sesterces, I count it one of the most prodigious enormities that a mans corrupt mind can bring forth.

But old men marvelled even in those daies at the mighty thick rampiers that K. *Tarquinius Priscus* caused to be made, the huge foundations also of the Capitoll that he laid, the vaulted sinks also and draughts (to speake of a piece of worke the greatest of all others) which he devised, by undermining and cutting through the seven hils whercupon Rome is seated, and making the city hanging as it were in the aire betic heaven and earth, like unto Thebes in Aegypt, whereof erewhile I made mention; so as a man might passe under the streets and houses with botes. But how would they be astonied now, to see how *M. Agrippa* in his Aedile-ship, after he had been Consull, caused seven rivers to meet together under the city in one main channell, and to run with such a swift streame and current, that they take all afore them what-soever is in the way, and carry it downe into Tyber: and being otherwhiles encreased with sodaine shoures and land-flouds, they shake the paving under them, they flank the sides of the wals about them: sometimes also they receive the Tyber water into

[1] The round church of *Nostre* dame, now at Rome (P. H.).

them when he riseth extraordinarily, so as a man shall perceive the streame of two contrary waters affront and charge one another with great force and violence within under the ground. And yet for all this, these water-workes aforesaid yeeld not a jot, but abide firme and fast, without any sensible decay occasioned therby. Moreover, these streames carrie downe eftsoons huge and heavie pieces of stones within them, mighty loads are drawne over them continually, yet these arched conduits neither settle and stoup under the one, nor be once shaken with the other; down many an house falls of it selfe, and the ruins beat against these vaults: to say nothing of those that tumble upon them with the violent force of skarefires, ne yet of the terrible earthquakes which shake the whole earth about them: yet for all these injuries, they have continued since *Tarquinius Priscus*, almost eight hundred yeres inexpugnable.

And here by the way I will not conceale from you a memorable example which is come into my mind by occasion of this discourse, and the rather, for that even the best and most renowned Chroniclers who have taken upon them to pen our Romane history, have passed it over in silence. When this K. *Tarquinius* surnamed *Priscus*, caused their vaults under the ground to be made, and forced the common people to labour hard therat with their own hands, it happened that many a good Roman citizen being now over-toiled in this kind of work (which whether it were more dangerous or tedious, was hard to say) chose rather to kill themselves for to be rid of their irkesome and painfull life; in such sort, that daily there were people missing, and their bodies found after they were perished. This king therefore, to prevent farther mischiefe, and to provide that his works begun might be brought to an end, devised a remedy which never was invented before, nor practised afterwards, and that was this, That the bodies of as many as were thus found dead, should be hung upon jebbets, exposed not onely to the view of all their fellow citizens to be despised as cursed creatures, but also to the wild and ravenous foules of the aire to be torne and devoured. The Romans (as they are the only nation under heaven impatient of any dishonor) seeing this object presented before their eies, were mightily abashed; and as this mind of theirs had gained them victory many a time in desperat battels, so at this present also it guided and directed them: and being (as they were) dismaied at this disgrace, they made account no lesse to be ashamed of such an ignominie after death, than they now blushed thereat in their life.

But to return again unto these sinks and water-works of ours under the ground: *K. Tarquine* above-named, caused them to be made so large and of such capacitie, that a good wain load of hay might passe within them. But al that ever I have said already is nothing or at leastwise very little, in comparison of one wonderful thing which I am content to set down before I come to our new and moderne buildings. In that yeare when *M. Lepidus* and *Q. Catulus* were Consuls at Rome (according as I find all the best writers to agree) there was not a fairer and more sumptuous house in all Rome, than that wherein *Lepidus* himselfe dwelt: but verily before five and thirty yeres were come and gone, there were a hundred houses and more braver than it by many degrees. Now, if a man list by this reckoning to make an estimat of the infinite masse of marble, as well in pillars as square Ashler, the rich and curious pictures, besides other sumptuous furniture, meet indeed for a king, which must of necessitie be emploied in a hundred such houses, as might not onely compare with that most beautifull and gorgeous house of *Lepidus*, but also exceed the same; as also the infinit number of other houses afterwards even until this day, which have gone beyond those hundred in sumptuosities; What would he say, and to what an unmeasurable proportion will all this arise? Certes, it cannot be denied, but fire (which burneth many a stately pallace) doth say well to the plucking down of mans pride, and punishing such wastfull superfluities; and yet these and such like examples, will not reforme the abuses that reign in the world: neither wil this lesson enter into our heads, That there is ought under heaven more fraile, mortall, and transitory, than man himselfe.

But what do I stand upon those glorious edifices, when two pallaces only have surpassed them all in costlines and magnificence. Twice in our time we have seen the whole pourprise of Rome to be taken up, for to make the pallaces of two Emperours, *C. Caligula*, and *Nero*: and as for that of *Nero* (because there might bee nothing wanting of superfluitie in the highest degree) he caused it to be all guilded, and called it was, The golden pallace. For why? Those noble Romans who were the founders of this our Empire, dwelt (no doubt) in such glorious and stately houses;[1] those I mean who went from the very plough taile, or els out of their country cabines (where they were found at repast by the fire side) to manage the wars, to atcheeve brave feats of armes, to conquer mighty nations, and to return with victory triumphant into the citie; such, I say, as had not so much free land in the whole world as would serve for one of the cellars of these prodigals. And here I cannot but think with my selfe, how little in proportion to the magnificent buildings of these daies, were those plots of grounds which in old time the whole state gave unto those invincible captaines by publick decree, for to build them houses upon, and how many of such places would go to one of these in our time, and yet this was the greatest honour that they could devise to bestow upon those valiant and hardy knights, as it may appeare by *P. Valerius Publicola*, the first consull that ever was at Rome, and had companion with him in that government *L. Brutus*, who had no other reward in recompence of his good service to the Common-weale, and so many demerits;[2] as also by his brother who in the same Consulship defeated the Samnites twice: where it is worth the noting that in the patent this branch went withall, *That they were allowed to open the gates of their houses outward, so as the doores might be cast to the street side*: this was in those daies the most glorious and honourable shew that such mens houses made, even those who had triumphed over the enemy.

Howbeit, as sumptuous in this kind, as either *C. Caligula* or *Nero* was, yet shal they not enjoy the glory of this fame, though you put them two and two together: for I wil shew, that al this pride and excesse of theirs in building their pallaces (princes though they were and mighty monarchs) came behind the privat works of *M. Scaurus*:[3] Whose example in his Aedileship was of so ill consequence, as I wot not whether ever there were any thing that overthrew so much all good manners and orderly civility: in such sort, as hard it is to say, whether *Sylla* did more dammage to the state, in having a son in law[4] so rich and mighty, than by the proscription of so many thousand Romane citizens.

---

[1] Meant in irony.
[2] Deserts or merits.
[3] See § 152 for a diatribe against the marble pillars of Scaurus and Crassus.
[4] For *Sylla* married the mother of *Scaurus* (P. H.).

And in truth, this *Scaurus* when he was Aedile, caused a wonderfull piece of worke to be made, and exceeding all that ever had been knowne wrought by mans hand, not only those that have been erected for a moneth or such a thing, but even those that have bin destined for perpetuitie; and a theatre it was: the stage had three lofts one above another, wherin were there hundred and threescore columnes of marble; (a strange and admirable sight in that citie, which in times past could not endure six small pillars of marble, hewed out of the quarry in mount Hymettus, in the house of a most honourable personage,[1] without a great reproch and rebuke given to him for it;) the base or nethermost part of the stage, was all of marble; the middle of glasse (an excessive superfluitie, never heard of before or after;) as for the uppermost, the bourds, planks, and floores were guilded; the columnes beneath, were (as I have said before) fortie foot high, wanting twaine: and between these columns (as I have shewed before) there stood of statues and Images in brasse to the number of three thousand. The theatre it selfe was able to receive fourescore thousand persons to sit well, and at ease. Whereas the compasse of *Pompeius* Amphitheatre (notwithstanding the city of Rome so much enlarged, and more people in his time) was devised for to contain no greater number than fortie thousand seats at large. As touching the other furniture of this Theatre of *Scaurus*, in rich hangings which were cloth of gold: painted tables, the most exquisit that could be found: plaiers apparrell and other stuffe meet for to adorne the stage, there was such abundance thereof, that there being caried back to his house of pleasure at Tusculum the surplusage therof, over and above the daintiest part, wherof he had daily use at Rome, his servants and slaves there, upon indignation for this wast and monstrous superfluitie of their master, set the said country house on fire, and burnt as much as came to a hundred millions of sesterces.

Certes, when I consider and behold the monstrous humours of these prodigall spirits, my mind is drawn away still from the progresse of mine intended journy, and forced I am to digresse out of my way, and to annex unto this vanity of *Scaurus* as great follie of another, not in masonry and marble, but in carpentry and timber: and *C. Curio* it was, he who in the civile warres between *Caesar* and

[1] L. Crassus (P. H.).

Pompey, lost his life in the quarrell of *Caesar*. This gentleman, desirous to shew pleasure unto the people of Rome at the funerall of his father deceased, as the manner then was, and seeing that he could not outgo *Scaurus* in rich and sumptuous furniture (for where should he have had such a father in law again as *Sylla*? Where could he have found the like mother to dame Metella, who had her share in all forfeitures and confiscations of the goods of outlawed citizens? and where was it possible for him to meet with such another father as *M. Scaurus*, the principall person of the whole city so long together, who parted stakes with *Marius* in pilling and polling of the provinces, and was the very receptacle and gulfe which received and swallowed all their spoiles and pillage?) and *Scaurus* himselfe verily, if he might have had all the goods in the world, could not have done as he did before, nor make the like Theatre, againe, by reason that his house at Tusculum was burnt, where the costly and rich furniture, the goodliest rare ornaments which he had gotten together from al parts of the world were consumed to ashes: by which fire yet this good hee got and prerogative above all other, That no man ever after him was able to match that sumptuositie of his Theatre.

This gentleman (I say) *Curio*, al things considered, was put to his shifts, and devised to surpasse *Scaurus* in wit since hee could not come neere him in wealth. And what might his invention be? Certes, it is worth the knowledge, if there were no more but this, that we may have joy of our own conceits and fashions, and call our selves worthily, as our manner is, Majores, that is to say, superiour every way to all others. To come then to *C. Curio*, and his cunning devise; he caused two Theatres to be framed of timber, and those exceeding big, howbeit so as they might be turned about as a man would have them, approch neere one to the other, or be removed farther asunder as one would desire, and all by the means of one hooke[1] apiece that they hung by, which bare the weight of the whole frame, the counterpoise was so even, and all the whole therfore sure and firme. Now he ordered the matter thus, that to behold the severall stage plaies and shews in the fore-noone before dinner, they shall be set back to back, to the end that the stages should not trouble one another: and when the people had taken their pleasure that way, he turned the Theatres

---

[1] Or pivot.

about in a trice against the afternoone, that they affronted one
another: and toward the latter end of the day, and namely, when
the fencers and sword-plaiers were to come in place, he brought
both the Theatres nearer together (and yet every man sat stil
and kept his place, according to his rank and order) insomuch, as
by the meeting of the horns and corners of them both together in
compasse, he made a faire round Amphitheatre of it: and there in
the middest between, he exhibited indeed unto them all jointly,
a fight and spectacle of sword-fencers fighting at sharpe, whom he
had hired for that purpose: but in truth, a man may say more
truly, that he carried the whole people of Rome round about at his
pleasure. . . .

Now let us come to the point, and consider a little better of this
thing. What should a man wonder at most therin, the deviser or
the devise it selfe? The workeman of this fabricke, or the master
that set him on worke? Whether of the twaine is more admirable,
either the venturous head of him that devised it, or the bold
heart of him that undertook it? to command such a thing to be
don, or to obey and yeeld to goe in hand with it? But when we
have said all that we can, the follie of the blind and bold people of
Rome went beyond al; who trusted such a ticklish frame, and
durst sit there, in a seat so moveable. Loe, where a man might
have seen the body of that people, which is commander and ruler
of the whole earth, the conquerour of the world, the disposer of
kingdomes and realmes at their pleasure, the deviser of countries
and nations at their wil, the giver of lawes to forrein states, the
vicegerent of the immortall gods under heaven, and representing
their image unto all mankind: hanging in the air within a frame
at the mercy of one only hook, rejoicing and ready to clap hands
at their owne danger. What a cheape market of mens lives was
here toward! What was the losse at Cannae to this hazard, that
they should complaine so much as they do of Cannae? How neere
unto a mischiefe were they, which might have happened hereby in
the turning of a hand?

Certes, when there is newes come of a city swallowed up by a
wide chinke and opening of the earth, all men generally in a publicke commiseration doe grieve thereat, and there is not one but
his heart doth yearne; and yet, behold the universall state and
people of Rome, as if they were put into a couple of barkes,

supported between heaven and earth, and sitting at the devotion
only of two pins or hookes. And what spectacle do they behold,
a number of fencers trying it out with unrebated swords? nay
ywis, but even themselves rather entered into a most desperat
fight, and at the point to break their necks every mothers son, if
the scaffold failed never so little, and the frame went out of joint.
Now surely by this proofe, *Curio* had gotten a good hand over the
people of Rome, and no Tribunes of the Commons with all their
orations could do more: from that time forward he might make
account to be so gracious, as to lead all the tribes after him in any
suits; and have them hanging in the air at his pleasure. What a
mighty man with them might he be (thinke you) preaching unto
them from the Rostra? What would not he dare to propose, having
audience in that publick place before them who could persuade
them thus, as he did, to sit upon such turning and ticklish Theatres.
And in truth, if we wil consider this pageant aright, we must
needs confesse and may be bold to say, that *Curio* had all the people
of Rome to perform a brave skirmish and combat indeed to honor
and solemnize the funerals of his father before his tombe.

And yet here is not all: for he was at his change and variety of
magnificent shewes, and when he perceived once that the hookes
of his frames were stretched ynough and began to be out of order,
hee kept them still close together round in forme of a perfect
Amphitheatre, and the very last day of his funeral solemnities,
upon two stages just in the middest, he represented wrestlers and
other champions to performe their devoire, and then all on a sud-
daine causing the said stages to be disjointed and hailed one from
another a contrary way, he brought forth the same day the fencers
and sword players who had woon the prize, and with that shew
made an end of all. See what *Curio* was able to do! And yet was he
neither king nor Caesar: he was not so much as a generall or commander of an army; nay, he was not named for any great rich
man: as whose principall state depended upon this, That when
the great men of the city, *Caesar* and *Pompey*, were skuffling
together by the eares, he knew well how to fish in a troubled
water.

But to leave *Curio* and such as he was, with their foolish and idle
expences, let us come to the miraculous workes that *Q. Marcius Rex*
performed, and that to some good purpose: which if we consider

and esteeme aright, passe all the other above rehearsed. This gentleman when he was Pretor, having commandement and commission both from the Senat, to repaire the conduits to the waters of Appia, Anio, and Tepula, which served Rome, did not that only, but also conveighed a new water into the city, which of his owne name he called Marcia: and notwithstanding that he was to pierce certaine mountaines, and make trenches quite through them under the ground, for to bring the water thither from the Spring, yet he perfourmed all within the time of his Pretourship. As for *Agrippa*, whiles he was Aedile, besides the conduits from all other fountaines which he scoured, repaired, and caused to keep their currant: he brought another of his own to the city, which is known by the name of Virgo: he made seven hundred pooles for receit of waters: a hundred and five conduits, yeelding water at rockes and spoutes, besides a hundred and thirtie conduit heads in the fields, and the most of them built strongly with vaults, and adorned right stately. Moreover, upon these workes of his he erected statues and images, to the number of three hundred, partly of brasse and partly of marble, besides foure hundred pillars of marble, and all within the compasse of one yeare. And if wee may beleeve his owne speech, discoursing of the acts done by him during his Aedileship, hee addeth moreover and saith, That the plaies and games which he exhibited that yeare, for to doe the people pleasure, continued threescore daies together, wanting one: that he caused a hundred threescore and ten baines or stouves to be made within the city, wherein people of all sorts and degrees might bathe and sweat of free cost, and not pay a denier: the which remain at this day, and have brought with them an infinit number of others.

But of all the conduits that ever were before this time, that which was last begun by *C. Caligula Caesar*, and finished by *Claudius Caesar* his successour, passeth for sumptuousnesse: for they commanded the waters from two fountaines, Curtius and Caeruleus, whose heads were 40 miles off: and these they carried before them with such a force and to such an height, that they mounted up to the top of the highest hils of Rome, and served them that dwelt therupon. This work cost three hundred millions of sesterces. Certes, if a man would well and truly consider the abundance of water that is brought therby, and how many places it serves, as well publicke as privat, in baines, stewes, and fishpooles, for kitchins and other houses of office, for pipes and little riverets to water gardens, as well about the citie, as in manors and houses of pleasure in the fields neere the city; over and besides, what a mighty way these waters be brought; the number of arches that of necessitie must be built of purpose for to conveigh them; the mountaines that be pierced and mined through to give way together; with the vallies that are raised and made even and levell with other ground: he will confesse, that there was never any desseine in the whole world enterprised and effected, more admirable than this.

In the ranke of these most memorable workes of man, I may well raunge the mountaine that was digged through by the same *Claudius Caesar*, for to void away the water out of the lough or meere Fucinus, although this work was left unfinished for hatred of his successour: which I assure you cost an incredible and inenarrable sum of mony, besides the infinit toil and labour of a multitude of workemen and labourers so many yeres together, as well to force the water which came upon the pioners from under the ground with devise of engines and windles up to the top of the hill... as to cut and hew through hard rags and rockes of flint: and all this by candlelight within the earth, in such sort that unlesse a man had bin there to have seene the manner of it, unpossible it is either to conceive in mind or expresse with tongue the difficultie of the enterprise. As for the peere and haven at Ostia (because I would make an end once of these matters) I will not say a word thereof, nor of the waies and passages cut through the mountaines, ne yet of the mighty piles and damns to exclude the Tuscane sea, nor the Lucrine lake, with so many rampiers and bridges made of such infinit cost. Howbeit, among many other miraculous things in Italy, one thing more I will relate out of mine author *Papyrius Fabianus*, a great learned Naturalist, namely, That marble doth grow daily in the quarries: and in very truth, the farmers of those quarries, and such as ordinarily do labour and dig out stone, do affirme no lesse; who upon their experience doe assure us, that looke what holes and caves be made in those rockes and mountaines, the same will gather againe and fill up in time: which if it be true, good hope there is, that so long as marbles do live, excesse in building will never die.

§ 159

The Load-stone

(Chap. 16)

NOW that I am to passe from marbles to the singular and admirable natures of other stones; who doubts but that the Magnet or Loadstone will present it self in the first place? for is there any thing more wonderfull, and wherein Nature hath more travelled to shew her power, than in it?

True it is, that to rockes and stones she had given voice (as I have already shewed)[1] whereby they are able to answer a man, nay, they are ready to gainsay and multiply words upon him. But is that all? what is there to our seeming more dull than the stiffe and hard stone? And yet behold, Nature hath bestowed upon it sence, yea and hands also, with the use thereof. What can we devise more stubborne and rebellious in its own kind, than the hard yron, yet it yeelds, and will abide to be ordered: for loe, it is willing to be drawne by the load stone: a marvellous matter that this mettall, which tameth and conquereth all things els, should run toward I wot not what, and the nearer that it approcheth, standeth still as if it were arrested, and suffereth it selfe to be held therwith, nay, it claspeth and clungeth to it, and will not away. And hereupon it is, that some call the load-stone Sideritis, others Heraclion.[2]

As for the name Magnes that it hath, it tooke it (as *Nicander* saith) of the first inventor and deviser thereof, who found it (by his saying) upon the mountaine Ida (for now it is to be had in all other countries, like as in Spaine also) and (by report) a neat-heard he was: who, as he kept his beasts upon the foresaid mountaine, might perceive as he went up and downe, both the hobnailes which were in his shooes, and also the yron picke or graine of his staffe, to sticke unto the said stone.

---

[1] *i.* The eccho (P. H.).

[2] Sideritis, σιδηρῖτις, of iron; perhaps from Heraclea in Lydia since Pliny later mentions a variety of loadstone obtained from the district of Magnesia in Lydia, in which Heraclea is believed to have been situated.

SEVEN AND THIRTIETH BOOKE
concludeth with pretious stones

§ 160

Of Amber

(Chaps. 2, 3)

BUT I wonder most at *Sophocles* the Tragicall Poet (a man who wrote his Poesies, with so grave and lofty a stile, and lived besides in so good reputation; being otherwise borne at Athens, and descended from a noble house, emploied also in the managing of state affaires, as who had the charge and conduct of an army) that he should go beyond al others in fabulous reports, as touching Amber: for he sticketh not to avouch, That beyond India it proceedeth from the tears that fall from the eies of the birds Meleagrides, wailing and weeping for the death of *Meleager*. Who would not marvell, that either himselfe should be of that beliefe, or hope to persuade others to his opinion? For what child is there to be found so simple and ignorant, who will beleeve, that birds should keep their times to shed tears every yere so duly, and especially so great drops and in such quantitie, sufficient to engender Amber in that abundance? Besides, what congruitie is there, that birds should depart as far as to the Indians and beyond, for to mourn and lament the death of *Meleager* when he died in Greece?

What should a man say to this? Are there not many more as goodly tales as these, which Poets have sent abroad into the world? And their profession of Poetry, that is to say, of faining and devising fables, may in some sort excuse them. But that any man should seriously and by way of history deliver such stuffe, as touching a thing so rife and common, brought in every day in abundance by merchants which were ynough to convince such impudent lies, is a meere mockerie of the world in the highest degree; a contempt offered unto all men, and argueth an habit of lying, and an impunitie of that vice intollerable.

But to leave Poets with their tales, and to speake resolutely and with knowledge, of Amber, knowne it is for certain, That engendered it is in certaine Islands of the Ocean Septentrionall, where it beateth upon the coasts of Germany: and the Almanes call it Glessum.[1] And in very truth, in that voyage by sea which *Germanicus Caesar* made into those parts, our countrymen named one of those Islands Glessaria, by reason of the Amber there found; which Island the Barbarians call Austeravia. It is engendred then in certaine trees, resembling Pines in some sort, and issueth forth from the marrow of them, like as gum in Cherrie trees, and rosin in Pines. And verily, these trees are so full of this liquor, that it swelleth and breaketh forth in abundance: which afterwards either congealeth with the cold, or thickeneth by the heat of Autumn. Now if at any time the sea rise by any extraordinary tide, and catch any of it away out of the Islands, then verily it is cast ashore upon the coast of Germany, where it is so apt to roule, that it seemeth (as it were) to hang and settle lightly upon the sands, whereby it is the more easily gotten.

§ 161

The Once stone

(Chap. 3)

THE froward peevishnes of some Authors who have written of Lyncurium, enforceth me to speak of it immediatly after Amber: for say that it be not Electrum or Amber, as some would have it, yet they stand stiffely in this, that it is a pretious stone; mary they hold, that it commeth from the urine of an Once,[2] by reason that this wild beast so soon as it hath pissed, covereth it with earth, upon a spight and envie to man, that he should have no good therby. They affirme moreover, That the Once stone or Lyncurium is of the same colour [as] that Ambre ardent which resembleth the fire, and that it serveth well to be engraven: neither

---

[1] For the perspicuitie and brightnes like unto glasse (P. H.).
[2] Lynx.

by their saying doth it catch at leaves only and strawes, but thin plates also of brasse and yron: and of this opinion was *Diocles* and *Theophrastus.*

For mine own part I hold all to be meere untruths: neither do I think, that in our age there hath been a man who ever saw any pretious stone of that name. Whatever also is written as touching the vertues medicinable of Lyncurium, I take them to be no better than fables, namely, that if it be given in drink, it wil send out the stone of the bladder: if it be drunk in wine, it will cure the jaundise presently, or if it be but carried about one, it wil do the deed: but ynough of such fantasticall dreames and lying vanities, and time it is now to treat of those precious stones, wherof there is no doubt made at al, and to begin with those that by al mens confession are most rich and of highest price. In which discourse I wil not prosecute this theame only, but also (for to advance the knowledge of posterity in those things that may profit this life) I meane eftsoones to have a fling at Magicians for their abhominable lies and monstrous vanities; for in nothing so much have they overpassed themselves as in the reports of gems and pretious stones, exceeding the tearms and limits of Physick, whiles under a color of faire and pleasing medicines, they hold us with a tale of their prodigious effects and incredible.

§ 162

Of the Emeraud

(Chap. 5)

EMERAUDS for many causes deserve the third place:[1] for there is not a colour more pleasing to the eie. True it is, that we take great delight to behold greene herbes and leaves of trees, but this is nothing to the pleasure wee have in looking upon the Emeraud, for compare it with other things, be they never so green, it surpasses them all in pleasant verdure. Besides, there is not a gem or precious stone that so fully possesseth the eie, and yet never contenteth it with sacietie. Nay, if the sight hath bin wearied and

[1] To wit, after Diamants and Pearles (P. H.).

dimmed by intentive poring upon any thing els, the beholding of this stone doth refresh and restore it againe, which lappidaries well know, that cut and ingrave fine stones; for they have not a better means to refresh their eies than the Emeraud, the mild green that it hath doth so comfort and revive their wearines and lassitude.

Moreover, the longer and farther off that a man looketh upon Emerauds, the fairer and bigger they seem to the eie, by reason that they cause the reverberation of the aire about them for to seeme green: for neither Sun nor shade, ne yet the light of candle, causeth them to change and lose their lustre: but contrariwise, as they ever send out their own raies by litle and little, so they entertain reciprocally the visual beams of our eies; and for all the spissitude and thicknesse that they seeme to have, they admit gently our sight to pierce into their bottome: a thing that is not ordinary in water. The same are shaped many times hollow, thereby to gather, unite, and fortifie the spirits that maintain our eie-sight. In regard of these manifold pleasures that they shew to our eies, by generall consent of all men spared they are, and lappidaries be forbidden expressely to cut and ingrave them: and yet the Emerauds of Scythia and Aegypt be so hard, as they cannot be pierced or wounded by any instrument: moreover, when you meet with a table-Emerauld hold the flat face therof against any thing, it will represent the said object to the eie, as well as a mirroir or looking glasse. And verily, *Nero* the Emperor was wont to behold the combats of fencers and sword-plaiers in a faire Emeraud.

§ 163

Epilogue

AND now having discoursed sufficiently of al the works of Nature, it were meet to conclude with a certain general difference between the things themselves, and especially between country and country.

For a finall conclusion therefore, go through the whole earth and all the lands lying under the cope of heaven, Italy wil be found the most beautiful and goodliest region under the Sun, surpassing all other whatsoever, and worthily to be counted the chiefe and principall in every respect: Italy (I say) the very lady and queen, yea, a second mother next to dame Nature of the world: chiefe for hardy men, chiefe for faire and beautifull women, inriched with captaines, souldiers, and slaves: flourishing in all arts and sciences, abounding with noble wits and men of singular spirit; scituat under a climat most wholsome and temperat, seated also commodiously (by reason of the coasts so ful of convenient havens) for traffick with all nations, wherein the winds are most comfortable (for it extendeth it selfe and lieth to the best quarter of the heaven, even in the midst just between East and West;) having waters at command, large forests and faire, and those yeelding most healthful air; bounded with mighty rampiers of high mountains, stored with wild beasts, and those harmlesse: finally, the ground so fertile for corn, the soile so battle for her herbage, as none to it comparable.

In sum, whatsoever is necessary and requisit for the maintenance of this life is there to be had, in no place better: all kinds of corne and grain, wines, oile, wooll, linnen, woollen and excellent boeufs; as for horse-flesh, I have alwaies heard, even from the mouth of those that be professed runners in the race with horse and charriot, That the breed of Italy passeth al others: for mines of gold, silver, brasse, and yron, it gave place to no country whatsoever, so long as it pleased the state to imploy it that way; and in lieu of those rich commodities which it hath still within her womb, she yeeldeth to us variety of good liquors, plenty of al sorts of corn, and abundance of pleasant fruits of all kinds. But if I should speake of a land after Italy (setting aside the monstrous and fabulous reports that go of India) in my conceit Spaine is next in all respects, I meane those coasts which are invironed with the sea.[1]

---

[1] The Bamberg MS. has here several more sentences listing the most excellent of Nature's products. Bostock and Riley thus translate the concluding sentence: 'Hail to thee, Nature, thou parent of all things! and do thou deign to show thy favour unto me, who, alone of all the citizens of Rome, have, in thy every department, thus made known thy praise.'

GLOSSARY

abroch, to set, to set afoot.
addition, distinguishing name.
aedile, a Roman magistrate.
aegre, eager, acrid, sharp.
affranchised, freed from slavery.
allec, a fish sauce, Roman Allies sauce.
ambry, cupboard, larder.
amphore, amphora holding 7 gallons.
anthias, sea fish, probably a wrasse.
arrereguard, rearguard.
arrugia, the shaft and pit of a gold mine.
ashler, ashlar, slab of stone.
asse, as, a Roman copper coin.
assurance, engagement.
ato-side, on one side.
avie, in emulation.

bain, bath.
balaenae, sperm whales.
hallaise, to balance.
barbel, the fish, and the fleshy filament that hangs from its mouth.
barton, an enclosure, a pen for chickens.
bastil, fortified tower.
battle, rich, productive.
beetle, mallet.
beraied, disfigured, defiled.
bespaule, to bespatter with saliva, to slander.
bias, obliquely.
big, a boil is Holland's usual meaning; pap or teat.
blast, blight.
bloudy-fals, blood blisters.
boeufs, cattle.
boleti, fungi with pores not gills.
boll, bowl.
bondgrace, veil on front of bonnet.
border, added plait of hair, switch.
borras, either crude borax (tincal) or used for malachite.
bouge, to bilge, to stave in a ship's bottom.
braied, pounded in a mortar.
branch, clause, section.
brizen, part of a pig, perhaps sweetbread.

buccinum, the shallow water purple-bearing shellfish.
bulk, stall, front of a shop.
burret, large winkle, whelk.
buskin, half-boot; the tragedian's thick-soled boot.

calamary, cuttlefish.
caltrope, three-pronged instrument for wounding horses' feet; plant with a spiny fruit.
carcanet, necklace.
cassidonie, chalcedony, a generic name for quartzes.
cast, device.
cataplasm, a plaster.
catch, a song, a round.
cater, caterer, purveyor.
cates, provisions.
cawle, netted cap.
cerecloth, cloth impregnated with wax or other glutinous material.
cerio, honeycomb, hence carbuncle.
chamber, metropolis, treasury.
champain, champaign, open level country.
champion, champian; variant of champain (q.v.) which became much more frequent than the normal form in the 17th cent.
chaplet, head wreath.
chapman, a dealer, a customer.
chase, haste, hurry.
chawdron, cauldron, vat.
chawne, chasm, cleft.
cinnabari, cinnambre, dragon's blood or, falsely, vermilion.
circulation, continuous distillation in a circulatory.
clave, cramp for glueing.
clees, claws.
clipping, embracing, hugging.
cod, husk containing seeds.
collect, to draw an inference.
collet, the setting of a stone in a ring.
collution, a mouthwash.

commodity, convenience.

conchylium, general term for all species of purple-bearing shellfish and for the purple dye.

concoction, digestion.

condite, pickled, preserved.

connivancie, pretended blindness or ignorance.

controlle, to object to.

conveighed, conducted.

converse, to be a companion, to be intimate.

coquil, shellfish.

costus, C. arabicus, an aromatic plant.

coulter, vertical iron of a plough.

cousenage, cozenage, deception.

cramp-fish, see *torpedo*.

crane, tunnel, tube.

culling, hugging.

cumin, cummin, aromatic plant like fennel.

curiositie, carefulness, niceness, subtlety.

curule aedile, Roman magistrate in charge of public spectacles.

cychramus, probably the ortolan.

cyperus, sweet rush, English galingale.

cypirus, a type of gladiolus.

decasticon, ten-line poem.

degree, step.

demerit, desert, merit.

denier, the Roman denarius, worth about 3*s*. at present values.

detersive, cleansing.

discuss, to disperse and cure a swelling.

divert, to deviate, to digress.

divisions, rapid melody, descant.

domaine, inheritable estate.

dorr, to deaden colour.

draught, cesspool.

drie-vat, vessel for dry goods.

dulced, appeased, soothed.

earst, soonest, earliest, in the first place.

ebbe, shallow.

eftsoons, again.

ell, the English ell measured 45 inches.

empalled, fenced in.

encountred, opposite one another.

ephemerides, astronomical almanac.

ere, to plough.

exemplify, to copy.

exigent, a writ commanding the defendant to appear in court.

exquisite, consummate, excellent.

extent, seizure of land and goods.

fellon, abscess, whitlow.

ferrer, blacksmith, farrier.

fisque, treasury.

flamin, a Roman priest.

flasket, a shallow basket.

flux, dysentery.

foist, light galley, barge.

fore-let, previously left undone, omitted.

fraile, basket, usually made of rushes.

frank, to fatten up in a frank or sty.

frumpe, a jeer.

galena, lead sulphide.

geason, rare, scarce.

gemmal, gemel, a double ring.

gestation, being carried or conveyed.

gist, halting place.

gladon, gladdon, the iris.

glosing, deceitful, flattering.

glottis, a plover.

god's-pennie, earnest money.

gore-moon, the November moon, perhaps because it rises red.

grain, scarlet dye from the kermes insect; the grain of wood.

graine, prong or ferrule of a stick.

guerdon, reward.

hasty, forward, early (of plants).

hautinesse, high-mindedness, eminence.

hipped, injured in the hip.

hippocampi, sea-horses.

holme, haulm, litter, stalks of beans, &c., used for thatching.

holothuria, echinoderms, especially sea-slugs.

hoove, hove, to blow up, to inflate.

horarie, lasting for an hour, short-lived.

hortyard, orchard, garden.

howlet, houlet, owl, night owl.

hoy, small sailing ship.

hucker mucker, concealment, secrecy.

huisher, usher, lackey.

impeach, to hinder, to damage.
impertinent, not pertinent.
impostume, a swelling, an inflammation.
indument, endowment.
inenarrable, indescribable.
informity, lack of form, deformity (perhaps an error for infirmity).
inquisition, investigation, research.

job, to peck, to stab.
joist, to pasture.
jugerum, the Roman land measure, approximately two-thirds of an acre.

kernel, gland.
kindled, brought forth young.
kindly, natural.

larg, the longest musical note, 2 or 3 longs.
laser-wort, lazar-wort, laserpitium, an umbelliferous plant.
latch, to catch.
latchet, shoelace.
lead, vat, copper.
leaud, see *lewd*.
leaudnesse, see *lewd*.
lewd, unlearned, common, vulgar.
lightly, probably, commonly.
like-owl, a horned owl.
limmer, limber, supple, weak, flabby, or bandy.
lin, to cease, to desist.
lingulaca, adder's tongue fern.
lively, living.
long, a musical note of 2 or 3 breves.
long of, because of.
lote-tree, the nettle tree.
louver, ventilator, type of chimney.
lupine, a lupin cultivated for fodder.
lurcher, petty thief, swindler.
lustie-gallant, a fashionable tint of light red named after a dance tune.
lute, to cement, to seal.
luzerne, lynx.
lyncurium, a fabulous precious stone.

manger, prepared dish, broth.
marish, marshy.
mast, acorns.
maugre, despite.

merry-gals, raw places.
meut, mute, to dung as birds (Johnson).
minium, vermilion.
mish-mash, medley, jumble.
modius, the Roman corn measure, a peck.
moile, to toil.
mordacitie, biting property, sting of nettle.
morisk, morris-dance.
mourron, morion, a 16th cent. helmet.
mowe, a wry mouth, a distorted face.
mue, mew, cage, aviary.
muffle, muzzle or nose.
mure, wall.
murex, purple-bearing shellfish; often used as *conchylium* (q.v.); large winkle, whelk.

nacre, see *pinna*.
nard, spikenard, scented root of a N. Indian plant.
navewe, kind of turnip.
neat-herd, cow-herd.
neece, *niece*, commonly used for granddaughter.
nereides, sea nymphs.
nice, over-refined, fastidious.
nitre, soda.
nones, nonce, purpose, occasion.
nource-garden, nursery.
nymphaea, water-lily.

oase, ooze.
obolus, a Roman weight equal to half a scruple, 10 grains or 0·6 gramme.
obsequent, compliant, serviceable.
occupier, merchant, dealer.
oilet, eyelet, eye, bud.
once, ounce, lynx.
orcae, orcs, killer whales.
origan, wild marjoram.
otis, great bustard.
ouvert, overt, uncovered.
overthwart, transversely.

paize, to weigh.
panicke, panic, Italian millet.
pantofle, slipper.
paroll, promise, agreement.
passe, to diverge from a course of action, to surpass.

pearle, an opaque spot on the cornea of the eye.

peise, to weigh; weight.

pelagium, deep-sea purple-bearing shell-fish.

pelting, petty, contemptible.

pensil, paintbrush.

pepin, pippin, pip, seed.

pepinnier, nursery for seedlings.

perspicuitie, transparency.

petie-glader, see *cypirus*.

physemata, bladders, hollow pearls.

pilling, skin.

pilling and polling, pillaging.

pin and web, inflammation of the eyes.

pinking, half-shut, peering (of the eyes).

pinna, the sea-pen or fan mussel.

pinnophylax, protector of the pinna, a crab.

pinnoter, protector of the pinna, a crab.

pioner, miner, labourer.

pismire, ant.

pistrices, whales.

plancher, planking, floor.

platforme, ground-plan.

poise, see *peise*.

pompion, pumpkin.

ponder, to weigh.

porphyrit, Egyptian granite.

port, deportment, bearing.

possess, to affect strongly, to engross the thoughts.

pouder, to pickle, to salt.

pourcelane, shellfish, cowrie.

pourcuttle, octopus.

pourfile, to profile, to outline.

pourprise, circuit, enclosure.

premeditat, planned, contrived.

press, cupboard.

prevent, to come before, to precede.

privitie, private knowledge.

puffen, unidentified ray.

pule, to whine, to cry.

pullein, pullen, hens.

pulmones, snails with simple lungs.

pultesse, a plaster.

pun, to ram, to beat.

purfle, to give an ornamental border.

purpura, the deep-sea purple-bearing shellfish.

pyrrie, pear.

rag, hard coarse stone.

rain, rein, kidney.

rampier, barrier.

raw, unfinished.

receive, to accept, to know.

record, to meditate.

reeke, seaweeds.

reliefe, pasture.

rendles, rennet.

repercussion, reflection.

reprehension, censure.

respective, worthy of reverence.

restie, fallow, untilled.

riveled, wrinkled.

rostra, platform for speakers in the Roman forum, adorned with beaks of ships.

roule, to roll, to move about.

rout, to roar, to make loud noises.

ruffle, to make a stir, to bear oneself proudly.

saccage, sackage, sack of a city.

sad, orderly, grave; *sad delay*, serious temperance.

sallat, light helmet without crest.

salve, to soothe.

savage, wild.

scalae gemoniae, the steps of lamentation on the Aventine hill.

schoene, 30 (or 40) stadia, some 4 to 5 miles.

scouring, cleansing.

scriptule, a scruple, 20 grains.

sea-dog, shark.

sea-frog, angler fish.

sea-nettle, jellyfish.

seednes, sowing.

seege, evacuation of bowel, stool.

seeled, covered, roofed.

seely, helpless, simple, weak, humble.

sen-greene, the house-leek.

sesterce, sestertius, the ordinary coin of the Romans, equal to a quarter denarius; worth about 9*d.* at present values.

shaftment, a span, 9 inches.

shag, matted hair.

share, groin.

shareman, shearman, who cut the nap of woollen cloth.

shindled, roofed with wooden shingles.

shittle, fickle, inconstant.
shroud, vault.
sink, sewer.
skarefire, a sudden fire.
skill, to know how, to have the ability, to understand.
soluble, producing laxity of the bowels.
sorance, disease producing sores.
sort, to consort, to join.
sowbread, a cyclamen the roots of which are eaten by swine.
spart, esparto grass.
sped, affected.
spiall, *in spiall*, on the watch.
spissitude, density, compactness.
splay, to spay, to remove the ovaries.
square, to strut, to swagger.
squinancie, quinsy.
staffe, stave, verse or stanza of a song.
stammel, woollen cloth or table cover of red colour.
stare, starling.
starke, rigid, stiff.
startop, startup, boot, legging.
stays, hat strings, holding up the brim or passing under the chin.
stele, stalk, stem.
stew, hot bath, fishpond.
stick, to hesitate.
stock, framework.
stock up, to root up trees.
stone, testis, ovary.
stopple, stopper.
stouve, stove, hot-house, sweating vault.
stuff, to furnish.
support, to maintain an opinion.
swaied, strained, curved down.
sword-grasse, see *cypirus*.

taber, tabor, drum.
table, the game of draughts or backgammon; the surface on which a picture is painted or the picture itself.
talent, said, in 1890, to have been worth £250, and perhaps £2,000 now.
tapissed, carpeted.
tettar, tetter, pustular skin disease.
tewed, steeped and beaten.

thornback, sting ray.
till, to wave up and down.
timbrel, percussion instrument, tambourine.
toll, to lure, to decoy.
torpedo, electric ray.
train, stratagem.
train, to persuade.
travail, toil; to toil.
travel, *travell*, see *travail*.
treatable, deliberate, distinct.
tritons, sea gods who blew through a shell to calm or raise the seas.
trot, an old hag.
truchman, interpreter.
tun, large cask or tub.
twillie, ribbed cloth.

ulex, gorse.
unneth, uneath, with difficulty, scarcely.
unrebated, sharp.

vaward, the van, the front.
venditat, to display.
vengible, very great, severe.
vent, market, outlet for sale.
ventosity, windiness.
vervaine, verbena, mallow.
viatores, wayfarers, travellers.
vinet, trailing design of branches or vines.
vitriol, iron sulphate.

wambling, rolling with nausea.
wanton, extravagant, unrestrained.
warrantize, sanction, guarantee.
weely, unproductive, marshy, poor.
weet, to know.
weld, to deal with successfully.
well-trussed, well-knit.
whitled, intoxicated.
wiffler, attendant who kept the way clear for public shows and processions.
windles, windlass.
wist, to know.
wistly, intently.
wood, furious, raging.
wraule, wrawl, to bawl, to squall.

ywis, indeed, truly.

INDEX OF NAMES

Abila, Abyla, a rocky hill at Ceuta in Morocco opposite Gibraltar and one of the pillars of Hercules, 29.

Achelous, a large river of central Greece reaching the sea at the S.W. corner of Epirus, 72.

Achilles, the Greek hero in the Trojan war, 298.

Acmodae, Shetland Islands, 35.

Acron, *fl.* 5th cent. B.C., a Sicilian physician from Agrigentum, 234.

Actium, in Epirus just S. of Preveza, 60, 201.

Aedemon, a freedman of king Ptolomaeus of Mauretania, 37.

Aegeum, Aegaeum, the Aegean Sea, 32.

Aesculapius, the Greek god of medicine and possibly a real physician, 233.

Aesope, *fl. c.* 570 B.C., the Greek fabulist of Phrygia, 302.

Aetheria, early name for Ethiopia, probably after Aether son of Chaos, 43.

Aethiops, said to be the son of Vulcan, 43.

Affricke, *see* Africa.

Africa, xix, 42, 70, 72, 74, 87, 150, 164, 176, 208, 301.

Agonaces, the teacher of Zoroaster, 241.

Agrigentum, a town in S. Sicily, now Girgenti, 234.

Agrippa, Marcus Vipsanius, 63–12 B.C., statesman and general, responsible for the Commentaries, a lost description of the Roman world under Augustus, and for the Pantheon, 35, 60, 307, 315.

Agrippa, Postumus, 12 B.C.–A.D. 14, posthumous son of M. Vipsanius Agrippa, 61.

Agrippina, wife of Claudius, 114, 116.

Ahenobarbus, Gnaeus Domitius, *fl. c.* 120 B.C., Roman general and proconsul in Gaul, 160–2.

Albanie, Albania, 60.

Albinus, Spurius, curule aedile in 161 B.C., 178.

Albion, *see* Britain.

Alcmena, mother of Hercules, 275, 278.

Alcon, a surgeon at Rome in the time of Claudius, 239.

Alexander, the Great, 356–323 B.C., king of Macedonia, 3, 39, 56, 139, 142, 274, 282, 283, 284, 304.

Alexander Cornelius, Polyhistor, *fl. c.* 90 B.C., a prolific Greek writer, 61.

Alexandria, 39, 137.

Alps, 26, 77, 208.

Amilo, an unidentified river in Mauretania, 66.

Ammianus Marcellinus, b. *c.* A.D. 325, the Roman historian whose history continues that of Tacitus, xx, xxvii.

Amphitryon, king of Thebes and husband of Alcmena in the Hercules story, 278.

Ampsanctus, a lake in Italy, now Lago d'Ansante, 27.

Anacreon, *fl. c.* 540 B.C., a lyric poet of Teos, 53.

Anaxilaus, *fl. c.* 30 B.C., a physician and philosopher of Larissa, 191.

Anaximander, b 610 B.C., a Greek philosopher of Miletus, 184.

Androcydes, *fl.* 400–377 B.C., of Cyzicus, a Greek painter, rival of Zeuxis, 278.

Andros, Edros, Bardsey Island, off the coast of Caernarvonshire, 35.

Anio, an aqueduct of Rome, 315.

Annibal, *see* Hannibal.

Antiochus, 324–261 B.C., king of Syria, 68, 234, 285.

Antipater, the Macedonian general who became sole master of Alexander's empire and died in 319 B.C., 68.

Antium, a town in Latium, now Porto d'Anzio, 249, 277.

Antonius, Marcus, 83–31 B.C., the triumvir, 53, 54, 59, 97, 98, 201, 202, 249.

Antony, *see* Antonius.

Anystis, courier of Sparta, 56.

Apelles, *fl.* 4th cent. B.C., the famous Greek painter of Sicyon, 3, 18, 279–86, 290, 291.

Apenine, the Apennine chain of mountains, 26.

Apia, old name for the Peloponnese, 32.

Apicius, Marcus Apicius Gabius, a notorious epicure of the time of Augustus and Tiberius, 82, 87, 192.

Apollo, god of the sun, divination, archery, poetry, and music, 3, 34, 157, 272.

Apollodorus, *fl. c.* 408 B.C., a Greek painter of Athens, 277.

Apollonia, a Milesian colony on the Black Sea, now Sozopol in Bulgaria, 272.

Appia, an aqueduct of Rome, 315.

Appia, the Appian Way from Rome to Capua and Brindisi, 118, 235.

Appio, Apion, a Greek grammarian of Oasis, teaching in Rome at the time of Tiberius and Claudius, 284.

Appius Junius Silanus, consul A.D. 28, 80.

Apuscorus, a Median magician, 242.

Aquilius, possibly Gaius Aquilius Gallus, the lawyer and orator, *c.* 65 B.C., 160.

Aquilius, Manius, consul 101 B.C.; captured and killed by Mithridates, 259.

Arabia, 93, 137.

Arcadia, in central Peloponnese, 61, 76, 202.

Archelaus, either the king of Cappadocia *c.* 34 B.C., or the king of Macedonia, *c.* 413 B.C., 176.

Aristides, *fl.* 360–330 B.C., a Greek painter of Thebes, 291.

Aristogeiton, co-murderer with Harmodius of Hipparchus, brother of the tyrant Hippias (sons of Peisistratus) in 514 B.C., 274.

Aristophanes, *fl. c.* 264 B.C., the grammarian of Byzantium in charge of the library at Alexandria, 69.

Aristotle, 384–322 B.C., the Greek philosopher, 72, 234, 241.

Arruntius, a Roman physician of the 1st cent. A.D., 235.

Arsinoe, a city of the Fayoum in lower Egypt, 299.

Asana, Asama, the Wadi Tensift in Morocco, on which Marrakesh stands, 37.

Asclepiades, early 1st cent. B.C., a physician from Prusa in Bithynia, 198, 216, 224, 226, 234.

Asclepiodorus, a Greek painter, contemporary with Apelles, 280.

Asia, 42, 304.

Asphaltites, *see* Dead Sea.

Assyria, 242.

Astura, a town in Latium near Antium, 249.

Athanatus, a strong man in the time of Pliny, 56.

Athens, 56, 135, 202, 244, 276, 296, 318.

Atlantia, early name for Ethiopia, probably after king Atlas, 43.

Atlas, the mountain range in N. Africa, 36–38.

Attalus, Philometor, d. 133 B.C., king of Pergamos, 176.

Attica, 202.

Attilius (Atilius), Gaius Atilius Regulus Serranus, consul 257 B.C., 175.

Aubrey, John, 1626–97, antiquary and author of *Minutes for Lives*, xxiii.

Augustus, Gaius Julius Caesar Octavianus, 63 B.C.–A.D. 14; emperor from 27 B.C., xxvi, 23, 55, 59, 86, 97, 131, 201, 234, 249, 285, 306.

Austeravia, another name for the amber islands, Glessariae, 319.

Avernus, lake, Lago Averno in Campania, 244.

Axantos, Isle d'Ouessant, Ushant, off Brittany, 35.

Axenos, another name for the Black Sea, literally, inhospitable.

Babylon, 242.

Bacchus, the Thracian name for Dionysus, god of fruitfulness and the vine, 74, 156, 274.

Baetica, Hispania Baetica, a province centred on the river Baetis, now the Guadalquivir, and corresponding to Andalusia, 88.

Baianum, Baiae, on the Italian coast opposite to Pozzuoli, 86.

Barbarus, Hermolaus, 1454–93, Italian scholar and editor of the *Natural History*, xxv.

Bassus, Aufidius, the historian of the time of Augustus and Tiberius whose general history Pliny continued, xix.

Bauderon, ?1540–1623, author of a famous pharmacopeia translated from French into Latin by Holland and published in 1639, xxvii.

Bergos, unidentified islands near Britain, 35.

Black Sea, 42.

Bocchus, *fl. c.* 106 B.C., king of Mauretania and father-in-law of Jugurtha whom he betrayed; *or* his son of the same name, d. 33 B.C., 70.

Bosphorus, 42.

Bostock, John, 1773–1846, physician and litterateur, part author of a translation of the *Historia Naturalis*, xv.

Brindisi, 119.

Britain, Britaine, Britannia, xxvii, 34, 165, 166, 242, 253.

Britannia, *see* Britain.

Browne, Sir Thomas, 1605–1682, author of *Religio Medici* and *Pseudo-doxia Epidemica*, xviii.

Brutus Callaecus, Decimus Junius Brutus (Callaicus), consul with P. Cornelius Scipio in 138 B.C., 298.

Brutus, Lucius Junius, first consul of Rome in 509 B.C., 310.

Brutus, Marcus Junius, *c.* 79–42 B.C., one of Caesar's assassins, 255, 296.

Busiris, a village near Memphis, said to be the modern Abousir, 300.

Bythinia, Bithynia, a country between the Sea of Marmora and the Black Sea, 54, 79.

Byzacium, a district of Tunisia, 164.

Caecilius, Lucius Caecilius Cilo, brother-in-law of Pliny and father of Pliny the Younger, xix.

Caeruleus, an aqueduct of Rome, 315.

Caesar, Gaius Julius Caesar, 102–44 B.C., 32, 56, 57, 183, 193, 228, 281, 285, 306, 307, 311, 312, 314.

Caesarea Philippi or Panias, built at the foot of Mt. Panium at a source of the Jordan; now Baniyas, 40.

Calamis, *fl. c.* 450 B.C., the sculptor of the great statue of Apollo at Apollonia, 274, 275.

Caledonia, Scotland, 35.

Caligula, Gaius Caesar, A.D. 12–41; emperor from A.D. 37 to 41, 32, 37, 96, 131, 136, 140, 249, 309, 315.

Callias, the inventor of vermilion in 405 B.C., 267.

Callirhoe, warm medicinal springs on the E. shore of the Dead Sea with the same name as the famous fountain on the acropolis at Athens, 40.

Calpe, the rock of Gibraltar, 29, 42.

Calvus, Gaius Licinius Macer, 82–47 B.C., orator and poet, 270.

Cambridge, xx.

Camden, William, 1551–1623, the historian and antiquary, author of *Britannia*, xx, xxiv, xxvii.

Camillus, Marcus Furius, d. 365 B.C.; the dictator, 267.

Campaine, *see* Campania.

Campania, the fruitful plain round Capua near Naples, now Terra di Lavoro, 30, 146.

Campaspe, Pancaspe, a favourite concubine of Alexander, 4, 283.

Candy, Candia in Crete, 136, 207, 304.

Cannae, a village in Apulia where Hannibal beat the Romans in 216 B.C., 151.

Canopicus, Canopus, the Canopic mouth of the Nile, 39.

Canopus, *see* Canopicus.

Capua, near Naples, 146.

Carambis, a promontory in N. Turkey near Sinopa, now Ince Burun, 110.

Carteia, an ancient seaport in Spain, on the bay of Algeciras, 90.

Carthage, 37, 118, 150, 151, 176, 194, 270.

Castabula, a city in Cilicia, S. Turkey, 79.

Castor, the brother of Pollux, sons of king Tyndareus of Sparta, 117, 291.

Cato, Marcus Porcius Cato Censorius, d. 149 B.C., the elder, 68, 150, 151, 169, 176, 238.

Catulus, Quintus Lutatius, *fl. c.* 100 B.C.; a colleague of C. Marius, 160, 309.

Catus, Sextus Aelius Paetus, consul 198 B.C., 271.

Caunos, a city on the coast of Caria, 286.

Cecil, Sir Robert, *c.* 1565–1612, Secretary of State to Elizabeth I and first Earl of Salisbury, xxvii, 3.

Celer, Asinius, consul in the time of Caligula, 80.

Cenchreae, a harbour of Corinth on the Gulf of Aegina, now the hamlet of Kekhries, 32.

Ceraunicum, Ceramicum, a street in Athens, 296.

Chares, *fl.* 3rd cent. B.C., sculptor and brass-founder of Lindos in Rhodes, 273.

Charles I, 1600–49, king of Great Britain, xxiii.

Charmis, Marcus, a physician of Marseilles in the time of Nero, 236, 239.

Charon, the ferryman of the dead, 27.

Chelidoniae, the Swallow Islands, off Cape Gelidonya in Turkey, 105.

Chelmsford, xix.

Chersiphron, *fl. c.* 560 B.C., of Cnossos, architect of the temple of Diana at Ephesus, 305.

Chrysippus, a physician of Cnidos at the time of Alexander the Great, 233, 234.

Cicero, Marcus Tullius, 106–43 B.C., the orator, 140, 184, 244, 245.

Cilicia, the Roman province in S. Turkey, 286.

Cincinnatus, Lucius Quinctius, dictator, 458 B.C., 175.

Circamnos, servant to king Necthebis, 304.

Circe, the sea-nymph famous for her magic, 242.

Claudius, Tiberius Claudius Drusus Nero Germanicus, 10 B.C.–A.D. 54, emperor A.D. 41–54, xix, 37, 39, 85, 114, 116, 131, 235, 239, 256, 272, 274, 315, 316.

Cleopatra, 69–30 B.C., queen of Egypt, 97, 201, 249.

Cleophantus, fl. early 3rd cent. B.C., a Greek physician, 225.

Clodius, Publius Clodius Pulcher, killed by Milo, 52 B.C., 307.

Gnaeus Domitius, who built the chapel in the circus of Flaminius, possibly Gnaeus Domitius Ahenobarbus, 160–2, 298.

Cnidos, a city in Caria on the peninsula opposite Cos, 297.

Collina, the gate of Rome near the Quirinal hill, 151.

Colophon, a city in Lydia, near Konieh in Turkey, 79.

Columella, Lucius Junius Moderatus, fl. c. A.D. 60, author of De Re Rustica and De Arboribus, 170.

Como, xix.

Consingis, wife of king Nicomedes of Bithynia; her name is usually given as Ditizela the Phrygian, 79.

Coos, see Cos.

Corduba, Cordova in Spain, 194.

Corinth Canal, 32.

Corinth, Gulf of, 32.

Cornelius Nepos, Roman historian, contemporary of Cicero, 29.

Cos, the Dodecanese island, 233.

Coventry, xv, xx.

Crassus, Lucius Licinius, b. 140 B.C., Roman orator, 160, 161, 162, 296.

Crete, 136, 207, 303.

Crinas, a physician of Marseilles at the time of Nero, 236.

Criumetopon, a promontory like a ram's brow in the Crimea, now Mys Sarych, 110.

Croesus, fl. c. 550 B.C., last king of Lydia, 132.

Cronium, the Arctic Ocean, 35.

Crotona, the Achaian colony in S. Italy, now Crotone, 56.

Ctesias, fl. 5th cent. B.C., a physician of Cnidus in Caria, author of Persica, a history of the East, 57.

Curio, Gaius Scribonius, tribune 50 B.C., 311, 312, 314.

Curius, Manius Curius Dentatus, fl. c. 280 B.C., the conqueror of Italian tribes, 174.

Curtius, an aqueduct of Rome, 315.

Cuvier, Georges Léopold Chrétien Frédéric Dagobert, Baron, 1769–1832, the French naturalist, xvi, xvii.

Cybele, a Phrygian goddess adopted by the Romans, known as Magna Mater, 27.

Cypres, see Cyprus.

Cyprus, 136, 146.

Daedalus, the mythical Athenian architect of the Minoan labyrinth, 302.

Dalechamp, Jacques, 1513–87, author, physician, and editor of the Natural History, xxv, xxvi.

Dalion, an unknown historian quoted by Pliny, 44.

Dando, a long-lived Sclavonian, 61.

Darius, d. 330 B.C., king Darius III of Persia, defeated by Alexander, 139.

Davies, John, ?1565–1618, poet and writing master of Hereford, xxiv.

Dead Sea, 40.

Delos, one of the Cyclades Islands, birthplace of Apollo, 34, 118.

Delphi, site of the oracle of Apollo, now Kastri, 27.

Demetrius, 'the philosopher', either Demetrius Phalereus, c. 345–283 B.C., or more probably Demetrius of Sunium, a contemporary of Pliny and Vespasian, 75.

Demetrius, Demetrius Poliorcetes, 337–283 B.C., king of Macedonia, 3, 32, 288.

Democritus, fl. c. 460–370 B.C., Greek philosopher from Abdera in Thrace, 20, 64, 179, 186, 187.

Demophilus, fl. c. 424 B.C., a Greek painter of Himera, 277.

Demosthenes, 384–322 B.C., orator and statesman of Athens, 253.

Demoteles, an unknown author who wrote of the buildings of Egypt, 302.

Diana, goddess of the moon and the chase, 189, 202, 203, 465, 467.

Diarrhytus, another name for Hippo, in Algeria, 87.

Dinochares, Deinocrates, Alexander's architect, 39.

Diocles, an unidentified author who wrote of the once stone, 320.

Domenichi, Ludovico, d. c. 1564, translator of the Natural History, xxvi.

Domitius, see Ahenobarbus.

Domitius Nero, Lucius D. N., A.D. 37–68, emperor from A.D. 54 to 68, 32, 161.

Dorotheus, fl. c. A.D. 60, a painter at Rome, 285.

Drusus Caesar, 15 B.C.–A.D. 23, son of Tiberius by Vipsania, 117, 238.

Drusus, Marcus Livius, tribune, 122 B.C., 258, 270.

Drusus, Nero Claudius Drusus, d. 9 B.C., younger brother of the emperor Tiberius, 56.

Dumna, unidentified island near Britain, 35.

Dupinet, Antoine, Seigneur de Noroy, d. c. 1584; the first and best French translator of the Historia Naturalis, xxvi.

Dyris, the S. range of the Atlas mountains, 37.

Dyrrhachium, Durazzo, now Durres in Albania, 193.

Echion, fl. c. 352 B.C., a Greek painter, 276.

Egypt, Aegypt, xviii, 26, 43, 69, 76, 77, 97, 129, 191, 192, 207, 291, 299, 301, 303, 304, 307, 321.

Electrides, see Glessariae.

Elis, in the W. Peloponnese, near Olympia, 56.

Elizabeth I, 1533–1603, English queen, xv.

Elpis, a Samian, 74, 75.

Empedocles, fl. c. 460 B.C., a natural philosopher of Agrigentum in Sicily, 234.

Endoeus, fl. c. 560 B.C., a Greek sculptor of Athens, 156.

Engedi, a city on the W. coast of the Dead Sea, now Eyn Gedi, 41.

England, xxii.

Ephesus, the city of Ionia, near Smyrna, 146, 156, 268, 304.

Ephorus, fl. c. 408 B.C., Greek historian from Cumae, 61.

Epirus, in N. Greece and Albania, 79, 257.

Erasistratus, fl. 3rd cent. B.C., a famous physician of Alexandria, said to be an adopted son of Aristotle's daughter, 234.

Erythrae, a city on the Ionian coast opposite to Chios, 129.

Esquiliae, the Esquiline Hill, the largest in Rome, with several summits, 21.

Ethiopia, Ethyopia, Aethiopia, 43, 44, 48.

Euanthes, an unidentified Greek writer, 76.

Euctemon, fl. 5th cent. B.C., of Athens, an astronomer and colleague of Meton, 184.

Eudemus, a Roman physician of the time of Tiberius, the lover of Livilla, 238.

Eudoxus, fl. c. 360 B.C., a Greek astrologer of Cnidus and disciple of Plato, 50, 241.

Eupompus, fl. c. 400 B.C., of Sicyon, a Greek painter, 278.

Europa, sister of Cadmus, carried off to Crete by Jupiter who took the form of a bull, 136.

Europe, 42.

Evans, Bergen, author of The Natural History of Nonsense, 1947, xviii.

Fabianus, Papirius, a Roman philosopher of the time of Tiberius, 86.

Fabius, Gaius Fabius Pictor, consul 269 B.C., 257.

Fabius, Paullus Fabius Maximus, c. 46 B.C.–A.D. 14, visited the banished Postumus with Augustus, supposed to have revealed the secret to Livia, 61.

Fabius, possibly Quintus Fabius Labeo, quaestor 196 B.C., 53.

Fabius, probably the historian Fabius Rusticus, a contemporary of Claudius, 77.

Fabius, Quintus Fabius Maximus Cunctator, d. 203 B.C., the general and dictator in the war against Hannibal, 258, 272.

Fabius Verrucosus, see Fabius Quintus Fabius Maximus (he had a wart on his lip).

Fannius, Gaius Fannius Strabo, consul 161 B.C., 119.

Farnaby, Thomas, ?1575–1647, the chief classical scholar and schoolmaster of his time, xxi.

Felicity, the goddess of happiness, 274.

Flaccus, a Roman surname, 130.
Flaminius, Gaius, d. 217 B.C., consul in 223 B.C., builder of the circus on the Campus Martius and of the Flaminian Way, 298.
Flavianus, probably Titus Ampius, *fl. c.* A.D. 60, 87.
Flavii, members of the family or gens Flavia, 9.
Flavius, or Flavus, Alfius, a rhetorician of the time of Augustus and Tiberius, 86.
Fonteius, Gaius Fonteius Capito, consul A.D. 59 with Vipstanus, 56.
France, 26, 165, 242, 253.
Fucinus, a lake in central Italy, now Lago di Fucino, near Aquila in the Abruzzi, 316.
Fufius Salvius, a weight-lifter, perhaps the actor Fufius mentioned by Horace, 56.
Fuller, Thomas, 1608-61, churchman and historian, author of *The Worthies of England*, xxi, xxiii.
Furius, Gaius Furius Chresimus, a freedman-farmer, 177.
Fut, a river or wadi in Morocco which reaches the sea at Mogador, 37.

Gades, a Phoenician colony in Spain, now Cadiz, 29, 84.
Galatia, an inland district of Asia Minor, 208.
Ganges, 50.
Gaul, France, 34.
Gelenius, Sigismundus, 1477-1554, German scholar and editor of the *Natural History*, xxv.
Genesara, the lake of Tiberias, the sea of Galilee, 40.
Genius, the tutelary deity of a person, 21.
Germanicus Caesar, 15 B.C.–A.D. 19, nephew and adopted son of Tiberius, 80, 117, 319.
Germany, xix, 34, 56, 153, 319.
Gesoriacum, Boulogne, 34.
Getulia, Gaetulia, S. Morocco, 37, 73, 204.
Gibraltar, Gibralter, 29.
Glessariae, islands near Jutland where amber was found, 35, 319.
Glycera, a garland-maker painted by Pausias, 200.
Gnidos, *see* Cnidos.
Gortyna, a town in Crete, 136.
Greece, xxi, xxii, 136, 170, 318.

Greece, Great, Magna Graecia, S. Ital colonized by the Greeks, 30.
Grenado, Granada, 118.

Haebudes, Hebrides Islands, 35.
Hall, John, 1627-56, the fat poet and pamphleteer of Cambridge and Gray's Inn, xxi.
Hannibal, Annibal, 247-183 B.C., the Carthaginian general, 151, 258, 265, 293.
Hanno, Carthaginian general who wrote a description of the W. African coasts, *c.* 500 B.C., 37.
Harington, Lady Anne, d. 1628, wife of the first Lord Harington, an heiress who brought her husband Combe Abbey near Coventry, xxiii.
Harmais, Harmachis, Horus, the Egyptian sun god, 300.
Harmodius, *see* Aristogeiton.
Harpocrates, the Egyptian god of silence, with his finger in his mouth, 256.
Helen, of Troy, wife of king Menelaus of Sparta, 215, 264.
Hellas, Greece, usually that part N. of the Isthmus of Corinth, 32.
Hellespont, the Dardanelles, 42.
Henry Frederick, Prince of Wales, 1594-1612, xx.
Heraclea, Heracleia, now Policoro in S. Italy, 277.
Heraclea, Heracleia Pontica, a coastal city of Bithynia, now Eregli, 203.
Heracleopolis, a town in Egypt at the entrance to the Fayoum, 302, 303.
Hercules, son of Jupiter, god of strength and guardian of riches, 29, 36, 129, 272, 273, 278.
Hercules Rusticellus, nickname for Vinnius Valens, q.v., 55, 56.
Hereford, xxiv.
Hermippus, *fl.* 3rd. cent. B.C., of Smyrna, wrote numerous biographies, 241.
Herodicus, *fl.* 5th cent. B.C., of Selymbria, the tutor of Hippocrates, 233.
Herodotus, b. 484 B.C., the Greek historian, 67, 299, 302.
Herophylus, *c.* 4th to 3rd cent. B.C., one of the most celebrated physicians of antiquity, 225, 234.
Hesiodus, *fl.* 850 B.C. according to Herodotus; Hesiod, the Greek poet, 143, 184.
Heywood, Thomas, d. 1650, dramatist

and translator with a 'maine finger' in 220 plays, xxiii.

Hibernia, *see* Ireland.

Hierapolis, a city in Phrygia between the rivers Lycus and Maeander, 27.

Hiero, Hieron, d. 467 B.C., ruler of Syracuse, 176.

Hippo, Bizerta in Algeria, 87.

Hippo, a town on the E. shore of lake Tiberias, 40.

Hippocrates, b. *c.* 460 B.C., the famous Greek physician of Cos, 233, 234.

Hippocus, an Arabian magician, 242.

Hippolytus, the son of Theseus and Hippolyte; he was torn to pieces by his horses and restored to life by Aesculapius, 233.

Holland, Philemon, 1552–1637, xv–xvii, xix–xxviii.

Homer, 51, 100, 215, 242, 264, 268.

Hymettus, Mount Hymettus above Athens, 296, 311.

Ialysus, the mythical founder of the town in Rhodes, subject of a picture by Protogenes, 4, 286.

India, 48, 50, 67, 70, 93, 190, 252, 276, 318, 322.

Ionium, the Ionian Sea, 32.

Ireland, 35.

Isidore, *see* Isodorus.

Islip, Adam, *fl. c.* 1600, the London printer, xv.

Isodorus, a Greek geographer of Charax, who lived under the early Roman emperors, 32, 34.

Italy, 61, 76, 146, 190, 226, 303, 321, 322.

Ivor, a river or wadi in Morocco entering the sea either at Cape Ghir or at Agadir, 38.

James I, 1566–1625, king of Great Britain, xx.

Janus, an old Italian god represented with one face to the front and another to the back, 258.

Jason, the Argonaut, 291.

Jerusalem, 41.

Jones, W. H. S., Honorary Fellow, St. Catharine's College, Cambridge; he continued Rackham's translation of Pliny, which has now been completed by D. E. Eichholz of Bristol University, xv.

Jordan, river, 40.

Juba, king Juba II of Numidia and Mauretania who wrote historical works in Rome, 38, 67, 69.

Judaea, xviii, 40, 41.

Julias, a town at the entrance of the Jordan into the lake of Tiberias, 40.

Juno, daughter of Saturn, sister and wife of Jupiter; the patron goddess of women, 21, 146.

Juno Lacinia, Juno Lucina, the protecting goddess of childbirth, 278.

Jupiter, Juppiter, Jove, the chief god of the Romans, xxiii, 22, 136, 146, 157, 221, 233, 267, 272, 278.

Jupiter Pompeianus, the statue of Jupiter dedicated by Claudius near the theatre of Pompey, 272.

Labicana, gate of Rome whence issued the road to Labicum, now La Colonna, 298.

Lacedaemon, Sparta, 56.

Lacetania, Lusitania in Spain, 218.

Landino, Cristofero, 1424–1504, translator of the *Natural History*, xxvi.

Languedoc, 203.

Lares, the Etruscan tutelary gods, of city or household, taken over by the Romans, 21.

Largus, Gaius Caecina, consul A.D. 42, 161.

Lathom, W., writer of a commendatory poem for Holland's *Cyrupaedia*, xxii.

Latro, Marcus Porcius, *fl. c.* 17 B.C., a Roman orator from Spain, 199.

Lccheae, Lechaeae, Lechaeum, the port of Corinth on the Corinthian Gulf, 32.

Lemnos, island in the N. Aegean, 303.

Lenaeus, Gnaeus Pompeius, a freedman of Pompey, 217.

Lepidus, Marcus Aemilius, d. 13 B.C., the triumvir, 59, 309.

Libo, probably Lucius Scribonius Libo, who celebrated games in 193 B.C., 307.

Licinus, Largius or Larcius, contemporary of the younger Pliny, praetor in Spain, xvii.

Limyra, a river and town in Lycia, 245.

Lindos, a town in the island of Rhodes, 264, 273.

Livia, Augusta, ?56 B.C.–A.D. 29, the empress, who married Tiberius Claudius Nero and then Augustus, 120, 147.

Livie, *see* Livius.

Livilla, wife of Drusus Caesar, son of Tiberius, 238.

Livius, Titus, Livie, Livy, 59 B.C.– A.D. 17, the celebrated historian, xx, xxvi, 3, 6, 8, 29.

Lollia, Paulina, wife of the emperor Caligula, 96, 97.

Lollius, Marcus Lollius Palicanus, consul 21 B.C., a rapacious governor of Galatia and Gaul, 97.

Lucrinus, the Lucrine lake, Lago Lucrino, near Baiae, 86, 316.

Lucullus, Lucius, *fl. c.* 150 B.C., proconsul of Hispania Baetica, 88, 90.

Lucullus, Marcus Licinius, who brought the statue of Apollo to Rome *c.* 150 B.C., 272.

Ludius, a Roman painter of the time of Augustus, 289.

Lybia, Libya, 73.

Lycia, a district in the S.W. of Turkey, 135.

Lysippus, a sculptor and brass-founder of Sicyon of the time of Alexander the Great, 272, 273.

Macedonia, Macedony, 255.

Macer, Baebius, *fl. c.* A.D. 100, a Roman magistrate and recipient of a letter from Pliny the Younger, xvii, xix.

Machaerus, a fortress on the E. side of the Dead Sea, Mukawir, near Ataruz about 10 km. from Callirhoe springs, 40.

Machaon, a famous surgeon, 'son of Aesculapius', at the time of the Trojan war, 233.

Maecenas, Gaius Cilnius, d. 8 B.C., a Roman knight, minister of Augustus, 60, 86.

Mago, date unknown, the famous Carthaginian writer on agriculture, 176.

Marcellus, Marcus Claudius, d. 208 B.C., the taker of Syracuse and five times consul, 57.

Marcellus, Marcus Claudius, 43–23 B.C., nephew and son-in-law of Augustus, 60.

Marcia, an aqueduct of Rome built by Q. Marcius Rex, 315.

Mareotis, lake Mariut, near Alexandria, 39.

Marius, Gaius, 157–86 B.C., the famous Marius, seven times consul, who beat back the Cimbrians in 101 B.C., 160, 312.

Marmaridus, a Babylonian magician, 242.

Mars, the god of war, 272, 298.

Marseilles, Marsils, Marsiles, Massilia, 146, 236, 239.

Marsils, Marsiles, *see* Marseilles.

Mary I, 1516–58, English queen, xix.

Mauretania Caesariensis, E. Mauretania, Libya, 204.

Mauretania, Morocco, 37, 38, 44, 66, 70.

Medea, the sorceress and lover of Jason, 291.

Mediolano, Joannes de, author of the Regimen Sanitatis Salernae in the 11th cent. A.D., xxvii.

Megara, a city between Athens and Corinth, 165.

Megasthenes, *fl. c.* 300 B.C., the Greek historiographer of India, 49.

Melanthius, *fl. c.* 332 B.C., a Greek painter of Sicyon, contemporary of Apelles, 276, 280.

Meleager, a fabulous Greek hero who died before the Trojan war, 318.

Meleagrides, Meleager's sisters who lamented his death and were changed into birds, 318.

Mellaria, a town in S. Spain, now Val de Vacca near Tarifa, 29.

Melos, one of the Cyclades islands, now Milo, 276.

Memphis, a capital of Lower Egypt, near Cairo, 299.

Menelaus, king of Sparta, 264.

Mentor, a Syracusan, 74.

Mephitis, a goddess who protected from deadly exhalations, 27.

Mercury, the Italian god of merchandise, later equated with Hermes the messenger of the gods, xxiii.

Messalina, wife of the emperor Claudius, 235, 238.

Metapontum, a town in S. Italy near Taranto, 146.

Metella, Caecilia, d. 81 B.C., mother of M. Scaurus, 312.

Metellus, Lucius Caecilius, *fl. c.* 240 B.C., 174.

Mictis, an island 6 days' sail from Britain, but St. Michael's Mount has been suggested, 35.

Milo, Milon, *fl. c.* 510 B.C., the athlete of Croton, 56.

Milo, Titus Annius, tribune in 57 B.C., 307.

Minerva, the Roman goddess identified with Pallas Athene, 156, 264.

Misenum, the N. promontory of the bay of Naples, xix.

Mithridates VI, Eupator, d. 64 B.C., king of Pontus, who failed to drive the Romans from Asia Minor, 216, 259.

Moeotis, the Sea of Azov, 42.

Moeris, now the Fayoum lake in lower Egypt, 299.

Moeris, king of Egypt about 1350 B.C., said to have made the Fayoum lake, 302.

Momus, the critic god who censured all except the goddess Aphrodite, 8.

Mona, Anglesey, 35.

Monapia, Isle of Man, 35.

Morini, a people of Gaul near the Channel, 34.

Moteris, see Moeris.

Mucianus, Licinius, consul in A.D. 52, 70, and 75; 67, 82, 135, 156.

Musa, Antonius, physician to the emperor Augustus, 234.

Muses, the nine goddesses of the arts, 3.

Mutianus, see Mucianus.

Narbon, Narbonne, 203.

Naxos, the largest of the Cyclades Islands, 206.

Nealches, fl. c. 245 B.C., a Greek painter, 287.

Necthebis, an unidentified king of Egypt, 304.

Nemesis, the Greek goddess of retribution, 228, 303.

Neptune, an Italian god of fresh water, later identified with Poseidon and god of the sea, 298.

Nerigos, probably part of Norway (Norge), then thought to be an island, 35.

Nero, Claudius Caesar Augustus Germanicus, A.D. 37–68, emperor A.D. 54–68, xix, 131, 140, 211, 235, 259, 270, 276, 285, 309, 310, 321.

Nero, the emperor Tiberius, 60.

Nero, A.D. 7–?29, son of Germanicus and Agrippina, 80.

Nero, Tiberius Claudius, husband of the empress Livia and father of the emperor Tiberius, 120.

Neseus, Neseas, a Greek painter preceding Zeuxis, 277.

Nestus, Nessus, a river in Thrace, now Nestos or Mesta with its mouth near Kavalla, 72.

Nicomachus, fl. c. 360 B.C., a Greek painter of Thebes, 276, 291.

Nicomedes I, d. 250 B.C., king of Bithynia, 79, 297.

Nicophanes, fl. 4th cent. B.C., Greek painter, contemporary of Apelles, 5.

Niger, Ger, a generic name for N. African rivers. Paulinus probably reached the river Dra, 38.

Niger, Trebius, fl. c. 150 B.C., an historian, companion of L. Lucullus, 88, 89, 91.

Nilus, the river Nile, 29, 39, 43, 299, 301.

Nulus, unidentified mountain in India, 49.

Numa Pompilius, the second king of Rome, 253.

Numantia, a city in the Spanish province of Tarragona, 118.

Ochimus, a mythical king of Rhodes, 286.

Ogulnius, Quintus Ogulnius Gallus, consul 269 B.C., 257.

Olympia, in the western Peloponnese E. of Pyrgos, site of the famous Panhellenic games, 277.

Olympus, the home of the gods, xxiii.

Orbona, the goddess of parents who had lost their children, 21.

Orcades, Orkney Islands, 35.

Ostia, the port of Rome, 85, 307, 316.

Otho, Marcus Salvius, A.D. 32–69, friend of Nero, 140.

Oxford, xx.

Padua, 3.

Palatium, the Palatine Hill, the first to be built upon in Rome, 21, 281, 296.

Pan, an Arcadian god of fertility and flocks and herds, sometimes said to be the son of Penelope, 278.

Panias, source of the Jordan, see Caesarea.

Pannonia, a Roman province stretching from Vienna to Bosnia, 60.

Papyrius, Fabianus, a natural philosopher of the time of Tiberius and Caligula, 316.

Papyrius, Gaius Papirius Carbo, tribune 89 B.C., 258.

Paris, son of king Priam of Troy, xxii.

Parrhasius, fl. c. 400 B.C., of Ephesus, a Greek painter working in Athens, 278, 279.

Paulinus, Gaius Suetonius, see Suetonius.

Paulus Aemilius, Lucius Aemilius Paullus, fl. c. 50 B.C.; he built a basilica in the Roman forum, 306.

Paulus, Lucius Aemilius, defeated king Perseus of Macedonia in 168 B.C., 271.

Pausias, *fl. c.* 350 B.C., a Greek painter of Sicyon, 200.

Peace, Pax, the goddess, 286, 307.

Pelasgia, old name for the Peloponnese, from the earliest inhabitants of Greece the Pelasgi, 32.

Peloponnesus, 32.

Penelope, the wife of Odysseus, 278.

Perimula, Malacca, 93.

Perseus, d. *c.* 162 B.C., the last king of Macedonia, 271.

Perseus, a son of Jupiter who killed Medusa, 36.

Persia, 204, 241, 274.

Persis, *see* Persia.

Perusia, in Etruria, now Perugia, 60.

Petesuchis, an Egyptian king and a god, 302.

Pharsalia, Pharsalus in Thessaly, where Caesar defeated Pompey, 57.

Phasis, the river marking the ancient boundary between Europe and Asia, the Rioni opening at Poti on the E. coast of the Black Sea, 227.

Phidippides, Pheidippides, *fl. c.* 490 B.C., the courier of Athens, 56.

Philemon, a Phrygian peasant who, with his wife Baucis, entertained Zeus and Hermes, xxiii.

Philinus, *fl. c.* 250 B.C., the philosopher of Cos, 75.

Philippi, in Macedonia, 59, 255.

Philonides, servant of Alexander the Great, 56.

Phoenice, Phoenicia, 206.

Phorcus, son of Neptune and father of the Gorgons, 298.

Phrygia, a kingdom in central Turkey, 306.

Phryne, a celebrated wealthy courtesan in Athens, 274.

Pisistratus, Peisistratus, d. 527 B.C., tyrant of Athens, 274.

Piso, Lucius Calpurnius Piso Frugi, *fl. c.* 130 B.C., the annalist, 178.

Pitheas, of Massilia, the Greek navigator of the time of Alexander the Great, 34.

Plancus, Lucius Munatius, consul 42 B.C., a general under Antony and Augustus, 98.

Plato, 428–347 B.C., philosopher of Athens, 241.

Plinius, Gaius Plinius Caecilius Secundus, Pliny the Younger, *c.* A.D. 62–113, xvii, xix.

Plinius, Gaius Plinius Secundus, Plinie, Pliny, A.D. 23–79, xv–xx, xxiv, xxv, xxvi, xxviii, 3, 6, 8, 9, 11.

Pliny, Plinie, *see* Plinius.

Plutarch, *c.* A.D. 46–120, the Greek biographer and philosopher of Chaeroneia, xx, xxiii, 9.

Pluto, god of the lower world, 273.

Podalyrius, a celebrated physician, 'son of Aesculapius', at the time of the Trojan war, 233.

Pollux, the brother of Castor, sons of king Tyndareus of Sparta, 117, 291.

Polybius, *c.* 204–122 B.C., a Greek historian from Arcadia, 72.

Polycletus, Polyclitus, *fl.* 5th cent. B.C., the Greek sculptor from Argos, 18.

Pompeius, Gnaeus Pompeius Magnus, 106–48 B.C., 55, 57, 216, 217, 224, 272, 311, 312, 314.

Pompey, *see* Pompeius.

Pomponius Secundus, a general in Germany in the time of Claudius, xix.

Pontus, a Roman province in Asia minor, 77, 110, 203, 204, 216, 272, 276.

Pontus Euxinus, *see* Black Sea.

Poppaea, wife of the emperor Nero, 270.

Populonium, a town in Tuscany near Piombino, 146.

Portugal, 208.

Praxibulus, archon of Athens in 315 B.C., 267.

Praxiteles, *fl.* 4th cent. B.C., the famous Greek sculptor, 273, 296–8.

Proculeius, a Roman knight and close friend of Augustus, 60.

Prodicus, a Greek philosopher contemporary with Socrates; his name may have been used in mistake for Herodicus (q.v.), 233, 234.

Propontis, the Sea of Marmora, 42.

Proserpina, goddess of spring and consort of Pluto, king of the lower world, 273.

Proteus, the sea-god who often changed his form, 242.

Protogenes, *fl. c.* 305 B.C., a Greek painter from Caria, working in Rhodes, 3, 280, 281, 283, 284, 286, 287, 288, 290.

Prusias II, d. 149 B.C., king of Bithynia, 54.

Psammetichus, 664–610 B.C., Egyptian pharaoh, 302.

Pterophoros, a fabulous country in the northern regions, 33.
Ptolomaeus, put to death by Caligula in A.D. 40, king of Mauretania, son of king Juba II, 37, 38.
Ptolomaeus, a reported son of Antiochus I of Syria, 234.
Ptolomaeus Lathyrus, d. 81 B.C., Ptolemy VIII, king of Egypt, 43.
Ptolomaeus I, Soter, d. 283 B.C., king of Egypt, 69, 284.
Publius, Publilius Syrus, *fl. c.* 45 B.C., a slave who became a famous playwright and poet, 82.
Publius Silius Nerva, consul in A.D. 28, 80.
Puteoli, on the coast of Campania, now Pozzuoli, 27, 67, 86, 244.
Pyraeicus, Pyreicus, a Greek painter shortly after the time of Alexander, 289.
Pyrrhus, *fl. c.* 280 B.C., king of Epirus, 3, 257.

Rackham, H., began the modern translation of the *Historia Naturalis* in 1938, xv, xxv.
Rediculi, a chapel to Rediculus, whose name meant turning back, erected at the second milestone from Rome where Hannibal stopped and turned back in 211 B.C., 118.
Rex, Quintus Marcius, praetor 144 B.C., builder of the Marcia aqueduct of Rome, 314.
Rhodes, 273, 280, 283, 287, 288.
Rhodope, Rhodopis, *fl. c.* 570 B.C., a fellow slave of Aesop and a courtesan, 301, 302.
Ricnea, Ricina, Islay, or Riginia, Rathlin, 35.
Riley, Henry Thomas, 1816–78, antiquary and translator, part author of a translation of the *Historia Naturalis*, xv.
Ripaean Hills, the name given to any mountain range N. of the known world, 33.
Rome, 306 et seq. and other pp. too numerous to cite.

Sabinus, Titius, *fl. c.* A.D. 15, a friend of Germanicus, 80.
Sala, a town on the W. coast of N. Africa, probably on the site of Rabat, 36, 37.
Saronian Gulf, the Gulf of Aegina on the E. of the Isthmus of Corinth, 32.
Scandia, probably part of Sweden, then thought to be an island by most geographers, 35.
Scaurus, Marcus Aemilius, curule aedile in 58 B.C., 294–6, 310–12.
Scipio, Allobrogicus, *fl. c.* 140 B.C., said to be a brother of Africanus minor, 270.
Scipio, Metellus Pius, d. 46 B.C., the general of Pompey, 57.
Scipio, Publius Cornelius Scipio Aemylianus, Africanus minor, *c.* 185–129 B.C., general in the 3rd Punic War, 72, 118, 270.
Sclavonia, approximately the area of Austria and Hungary, 60.
Scopas, *fl.* 395–350 B.C., a famous Greek sculptor of Paros, 298, 305.
Scythia, the steppe country between the Carpathians and the river Don, 321.
Seneca, Annaeus, the philosopher and poet of the time of Nero, 236.
Serapio, Serapion, a painter of unknown date, 289.
Serenus, Anneus, Captain of the Guard to the emperor Nero, 211.
Seres, people of China, 134.
Servilius, Marcus Servilius Nonianus, consul A.D. 35, 118.
Servius Clodius, Servius Claudius, a Roman knight, 220.
Servius Tullius, the sixth king of Rome, 253, 257.
Sestius, Gaius Sestius Gallus Camerinus, consul A.D. 35, 118.
Sextius, Quintus, a Roman philosopher of the time of Julius Caesar, 187.
Shakespeare, William, 1564–1616, xxvii.
Siambis, Rackham gives Sian; the island may have been the Isle de Sein near Ushant, 35.
Sicily, 60, 234.
Sicyon, in the N. Peloponnese, now Vasiliko, 56.
Silanus, Decimus Junius, translated Mago's works from the Punic in 146 B.C., 176.
Silimnus, Silumnus, Dalkey Island near Dublin, 35.
Silures, the people of S. Wales, 35.
Silymbria, Selymbria, in Thrace, 44 miles W. of Constantinople, 233.
Sinuessa, Sinope in Campania near Monte Dragone, 27.

Sodom, lake of, *see* Dead Sea.
Sofigenes, a mathematician and astronomer of the time of Julius Caesar, 183.
Sophocles, 495–406 B.C., the Greek tragedian of Athens, 318.
Soracte, a mountain in Etruria, now Monte San Oreste, 27.
Spain, xix, 34, 118, 218, 265, 317, 322.
Speed, John, 1552–1629, the cartographer, xxvii.
Stertinius, Quintus, a Roman physician of the 1st cent. A.D., 235.
Stesichorus, 632–?556 B.C., a Greek poet of Himera, 113.
Stoidis, an unidentified island off the coast of Baluchistan, 93.
Stolo, Gaius Licinius, traditionally tribune of the plebs, 376–367 B.C., 174.
Strabo, Marcus Laenius, *fl. c.* 50 B.C., of Brindisi, a friend of Varro, 119.
Suetonius, Gaius Suetonius Tranquillus, *fl. c.* A.D. 98–138, the Roman historian, author of the *Lives of the Caesars*, xviii, xx, xxvii.
Suetonius Paulinus, Gaius, *fl.* A.D. 60, propraetor in Mauretania in A.D. 42 and later commander in Britain, 38.
Sylla, Sulla, Lucius Cornelius Sulla Felix, 138–78 B.C., the dictator, 310, 312.
Syracuse, Syracusa, 74.
Syria, 72, 74.
Syrtes, the gulfs of Sirte and Gabès, in N. Africa, 70.

Tacitus, Cornelius, *c.* A.D. 55–120, the greatest historian of the imperial period, xix, 9.
Tanais, the river Don, 29.
Taprobane, Ceylon, 93.
Tarentum, Taranto in S. Italy, 272.
Tarichion, the lake of Tiberias, 40.
Tarquinius Priscus, Lucius, *fl. c.* 600 B.C., the fifth king of Rome, 307–9.
Tauron, an unidentified writer on India, 50.
Taurus, mountain range in S. Turkey, 105.
Tepula, an aqueduct of Rome, 315.
Thales, *fl. c.* 580 B.C., a Greek philosopher of Miletus, 184, 301.
Thapsus, near Ras Dimas, S. of Sousse in Tunisia, the site of Caesar's victory over Scipio and Juba in 46 B.C., 57.
Thebes, a capital of Upper Egypt, now Luxor, 307.

Themison, *fl.* 1st cent. B.C., a famous physician of Laodicea in Syria, 234.
Theophrastus, a Greek philosopher of Eresus in Lesbos, the disciple of Plato and Aristotle, 267, 320.
Thessalus, a physician of the time of Nero, 235.
Thetis, chief of the Nereids and mother of Achilles, 298.
Thomasius, Thomas, 1553–88, first printer to the University of Cambridge and author of a Latin dictionary, xxvii.
Thrasymenus, Lake Trasimene, now Lago di Perugia, in central Italy where Hannibal beat the Romans in 217 B.C., 151.
Thule, the northern island described by Pytheas as 6 days from Orkney. It was probably Iceland, or perhaps the Shetlands or N. Norway, 35.
Tiber, Tyber, 80, 307.
Tiberias, the principal town of Galilee, close to the hot springs of Emmaus, 40.
Tiberius Nero, Tiberius Claudius Nero Caesar, 42 B.C.–A.D. 37, the emperor, 56, 60, 61, 117, 120, 131, 192, 229, 242.
Timaeus, *c.* 352–256 B.C., the celebrated Greek historian from Tauromenium in Sicily, 35, 257.
Timanthes, of Cythnos, a Greek painter contemporary with Zeuxis, 278.
Timomachus, a painter of Byzantium, possibly working in the 1st cent. B.C., 291.
Tithoes, an Egyptian god, 302.
Titus, Flavius Sabinus Vespasianus, emperor A.D. 79–81, xvii, 17.
Toranius, a slave merchant in about 40 B.C., 53.
Trebia, the river Trebbia, a tributary of the Po, where Hannibal beat the Romans in 218 B.C., 151.
Tritanus, a fencer, 55.
Troy, 268.
Tullius, Laurea, a freedman of Cicero, 244.
Turner, Paul, author of *Selections from the History of the World*, 1962, xiv.
Turranius Gracilis, probably Decimus Turranius Niger, friend of Varro and Cicero, 29.
Tuscany, 146.
Tusculum, an Italian city 15 miles from Rome, 311, 312.
Tyrus, Tyre in Phoenicia, 208.

Ulysses, Odysseus, king of Ithaca at the time of the Trojan war, 242.

Utica, now Boushater near Tunis, a Phoenician town said to have been founded c. 1100 B.C., 157.

Valens, Vettius, a Roman orator and physician of the time of Claudius, 235, 238.

Valerianus Cornelianus, a writer on agriculture, 147.

Valerius, fl. c. 190 B.C., the architect of Ostia, 307.

Valerius, Publius Valerius Publicola, first consul of Rome in 509 B.C., 310.

Varro, Marcus Terentius, 116–28 B.C., the most voluminous of Roman authors, 55, 174, 176, 198, 220, 225, 233, 289.

Varus, Publius Quintilius, defeated by the Germans in A.D. 9, 61.

Vectis, Isle of Wight or White-horn, 35.

Velitrae, now Velletri, a town below the Alban hills near Rome, 136.

Venice, xvi.

Venus, the Latin goddess of gardens, later equated with Aphrodite, goddess of love, 274, 291, 297, 298.

Venus Anadyomene, Venus rising from the sea, title of a picture by Apelles, 4, 283, 285.

Verona, xix, 3.

Verrius Flaccus, a grammarian of the time of Augustus and Tiberius, 267.

Vespasianus, Titus Flavius Vespasianus Sabinus, A.D. 9–79, emperor A.D. 69–79, xix, 9, 256, 307.

Vesuvius, xix.

Vetus, Gaius Antistius, fl. c. 30 B.C., who bought Cicero's house, 244.

Viminalis, the Viminal Hill of Rome, on which stood a willow copse, 160.

Vindex, Gaius Julius, fl. c. A.D. 60, a rebel against Nero, 199.

Vinnius Valens, a centurion of the time of Augustus, 55.

Vipstanus, Gaius Vipstanus Apronianus, consul A.D. 59; 56.

Virgil, Publius Vergilius Maro, 70–19 B.C., 145.

Virgo, an aqueduct at Rome built by Marcus Vipsanius Agrippa, 315.

Vulcan, the fire god, 43.

Ward, Samuel, d. 1643, Master of Sidney Sussex College, Cambridge, when Fuller was one of his pupils, xxiii.

Whibley, Charles, 1859–1930, scholar and wit, edited Holland's translation of Suetonius, xix, xxiv, xxvi.

White, John S., editor of a selection from the Historia Naturalis, 1885, xv.

Xenophilus, a Pythagorean philosopher and musician, 62.

Xenophon, b. c. 430 B.C., the Greek historian, xx, xxii, xxvii, 61, 176, 184.

Xerxes, king of Persia from 485 to 465 B.C., 274.

Zaratus, a Median magician, 242.

Zarmocenidas, an Assyrian magician, 242.

Zeland, Netherlands, 152.

Zeuxis, fl. c. 424 B.C., a Greek painter of Heracleia, 277–9.

Zoroaster, founder of the Magian religion of Persia, before the time of Darius, 241.

PRINTED IN GREAT BRITAIN
AT THE UNIVERSITY PRESS, OXFORD
BY VIVIAN RIDLER
PRINTER TO THE UNIVERSITY